Preface

This book grew directly out of a three-day conference held in Oslo, Norway, during August 1980 under the auspices of the International Ergonomics Association and the Nordic Ergonomics Society. The conference had a clear practical orientation with the primary aim of addressing the important question: how do we move from ergonomic theories, data, principles and methods to their implementation in the real work place? Nearly 70 conference presentations offered at least some partial answers to this question. No formal proceedings were published from the conference, but some of the papers appeared in a special issue of the journal *Ergonomics* (**23**, No. 8, 1980).

Two of the chapters in this book, Chapters 7 and 8, have been reprinted from that *Ergonomics* issue, whilst Chapter 16 represents a combined and modified version of the authors' individual papers in the journal issue. Additional chapters of the book represent a selection of the conference papers. The selection process was aided by the advice from a number of reviewers.

The sixteen chapters, which are concerned with certain applied aspects of ergonomics and based on empirical data collected from real work situations, are not grouped into any specific sections. However, the first nine chapters tend to focus on guidelines and issues relevant to workstation design, and include some specific cases of ergonomic implementations such as Chapters 6, 7 and 8. The subsequent chapters 10 through 15 are primarily concerned with ergonomics methodology. Chapter 16 provides an analysis of the ergonomic implementation process and some of its causal factors based in part on data from an empirical study. The Appendix 1 has been prepared specifically for this book as a guide to the published literature on ergonomics.

It is not intended that this book should serve as any general text of ergonomics; several other textbooks serve that purpose quite well (see Appendix 1). Instead, the chapters of this book combine to give an account of some practical job design tools and efforts to achieve propagation of ergonomics to the real work place. The volume as a whole should be of interest to practitioners, researchers and teachers of ergonomics.

Editing a book of this nature involves a cooperative venture between the contributors, the editor, and the publisher. I am indebted to the many individual authors who contributed their time and effort, and to the publishers for their cooperation and for suggesting this book project. I would also like to express my appreciation to Taylor & Francis Ltd for their permission to reprint some of the articles from the special issue of *Ergonomics*.

Finally, I want to thank my wife, Amy, for her support and clerical assistance during the project.

Minneapolis, Minnesota   Tarald O. Kvålseth
December, 1982

John Ridd '83

Ergonomics of workstation design

Ergonomics of workstation design

Edited by
Tarald O. Kvålseth
University of Minnesota

Butterworths
London Boston Durban Singapore Sydney Toronto Wellington

First published, 1983

© **Butterworth & Co (Publishers) Ltd, 1983**

British Library Cataloguing in Publication Data

Ergonomics of workstation design.
   1. Office furniture – Congresses
   2. Human engineering – Congresses
   I. Kvålseth, T. O.
   651'.23   HF5521

   ISBN 0-408-12653-6

Photoset by Butterworths Litho Preparation Department
Printed in England by Mackays of Chatham Ltd, Chatham, Kent

List of contributors

Ayoub, M. A. Department of Industrial Engineering, North Carolina State University, USA

Bellamy, L. Department of Engineering Production, University of Birmingham, England

Corlett, E. N. Department of Production Engineering and Production Management, University of Nottingham, England

Das, B. Industrial Engineering Department, Texas A & M University, USA

Edwards, M. Department of Engineering Production, University of Birmingham, England

Ekblom, B. Department of Human Work Sciences, University of Luleå, Sweden

Galer, I. A. R. Department of Human Sciences, University of Technology, Loughborough, England

Grady, R. M. Industrial Engineering Department, Texas A & M University, USA

Grandjean, E. Institut für Hygiene und Arbeitsphysiologie, Eidgenössische Technische Hochschule, Zürich, Switzerland

Hagberg, M. Work Physiology Division, National Board of Occupational Safety and Health, Umeå, Sweden

Hünting, W. Institut für Hygiene und Arbeitsphysiologie, Eidgenössische Technische Hochschule, Zürich, Switzerland

Jonsson, B. Work Physiology Division, National Board of Occupational Safety and Health, Umeå, Sweden

Knauth, P. Institut für Arbeitsphysiologie, University of Dortmund, West Germany

Kukkonen, R. Institute of Occupational Health, Vantaa, Finland

Kvålseth, T. O. Department of Mechanical Engineering, University of Minnesota, Minneapolis, USA

Landeweerd, J. A., Medical Psychology, Faculty of Medicine, Maastricht State University, Maastricht, The Netherlands

Läubli, Th. Institut für Hygiene und Arbeitsphysiologie, Eidgenössische Technische Hochschule, Zürich, Switzerland

Luopajärvi, T. Institute of Occupational Health, Vantaa, Finland

Maeda, K. Institut für Hygiene und Arbeitsphysiologie, Eidgenössische Technische Hochschule, Zürich, Switzerland

Megaw, E. D. Department of Engineering Production, University of Birmingham, England

Noro, K. Human Factors Engineering Department, University of Occupational and Environmental Health, Japan School of Medicine, Kitakyushu, Japan

Powell, J. Department of Engineering Production, University of Birmingham, England

Ridd, J. E. Materials Handling Research Unit, Institute of Industrial and Environmental Health and Safety, University of Surrey, Guildford, England

Rookmaaker, D. P. Central Ergonomics Group, Netherlands Railways, The Netherlands

Riihimäki, V. Institute of Occupational Health, Helsinki, Finland

Rutenfranz, J. Institut für Arbeitsphysiologie, University of Dortmund, West Germany

Shackel, B. Department of Human Sciences, University of Technology, Loughborough, England

Stammers, R. B. Department of Applied Psychology, University of Aston, Birmingham, England

Strandberg, L. Occupational Health Department, National Board of Occupational Safety and Health, Solna, Sweden

Winkel, J. Department of Human Work Sciences, University of Luleå, Sweden

Yap, B. L. Department of Human Sciences, University of Technology, Loughborough, England

Contents

x   Contents

Chapter 1

Analysis and evaluation of working posture

E. N. Corlett

Introduction

There are many examples of the injurious effects of consistently and repeatedly loading the same muscle groups over long periods of time. The body adapts to its demands as best it can, leading to physical distortion, and where adaptation is not possible disease usually results. Where work is designed to satisfy only technical requirements, or where engineering-based criteria are used to decide on human behaviour at work, as is the case with much method study, these results are common. If improvements in this situation are to be made, the criteria for designing work activities and the resulting postures must be based on the body's requirements as a living organism. Utilising these criteria, it must be possible to record and analyse the postures adopted, understand the relationships between the postures and the observed effects, both on the individual and the perform-ance, and assess the results of any design activity intended to improve the work postures.

In the context of ergonomics, therefore, the study of posture is related to the well-being and effective performance of people; it is not an end in itself. To design for better performance in relation to improved posture there must be methods for recording postures, the times they are held and the sequences of postures which are adopted. In addition it is necessary to record the performances before and after any changes and the effects on the people concerned, whether these are discomfort or diseases. If the study of posture in the context of ergonomics is to be useful it must be possible to interpret, from such measures as are taken, the causes of any observed effects and, hence, what must be done to improve the situation. This requires a sound understanding of the physiology and biomechanics of the working body.

The adoption of postures is, obviously, a necessary result of performing physical work and the continuity of work implies continuity of postures. For the maintenance of health it is evident that there must be sufficient opportunity to recover from the effects of posture, either by a change of posture during other parts of the work activity or by relaxation or rest away from work, so that the desired daily work may be achieved. As yet there are no techniques which permit the calculation of postural load and of recovery from its effects. Even the criteria which are put forward to specify when postural load is to be considered inadequate are difficult to relate to particular cases and by no means specific enough to permit the evaluation of the effects of posture in a given situation.

Working situations can have great variety and are the common experience of many millions across the globe. If real improvements are to be achieved the techniques for workplace design must be usable by technicians of modest ability and be reliable in their hands. Obviously this is not always possible but no serious improvements will arise unless ergonomists address themselves to the problem of creating methods usable by lower management and workpeople themselves. In the following some techniques appropriate for use by these personnel have been included.

The recording of posture

The evaluation of posture requires some measures of it which will allow comparison against standards or permit appropriate manipulations to produce values on a scale of severity. Posture is not just the orientation of the limbs in space, but includes the muscular forces produced and the times for which they are held. The sequence in which postures are produced is also relevant, since this influences the opportunities for recovery which may arise as postures are changed.

The first stage in this process is the recording of the posture. This is not only the problem of transferring to a permanent and analysable format the particular body positions observed, but also of providing a record of the forces present, the times for which various postures are held and their sequence. Techniques for this have been sought for at least three centuries, primarily for recording ballet, and it is reported that posture symbols have been identified in Tibetan, Egyptian and Chinese writings, some of pre-Christian date (Hutchinson 1954).

Intitially photography is attractive as a method but a brief consideration reveals that it only transfers what is seen at the worksite from there to the laboratory. It permits body positions as well as holding times to be measured and the same scene to be viewed repeatedly, but the filmed record is scarcely more readily analysed than the direct observations. Most other recording methods suffer from the opposite fault, they permit analysis of the postures but do not record times and sequences. These must be obtained from an additional recording procedure. Very few are able to record forces.

Ballet recording

One procedure which combines several features is *Labanotation* (Hutchinson 1954). It is written on a staff, divided, as is the musical staff, by bar lines to indicate timing but written from bottom to top of the paper rather than from left to right. From the vertical centre of the staff, leg and arm movements, trunk, head and, eventually, detailed movements of the smallest gesture are recorded, each with a length equal to the time it is held. Modifications to the symbols can cope with every gesture and movement in ballet and Preston-Dunlop (1969) illustrates as an industrial example, a person using a rake. The effort involved has also been considered as a factor to be recorded, using the judgement of the recorder (Laban and Lawrence 1947).

Whilst very precise, the technique requires a high level of skill. An abbreviated form of recording which does not include effort has been introduced and is widely taught to teachers of dance, but even this requires some three months for proficiency. To incorporate the time scale it is usually necessary to record movements first and then measure the time involved during subsequent repetitions of the movement, a procedure necessary even in straightforward industrial time study.

Other techniques which have been developed do not incorporate a time base, making it difficult to illustrate rhythmic or co-ordinated movements. An example of another ballet recording technique used for industrial ergonomics purposes was given by Kember (1976). Although written on a staff, and permitting the path of movement from one posture to another to be illustrated, it does not allow the introduction of a time scale. It was also noted by Kember that an intensive course of three months would probably be required to learn the procedure adequately.

There have been other procedures advanced for recording postures during work but they are frequently just records of body position. The two ballet procedures described above permit forces and balance to be described, data which are essential for any study of posture. However, they are not linked to a model which would allow their interpretation in ergonomic terms, which is not surprising since they were not designed for this. The procedures now to be described are all developed in relation to concepts of postural load and stress, providing some links which enable the investigator to move from his records to proposals for change which will benefit the subjects of his records.

The OWAS system

An outline of this system was recently pulished by Karhu *et al.* (1977). The posture was classified by a three-figure code according to the definition of Table 1.1. The position of the back, upper and lower limbs were noted and

Table 1.1

	1	2	3	4	5	6	7
Back	straight	bent	straight and twisted	bent and twisted			
Upper limbs	both at or below shoulder	one at or above shoulder	both above shoulder				
Lower limbs	loading on both: straight	loading on one: straight	loading on both: bent	loading on one: bent	loading on one: kneeling	body is moved by limbs	both hanging free

recorded in that order, using the appropriate number from the top of the table.

When recording a posture the recorder noted where forces were being applied, and their direction. The resulting classification was then referred to a chart on which each possible posture had been specified in terms of

(1) a normal posture which, except in special cases, needs no attention;
(2) a posture which should be considered at the next regular check of the working method;
(3) a posture which must be considered in the near future;
(4) a posture requiring immediate consideration.

These criteria arose from an amalgamation of judgements, by workers and specialists, of the postures adopted by workers in the steelworks concerned. These had been photographed, analysed and then posed for rephotographing to provide a consistent set of pictures.

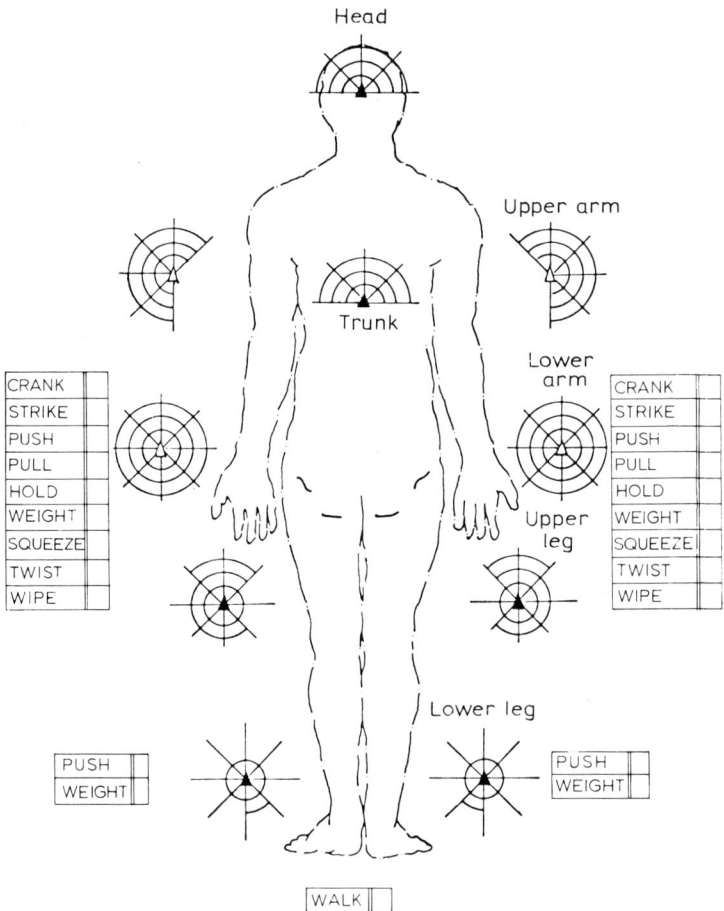

Figure 1.1 Posture targetting diagram showing the 'standard' position from which all changes in posture are estimated

As will be seen, the method permits technicians, after a short training, to assess working postures quickly and routinely. The very simplicity of the method is an advantage and it was reported that it is in regular use in the company concerned (Ovako Oy, Finland) and has led to the widespread improvement of the comfort of individual jobs and a heightened interest in working conditions across the firm. The authors point out, however, that 'before OWAS can be useful as a tool for improving working conditions, company policy towards working conditions must be decided. Otherwise the work study engineer's use of OWAS has no meaning'.

Posture targetting

This procedure (Corlett *et al.* 1979) enables a posture to be recorded from observation of a prearranged group of ten targets. These targets are of the form shown in Figure 1.1 and refer to the part of the body adjacent to them. In practice the 'standard' body position shown is not on the form but the targets are grouped in the same format, close together. This permits several sets of targets to appear on one sheet of paper, Figure 1.2.

To represent departures, in the horizontal plane, of the body part from the standard position, a mark is made on a target according to its radial displacement, the straight-ahead position being vertially upwards on the target. Displacement in the vertical plane is recorded by treating the concentric circles as a scale of 45°, 90°, 135°, etc. from the target centre;

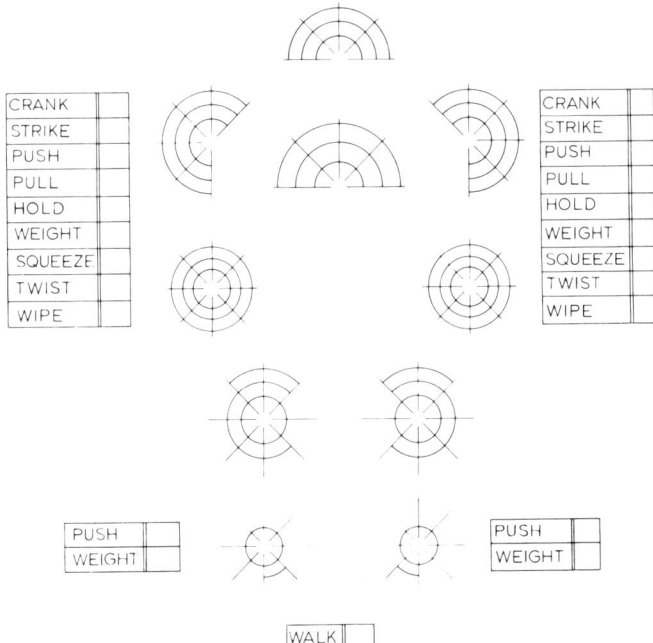

Figure 1.2 Posture targetting form for field use

thus a vertical displacement of 90° from the standard position would be marked on the second circle. Any forces or actions by a limb would be indicated by a check mark in the adjacent panels.

There have been several attempts at posture recording on similar lines but this is the simplest. The record is readily transferable to a computer, since each of the targets may be listed, using $R\theta$ co-ordinates, in a predetermined sequence. The analysis of large amounts of data is thus possible. The precision and accuracy of recording have been tested (Corlett *et al.* 1979; Simpson 1980).

The evaluation of posture

The evaluation of posture involves not just the configuration of the body, but the forces exerted in that configuration and the time for which it is held. If one asks the question, 'Is that a good posture?', the judgement is often on the basis of the currently observed position of the body, independently of the work being done. This is frequently the case when industrial seating is being discussed, such points as lumbar support and under-thigh pressure being qualitatively evaluated. Yet many seats which would be rated 'good' on such criteria are evidently hopeless for the workers concerned. It was demonstrated by Shackel *et al.* (1969) that very different choices were made by people, using chairs for various purposes, according to the tasks they were doing and these did not accord with the judgements of experts on seating.

This is not to say, however, that qualitative judgement is totally inadequate, only that the basis on which it is made must be appropriate. Postures result from trying to do a task and the task activities must be taken into account when judgement is made. Many decisions about workplaces use as a basis for judgement and decision the 'Principles of Motion Economy' (Barnes 1963). These present requirements for the layout of workspaces which then produce the postures from those doing the work. If these principles were based on sound ergonomic knowledge they would both engender good workplaces and provide a basis for the judgement of workplace quality. This is, unfortunately, not the case and the result is that the view of what is appropriate for the human body at work is based on mechanistic concepts of its operation, bearing little relation to the biological facts.

Where knowledge is scanty there is still a need for guiding principles, but these require up-dating as knowledge advances. It is important that such principles should, together, present a view of a person at work which is person–oriented and will allow the engineer or technician to apply the concepts in a wide range of situations. Table 1.2 lists ten such principles which were developed specifically for use by technicians engaged in workplace design (Corlett 1978). They are based on the results of ergonomics studies and give a framework of understanding concerning human posture and effort which is in line with the physiological and anatomical facts and thus will assist in the making of decisions regarding posture which are more likely to be correct than where uninformed judgement and experience alone are utilised.

Table 1.2 *Ten principles for the arrangement of work places*

(1) The worker should be able to maintain an upright and forward-facing posture during work.
(2) Where vision is a requirement of the task, the necessary work points must be adequately visible with the head and trunk upright or with just the head inclined slightly forward.
(3) All work activities should permit the worker to adopt several different, but equally healthy and safe postures without reducing capability to do the work.
(4) Work should be arranged so that it may be done, at the worker's choice, in either a seated or standing position. When seated, the worker should be able to use the back rest of the chair at will, without necessitating a change of movements.
(5) The weight of the body, when standing, should be carried equally on both feet, and foot pedals designed accordingly.
(6) Work should not be performed consistently at or above the level of the heart; even the occasional performance where force is exerted above heart level should be avoided. Where light hand-work must be performed above heart level, rests for the upper arms are a requirement.
(7) Rest pauses should allow for all loads experienced at work, including environmental and information loads, and the time interval between successive rest periods.
(8) Work activities should be performed with the joints at about the mid-point of their range of movement. This applies particularly to the head, trunk and upper limbs.
(9) Where muscular force has to be exerted it should be by the largest appropriate muscle groups available and in a direction co-linear with the limbs concerned.
(10) Where a force has to be exerted repeatedly, it should be possible to exert it with either arm, or either leg, without adjustment to the equipment.

It will be seen that these principles are very general and none can be said to be law in the sense that it is always applicable. They are arranged such that principles higher on the list should, in general, take precedence over those lower down. Experience and judgement are necessary for good utilisation of these and other qualitative methods, and it is unlikely that the situation will ever arise where quantitative methods alone will be adequate for workplace design.

Postural loading

The length of time for which a posture may be held may depend on the most highly loaded muscle group. As Rohmert (1973) has shown, the holding time of a muscle group is related logarithmically to the proportion of its maximum force it is required to maintain. Rohmert has proposed that 15% or less of this maximum can be maintained 'indefinitely'. Our studies suggest that not more than 8% could be so maintained and probably 5% is nearer the mark, a conclusion arrived at independently by Björksten and Jonsson (1977). However, much industrial work is concerned not so much with constant holding to exhaustion but with repeated postures. The recovery from, and frequent repetition of, postures are of major interest.

Maintenance of a posture implies that the muscles involved are exerting a continuous force. The internal pressure generated in these muscles will restrict blood supply to them and, hence, opportunity for the muscle to recover from its activity is reduced. Recovery will occur when the muscle is relaxed and will be related to the amount of effort produced.

The limitation on holding the posture will be the holding time of the most severely loaded group of muscles, if this group can be identified and its maximum voluntary contraction (MVC) measured. Rohmert (1973) has proposed a method for the estimation of recovery periods from the data. Figure 1.3 shows the relationship between holding time and the percentage of MVC, plotted directly and as a logarithmic function. The shape of the curve is informative, demonstrating that there is still a limit to holding time even with very small proportions of MVC.

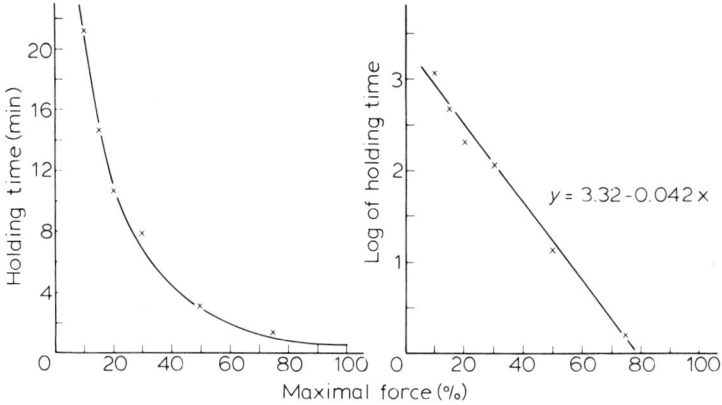

Figure 1.3 Curve of maximum holding time against % MVC (horizontal pull)

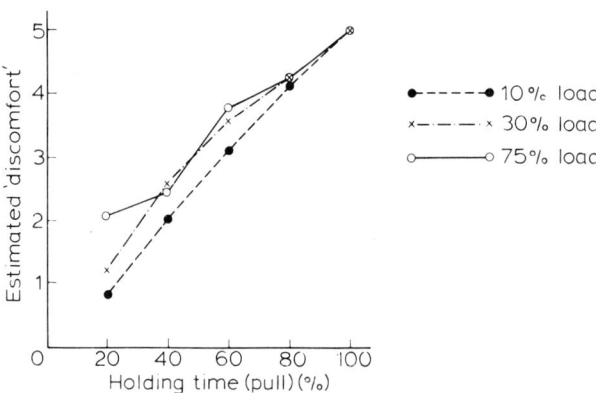

Figure 1.4 Relationship between changes in discomfort and holding time for various proportions of MVC

The use of the procedure depends on the feasibility of measuring the MVC of the selected muscle group. MVC is not the peak value which the muscle can achieve but is usually taken as that force which can be just maintained for three seconds. When measurments are taken the limb or other body part must be in the configuration adopted in the posture under consideration and the muscle group being measured must not be aided by other muscles.

Identification of posturally severely loaded muscles is assisted by the presence of discomfort, increasing to severe pain if relaxation is not possible. The growth of discomfort as a posture is maintained has been shown to be linear with time for both an identifiable muscle group, e.g. the biceps exerting a steady pull with the elbow at 90°, and for a posture where many groups operate but a discomfort site can be identified. Figure 1.4 (Barbonis 1978) illustrates the linear relationship between holding time and discomfort level for a horizontal pull in which the upper arm was horizontal and the forearm vertical. Although three different forces were used, each having very different maximum holdings times, the growth of discomfort over time was substantially the same.

Postural discomfort

The relationships illustrated above gave rise to a procedure for using postural discomfort as an indication of the effects of posture (Corlett and Bishop 1976). The procedure uses an outline diagram of the body, Figure 1.5, divided approximately according to the areas of discomfort found during pilot trials, as a map to define the distribution of discomfort across the body. A subject is asked to point to the body areas which are currently

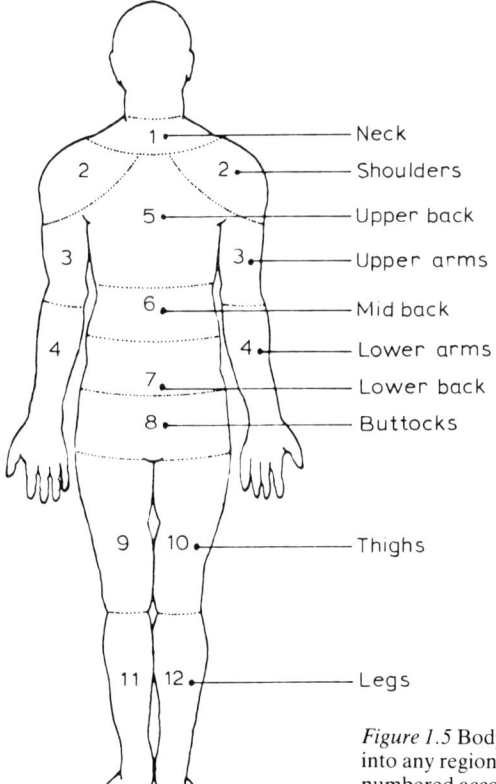

1 — Neck
2 — Shoulders
5 — Upper back
3 — Upper arms
6 — Mid back
4 — Lower arms
7 — Lower back
8 — Buttocks
10 — Thighs
12 — Legs

Figure 1.5 Body regions diagram. This may be divided into any regions appropriate for the investigation and numbered accordingly. No wording should appear on the test sheet

giving the grestest discomfort. After noting the response, which may involve more than one of the areas, he is then asked for the area or areas which are next in their level of discomfort. This questioning is continued, identifying successively less severe levels of discomfort, until the subject offers no further responses. Thus he has specified various body areas, each at a distinguishable level of discomfort. At intervals over the working day the procedure is repeated and the growth of discomfort in each area, or functionally related group of areas, can be plotted on a time base. The procedure may be repeated after several days, using the same subjects on their own jobs, to assess the repeatability and to give confidence in the recorded values. As small changes in body dimensions may permit a big change in the orientation of different individuals to the same workplace, similarity of results between subjects should not necessarily be expected and result over subjects should be averaged with caution. Repeatability with regard to the same subject is a better test of the reliability of the findings than similarity between subjects.

Figure 1.6 illustrates how the records may appear. It is particularly noticeable that even though a three-quarter hour lunch break has been given, the pattern of discomfort in the afternoon does not repeat that of the morning. Indeed it is more as if the afternoon period encouraged a rapid return to the level and trend reached at the end of the morning work period. What is very clear is that recovery from postural loads sufficiently severe to result in the experience of considerable pain, is not rapid and cannot be achieved during a lunch break.

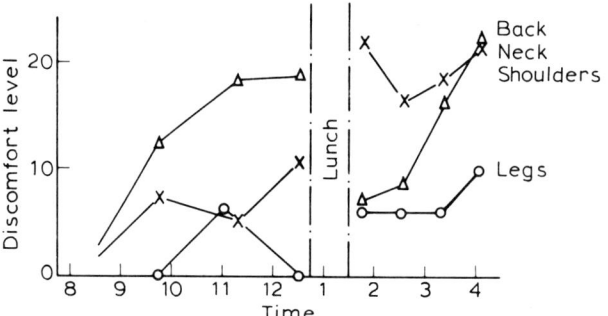

Figure 1.6 Average discomfort scores for four coil winder operators recorded over the whole of a working day

The effect on discomfort in the lower back of changing the work height for spot welders (Corlett and Bishop 1976) is shown in Figure 1.7. The vertical scale, which is arbitrary, represents a range from 'no noticeable discomfort' to 'extreme discomfort', whilst the horizontal scale covers about half a working day. The improvement could be directly linked, via relationships listed in Table 1.3, to the machine changes introduced. These relationships, from van Wely (1970) were deduced from a study of the workplaces of patients who attended an industrial surgery. The reported diseases were linked to postures adopted to pursue their jobs. This study is an example which needs extensive replication.

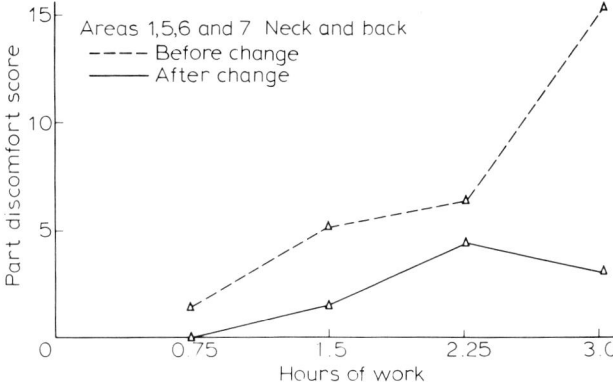

Figure 1.7 Back discomfort before and after changes to spot welding
machines

A procedure to develop extensive data relating working postures to ill
health and injury was described by Grieco *et al.* (1978). Their approach
involved the provision of two recording forms on which either a fixed or a
variable posture was specified. They then assessed the tolerance of these
postures against nine aspects, each of which was assessed judgementally by
a clinician. The third component in their study was a procedure for
clinically examining large numbers of people who had been exposed to
unsatisfactory working postures. They presented a sequence of measures
to be made when the subject adopts certain selected postures. These
postures were chosen to emphasise the extent of movement of major joints
of the limbs and trunk as well as the shape of the spine. This important
section of their study was to provide that essential segment of information

Table 1.3 *'Bad postures' versus probable sites of symptoms (after van Wely 1970)*

Bad postures	*Probable site of pain of other symptoms*
Standing (particularly a pigeon-footed stance)	Feet, lumbar region
Sitting without lumbar support	Lumbar region
Sitting without support for the back	*Erector spinae* muscles
Sitting without good footrests of the correct height	Knee, legs and lumbar region
Sitting with elbows rested on a working surface which is too high	*Trapezius, rhomoideus* and *levator scapulae* muscles
Upper arm hanging unsupported out of vertical	Shoulders, upper arms
Arms reaching upwards	Shoulders, upper arms
Head bent back	Cervical region
Trunk bent forward; stooping position	Lumbar region, *erector spinae* muscles
Lifting heavy weights with back bent foward	Lumbar region, *erector spinae* muscles
Any cramped position	The muscles involved
Maintenance of any joint in its extreme position	The joint involved

which, as yet, is unavailable, concerning the long-term effects of working posture on the adaptation of the human body. As yet no data from this project have been reported.

Holding time and recovery

It was mentioned earlier that the holding time for static muscular work depended on the intensity of muscular contraction and that the relationship between the percentage of maximum voluntary contraction and time was a logarithmic one. It is not always possible to assume that a posture will follow the same rule as a single muscle group, as it may be feasible to transfer the postural load between several groups, particularly if the individual is substantially in balance and stable.

The effect of changes in posture on holding time is illustrated by Figure 1.8. The working positions, specified by the percentages at the foot of the figure, are proportions of the shoulder height and maximum reach of each

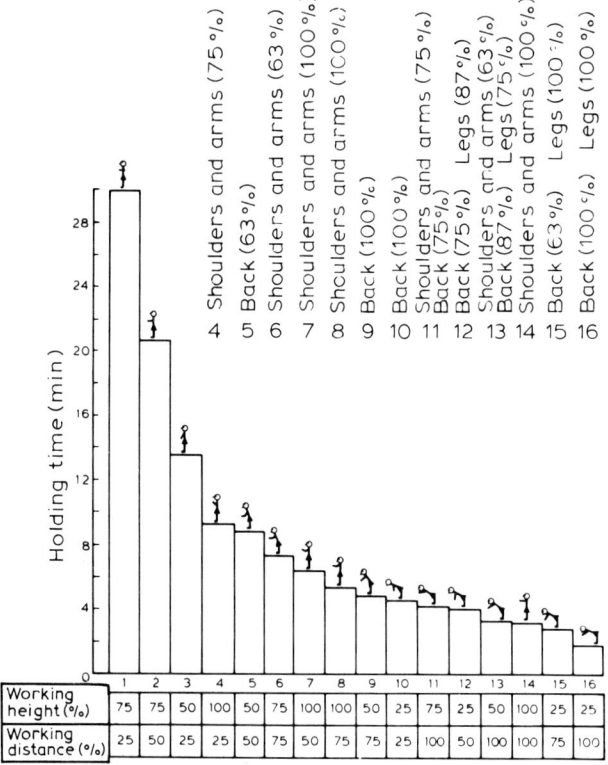

Figure 1.8 Changes in holding time with increasing severity of forward bend and reach. The data are from an experiment involving several subjects

subject. The study is described in Barbonis (1978). As the position adopted became more extreme, moving from left to right on the figure, the most common sites of extreme discomfort moved from the shoulders, via the neck and back to the legs.

Recovery from five postures selected from the set of Figure 1.8 was investigated in greater detail. It was found that where a posture had been maintained for its maximum period, even a rest pause equal to twelve times the holding time was not sufficient for full recovery, only between 80% and 90% of the original holding time being possible. The proportion of recovery with different rest periods, expressed as a percentage of the original holding time, is shown in Figure 1.9 for two of these five postures. It will be noted that the recovery curves for both are substantially similar, that some 75% of recovery has occurred within a 100% rest pause but that full recovery does not appear to be reached within the scope of the graph.

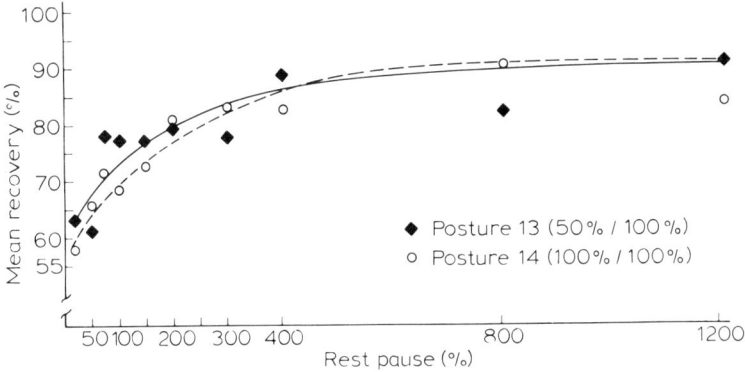

Figure 1.9 Recovery curves for two different forward-bending postures after holding to maximum discomfort. Recovery periods are expressed as percentages of the maximum holding time of the posture on the first trial

Further investigation of the data revealed that the major factor affecting the length of the second work period was the length of the first work period and a combination of the data from the five postures studied gave the formula presented in Figure 1.10. This formula explained 97% of the variation about the mean and thus was a highly reliable predictor for the second holding time. Figure 1.10 shows the formula plotted for various values of T_1, the holding time for the first trial, and a rest pause of 1200% of T_1. The horizontal axis gives the predicted second holding time and it will be seen that, for other than very short periods of T_1, only about 80% of the first holding time can be achieved on the second trial.

Comparison with Figure 1.6 will illustrate this finding in practice. The discomfort experienced in static work is related to the blood lactate level which develops due to the anaerobic metabolism in the muscle. Where this develops quickly the pain level will cause the posture to be changed, where it is slower to develop, muscle glycogen can also be utilised in the muscle metabolic process. Whilst pain is related to lactate levels, stamina depends on the availability of glycogen but, once used, this takes a long time to

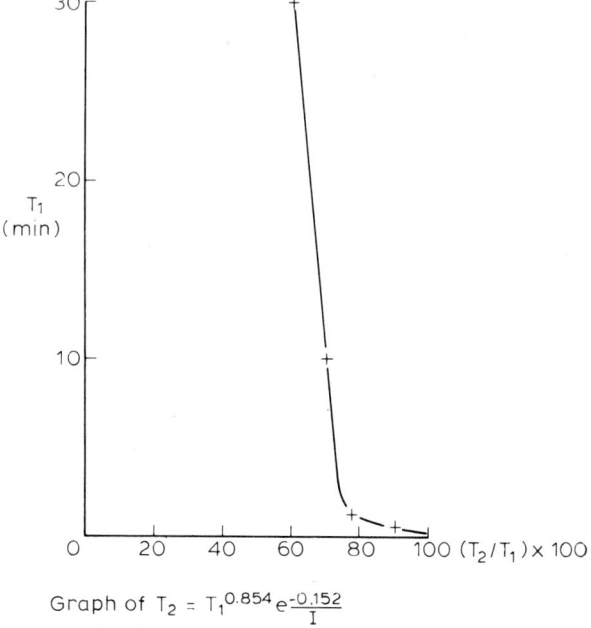

Graph of $T_2 = T_1^{0.854} e^{-\frac{0.152}{I}}$

for $I = 1200\% \, T_1$

Forward bending posture

Figure 1.10 The relationship between the first maximum holding time for a forward bend posture and the second time, when a rest pause of twelve times the first holding time is given

replace. The slow development of pain represented by Figure 1.6 suggests that glycogen is being depleted during the morning which is not completely replaced over the lunch period. Consequently, the capacity is not available to maintain the posture for such a long period during the second half of the day.

Mechanical loading, holding time and discomfort

The postures illustrated in Figure 1.8 and described above utilised the maximum holding time as an indication of their severity. However, the loading at the joints, expressed as the torque to resist external forces including gravity, may be readily calculated as described by Grieve and Pheasant (1976). The stability of the posture can be expressed diagrammatically, as they have shown.

A study of the forward bend, using four postures corresponding to numbers 14, 11, 13 and 16 on Figure 1.8, was conducted to compare calculated resisting torques, reported discomfort and holding time (Corlett *et al.* 1981a). Torques were calculated about hip, knee and ankle joints and the rate of increase of discomfort calculated from the discomfort scores. Analyses were done to find how closely the resisting torques at each of the joints correlated with the discomfort measures.

It was shown that the resisting torque at the ankle correlated most closely with discomfort in the lower leg but, probably due to the sharing of the load required to support the superincumbent parts of the body between several groups of muscles at the other joints, the relationship between discomfort growth and resisting torque at the other two joints was less close. The distribution of load between muscles at each posture, and the changes in the distribution with changes in posture, were demonstrated by the changes in discomfort as shown in Figure 1.11.

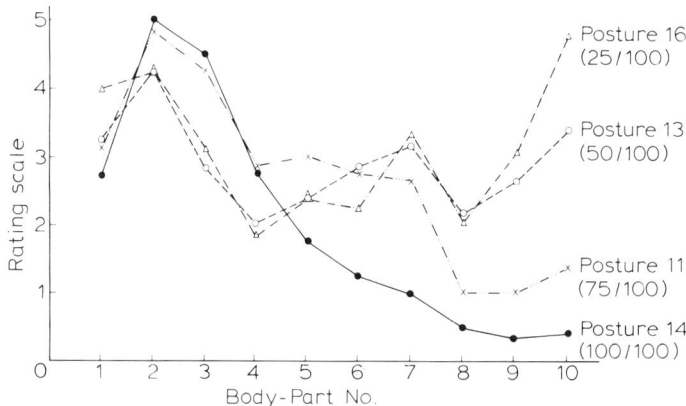

Figure 1.11 Discomfort intensity at the end of postural work in the various parts of the body for each of four postures

The possibility of utilising biomechanic analysis for estimating holding times, given an understanding of the discomfort distribution to be expected, is suggested by this study. The eventual computerisation of such analyses for workplace design would not be difficult if the link between posture and discomfort could be made.

EMG in relation to posture

The electromyogram (EMG) reveals in a unique way the actual activity of the muscle. Early use of EMG records relied on a visual classification into 'slight', 'moderate', etc. levels and it was in the mid-fifties that more quantitative measures were introduced. An early measure was the integrated EMG, which indicated the total muscular activity but did not differentiate between increased frequency and increased amplitude in the signal. It was found that during static muscular contraction there was an increase in the EMG level over time, identified as arising from fatigue, and later studies showed that there was also a change in the frequency spectrum, towards an increase in the low frequencies.

For the forward-bend posture, although increases in integrated EMG [IEMG] (where the rectified raw signal is accumulated to a given voltage level and the time to reach this level is recorded) can be demonstrated with increased angle of bend, when the bend reaches 80° or 90° the EMG becomes 'silent'. This has been stated to occur when the trunk is virtually supported by the stretched ligaments of the back. Whilst discomfort recording shows this to be a painful posture, the IEMG record shows little evidence of muscular force being exerted.

Studies reported by Grieve and Pheasant (1976) indicate that for the three muscle groups they tested (*erector spinae, biceps brachii* and *triceps surae*) there was a decrease in maximum electrical activity in isometric contraction as the muscle length was increased, i.e. by having differing degrees of flexion or extension for different trials. They interpret their results as indicating that a stretched muscle requires fewer action potentials per unit time to achieve maximal tension than does a shortened muscle and that evidence of low EMG activity must not be taken to indicate no muscular effort. Equally, where test contractions are used to provide data for normalising EMG records the contractions must occur with similar postures to those under investigation.

The difficulties inherent in the use of EMG records to identify the postural stress experienced by a subject is demonstrated by Figure 1.12.

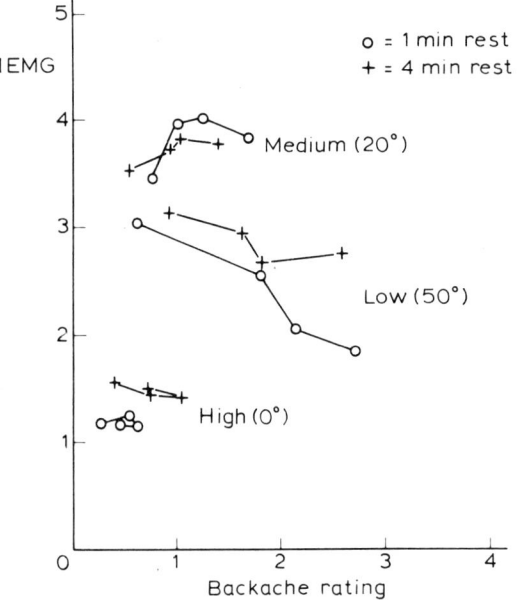

Figure 1.12 Minute by minute changes in totalled scores for IEMG and backache ratings for three forward-bending postures. Four-minute trial duration

The graph (from Corlett *et al.* 1981b) shows the changes in IEMG minute by minute during a forward bend lasting four minutes, plotted against the changes in reported back discomfort. The experiment involves two successive tests with either a one- or a four-minute rest pause, and six subjects were used, their averaged results being plotted in the figure.

The forward-bending postures used were such as to avoid the 'silent period' occurring when a low bend occurs, yet IEMG scores fell markedly with a 50° bend compared with the results for the 20° bend. The biomechanic considerations make it evident that the back is not under a reduced load; the phenomenon discussed by Grieve and Pheasant (1976) is probably the cause of the observed decrease. The discomfort records, using a time-related indicator of discomfort, support the data of Figure 1.8, showing increased discomfort with increasing degrees of bend.

A further promising analysis of EMG arising during working postures was reported by Jonsson and his colleagues (see Jonsson 1978). This involves the construction from the rectified EMG recording of an amplitude probability distribution function. Hagberg and Jonsson (1975) indicated that this may be normalised on the basis of appropriate test contractions or may utilise the microvolt values themselves. The latter, however, will not provide indications of the force being exerted by the muscle unless microvolt values during test contractions have been ascertained at the same experimental session.

The value of the procedure is stated to be its potential for separating the static and dynamic components of muscular activity and being able to relate them to criteria which will indicate the intensity of the muscle load. This has not previously been possible but the use of the amplitude probability distribution function introduces a new opportunity to specify muscular load limits for static muscle work when it would otherwise be confounded with the active use of the same muscle.

With the arrival of inexpensive electronic analysis equipment the frequency and amplitude spectra of EMG signals may readily be obtained under field conditions where surface electrodes are feasible. The amplitude spectrum plot allows the minumum level of activity to be defined, the 'static' component of the activity identified and also the mean and peak levels to be indicated. Where test contractions have been done, the percentage of MVC will be identifiable on the graph, together with the proportion of time for which each percentage is maintained. Whereas much work on posture has had to rely on subjective evaluation combined with body displacement measures and their mathematical assessment, the opportunity to assess in more detail the actual behaviour of the muscles used to maintain the postures, when combined with other methods, should enable body loads to be more precisely identified and a greater understanding of the effects of posture to be achieved. This paper has outlined some procedures for the analysis of working postures and the progress made towards a comprehensive system for dealing with posture in the context of work design.

Conclusion

Increased understanding of the course of postural fatigue is evident and some practical procedures for dealing with workplace evaluation are available. However, a clear understanding of the nature of this fatigue, and of its recovery, is not yet available. Indeed, some of the criteria put forward by some workers clearly clash with those of others, as will be evident from this overview. It is likely that postural fatigue arising from a severe posture which gives rise to early discomfort is different in nature from that arising from frequently adopted, less severe postures where the discomfort builds up over a period of several hours. The creation of a comprehensive model of postural load applicable to field situations awaits the resolution of a number of anomalies already evident in the extensive literature.

Acknowledgements

Apart from those indicated as collaborators in the referenced papers, mention must be made of the major contributions from Dr I. Manenica and Dr P. A. Barbonis. Some of the work of S. Mason, M. Tighezza, P. J. Goillau and M. Boussena has also been incorporated into the above discussion.

References

BARNES, R. M. (1963). *Motion and Time Study*, Wiley, New York.
BARBONIS, P. A. (1978). *Measurement and Modelling of Postural Work Load*, Ph.D. thesis, University of Birmingham.
BJÖRKSTEN, M. & JONSSON, B. (1977). 'Endurance limit of force in long-term intermittent static contraction', *Scand. J. Work Environ. and Hlth*, **3**, 23–27.
CORLETT, E. N. (1978). 'The human body at work: new principles for designing work spaces and methods', *Management Services*, May, 8pp.
CORLETT, E. N. & BISHOP, R. P. (1976). 'A technique for assessing postural discomfort', *Ergonomics*, **19**, 175–182.
CORLETT, E. N., MADELEY, S. J. & MANENICA, I. 'Posture targetting: a technique for recording working postures', *Ergonomics*, **22**, No. 3, 357–366.
CORLETT, E. N., BOUSSENNA, M. & PHEASANT, S. T. (1982). 'Is discomfort related to the postural loading at the joints?', *Ergonomics*, **25**, No. 4, 315–322.
CORLETT, E. N., MANENICA, I. & GOILLAU, P. J. (1983). 'The relationship between EMG activity and the sacrospinalis and reported back discomfort', *Eur J. Appl. Physiol.*, **50**, 213–222.
GRIECO, A. *et al.* (1978). 'Development of a new method for evaluation of risks of injury induced by working postures', *translation from La Medicina del Lavoro*, **69**, Supp. 3.
GRIEVE, D. W. & PHEASANT, S. T. (1977). 'Myoelectric activity, posture and isometric torque in man', *Electromyogr. clin. Neurophysiol.* **16**, 3–21.
HAGBERG, M. & JONSSON, B. (1975). 'The amplitude distribution of the myoelectric signal in an ergonomic study of the deltoid muscle', *Ergonomics*, **18**, No. 3, 311–319.
HUTCHINSON, A. (1954). *Labanotation*, Oxford University Press, London. (There is a second edition, 1970.)
JONSSON, B. (1978). 'Kinesiology', (in *Contemporary Clinical Neurophysiology*, Cobb W. A. & van Duijn, H. (eds.), E.E.G. Suppl. 34, 417–428), Elsevier, Amsterdam.
KARHU, O. *et al.* (1977). 'Correcting working postures in industry, a practical method for analysis', *Applied Ergonomics*, **8**, 199–201.
KEMBER, P. A. (1976). 'The Benesh movement notation used to study sitting behaviour', *Applied Ergonomics*, **7**, No. 3, 133–136.
LABAN, R. & LAWRENCE, F. C. (1947) *Effort*, Macdonald and Evans, London.
PRESTON–DUNLOP, V. (1969). *Practical Kinetography Laban*, Macdonald and Evans, London.
ROHMERT, W. (1973). 'Problems in determining rest allowances', *Applied Ergonomics*, **4**, 91–95; 158–162.
SHACKEL, B. *et al.* (1969). 'The assessment of chair comfort', *Ergonomics*, **12**, 269–306.
SIMPSON, G. (1980). (Referred to in Graveley *et al.*) *An Investigation of Stress on Coal Face Workers*, NCB Report, October, Institute of Occupational Medicine, Edinburgh.
van WELY, P. (1970). 'Design and disease', *Applied Ergonomics*, **1**, 262–269.

Chapter 2

Constrained postures at office workstations

E. Grandjean, W. Hünting, K. Maeda & Th. Läubli

Postural efforts

Postural efforts are static efforts, they are associated with long-lasting static contractions of muscles. Static effort compresses blood vessels and reduces blood irrigation of the muscles. Therefore, the statically loaded muscle has a decreased supply of energy and oxygen, whilst waste products (lactic acid, carbon dioxide and others) are accumulated. These waste products cause acute localised fatigue in the statically loaded muscles; tiredness, pains and even cramps are the symptoms of excessive static load.

Examples of postural efforts

Our bodies must often perform static efforts during everyday life, but the most common static load is required by some long-lasting postures. Thus, when standing, a whole series of muscle groups in the legs, hips, back and neck are strained for long periods. Thanks to those static efforts, we can keep selected parts of our bodies in any desired attitude. A few examples of typical situations illustrate such postural efforts.

Bending the trunk either forwards or sideways causes a heavy static load on the muscles of the back.
Holding extended arms forward is a static effort, especially if the hands are carrying a weight.
Keeping an arm and hand outstretched in order to operate a machine for many hours is a static effort associated with the risk of painful muscle fatigue in the shoulder.
Standing in one place is bad for the blood circulation as well as for static efforts; it is associated with an increased hydrostatic pressure of the blood in the veins and causes venous congestion. When walking or moving, the muscles of the legs can act as a pump; this is a favourable circulatory condition.

Thus, pedals for standing work are undesirable; they produce not only a high static load on one leg but are also a hazard for the blood circulation. The inclination of the head is another postural problem. It is recommended that the angle between a line from the eye to the display on the one hand, and a horizontal line on the other should be in the range of 15°–45° when standing and 26°–50° when sitting. Furthermore, experts in the field recommend that the angle between a prolongation of the back line and a line 'neck to head' should not exceed 20°.

Medical aspects of postural efforts

Postural efforts not only decrease performance and productivity, but in the long run they also affect well-being and health. In fact, if postural efforts are repeated daily over a long period, more or less permanent aches will appear in the limbs concerned, and may involve not only the muscles but also the joints, tendons and other tissues. Long-lasting postural efforts can lead to deterioration of joints, ligaments, tendons and other parts of the connective tissue.

Several field studies as well as general experience show that postural efforts are associated with an increased risk of

inflammation of the joints;
inflammation of the tendons sheaths;
inflammation of the attachment points of tendons;
symptoms of chronic degeneration of the joints in the form of chronic arthroses;
painful induration of the muscles;
disc troubles.

Persistent pains in the overloaded tissues appear particularly among older operatives. Table 2.1 shows possible relationships between postural efforts and risk of pain or disease.

Table 2.1 *Possible relationships between unfavorable postures on one side and risks of pains or deseases on the other side*

Postures	Risks of pains or diseases
Standing in one place	Feet and legs, varicose veins
Sitting erect without back support	Extensor muscle of the back
Seat too high	Knees, neck
Seat too low	Shoulders and upper arms
Trunk curved forwards when sitting or standing	Lumber region; deterioration of intervertebral discs
Head inclined forwards	Neck, deterioration of intervertebral discs

Ergonomic principles to avoid postural efforts

A major objective in the design and layout of jobs, workplaces, machines and tools should be to minimise static efforts due to inadequate posture. To reach this objective, two principles must be taken into consideration.

All workplace dimensions (including tools) should be suited to the body size of the operator as well as to biomechanical requirements; thus postural efforts can be minimised.
Postures must be adopted which will allow as many muscles as possible to contribute; thus the muscles will be most efficient and most skilful.

These principles are essential for the assessment of

adequate working heights;
comfortable head positions;
adequate vertical and horizontal grasping space;
adequate operating space for the legs;
comfortable handgrips, knobs and other controls.

Postural problems at VDTs and other business machines

An important consequence of the introduction of VDTs at workplaces is the integration of operators in a man–machine system. The space of action of the employee is restricted; the movements are limited and stereotyped for the fingers, hands and arms. The position of the head is imposed by visual angle and visual distance; the position of the hands is given mainly by the keyboard, and to some extent, by the source of documents. Many jobs have a repetitive character with special demands on vigilance. All these elements further constrained postures, and they are characterised by a restriction of free movements and by long-lasting static postural efforts.

This state of affairs was the background of two field studies (Hünting *et al.* 1980a; Läubli *et al.* 1980; Hünting *et al.* 1980b). Systematic investigations at various workplaces equipped with VDUs, accounting machines or typewriters were carried out in banks, post offices and in some typing pools. The study comprised the following groups of operators: 53 on data entry terminals, 109 on conversational terminals, 119 accounting machine operators, 78 full-time typists and 55 employees occupied with traditional office work.

The following investigations were carried out. The incidence of physical impairment was recorded with a self-rating questionnaire, medical examination of muscles and joints involved was made, workplace dimensions and some postural characteristics were determined. Some interesting results of both studies are summarised below.

Postural efforts at accounting machine workstations

Figure 2.1 shows an accounting machine operator in a typical working posture. The main task of the accounting machine operator was to read figures from coupons and to type them into a keyboard. The operator

Figure 2.1 View of an accounting machine operator. Right hand: operating keyboard; Left hand: turning over coupons. main visual line towards coupons

maintained a continuous sitting posture, the two hands having different tasks.

With the left hand the operator had to turn the coupons over, the left elbow lying on the desk. The main visual line was orientated to the coupons, causing some rotation of the head to the left and some forward bending of the neck. The right hand was exclusively used to operate the numerical keyboards.

The working day was 8½ h. It was estimated that, on average, 5–6 h were spent operating the accounting machine. The keying speed varied between 8000 and 12 000 strokes/h. Some of the physical complaints of the 119 accounting machine operators were compared with a group of shop girls of the same age (see Figure 2.2).

The following conclusions were derived.

The incidence of impairment in hands and arms was more than twice as frequent in the accounting machine operators than in the shop girls.
In the accounting machine operators, this impairment was significantly more frequent on the right than on the left side.

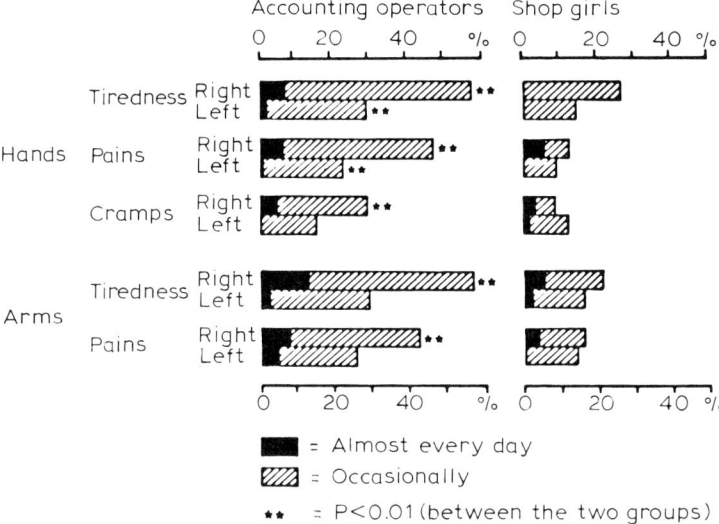

Figure 2.2 Impairments in hands and arms of accounting machine operators and shop girls. 119 accounting machine operators = 100%. 57 shop girls = 100%

These results lead to the assumption that impairment in hands and arms of the accounting machine operators was related to the working posture, and that of the right side to the special load of the keyboard operations.

In order to check possible effects of body postures on the incidence of impairment, we divided 57 subjects into three groups of different body posture characteristics. The comparison of these data showed relationships between three ranges of body angles and impairment shown in Figures 2.3 and 2.4.

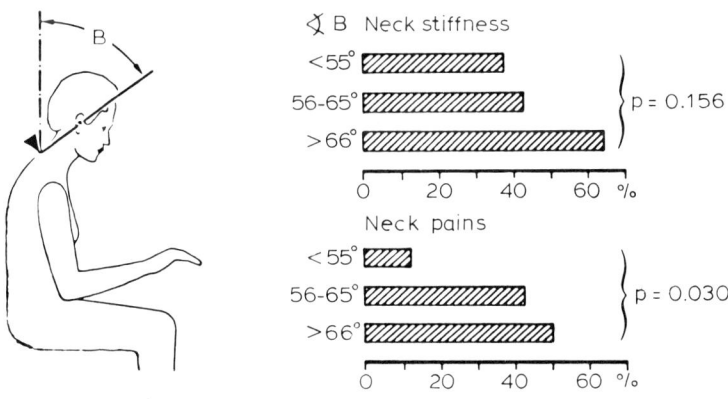

Figure 2.3 Incidence of impairments in the neck related to the neck–head angles (B) of 57 accounting machine operators

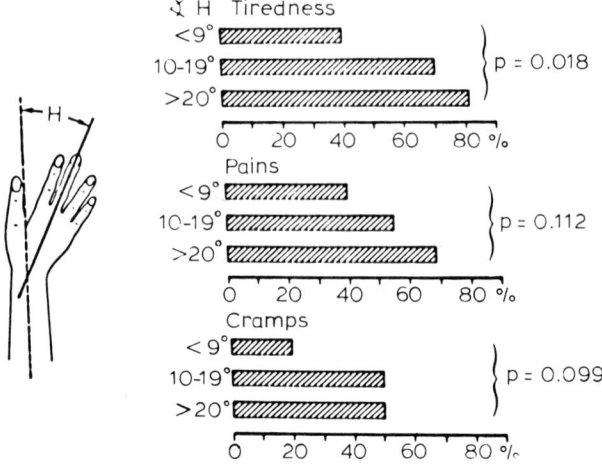

100 % = subjects in each of the three angle-groups

Figure 2.4 Incidence of impairments in the right hand, related to the ulnar (lateral) deviation of the right hand of 57 accounting machine operators

Not all the reported relations are statistically significant. Nevertheless, the general tendency is obvious and we can deduce the following statements from the two figures.

The incidence of stiffness and pains in the neck increased with the degree of forward bending of the head (Figure 2.3).
The incidence of tiredness, pains and cramps in the right hand increased with the degree of the ulnar deviation of the same hand (Figure 2.4).

Analysis of workplaces revealed a faulty design: both the table level and the keyboard level were too high.

Study of working postures gave the following results: in order to compensate for the high keyboard level, the subjects prefered relatively high seat levels, which imposed a marked forward bending of the head. Furthermore, the high keyboard level was associated with a greater forward extension of the upper arm. Cause and effect were clear: the faulty design determined an adverse posture of head and arms and caused impairment in neck and shoulders. The study also revealed an adverse effect of the traditional keyboard design: in order to keep the right hand parallel to the banks of the keyboard, the subjects were forced to hold the right hand in an ulnar deviation (see Figure 2.1).

An important factor of the studied workplace is certainly the position and quality of the source documents. The coupons were of rather poor legibility and the continuous reading must be considered as a relevant visual load causing eye complaints. In order to facilitate the reading task, the subjects rotated trunk and head to the left and kept the head in a forward-bending position. Therefore, position and quality of the source documents aggravated the body postures which were already badly determined by the high level of the keyboard.

The observed adverse body postures would be without importance if they did not last for many hours per day thus leading to constrained postures. All the results lead to four main recommendations.

The keyboard should be rotated anti-clockwise by 15°–20°. This should prevent the ulnar deviation of the right hand.

The desk level supporting the keyboard should be adjustable in order to allow the operators to choose a working level according to anthropometric and functional needs.

The position of the source document should be such that, within normal visual distances, the bending of the head can be reduced to a comfortable head–neck inclination. The source documents themselves should have an inclination of at least 15° which would also prevent an excessive bending of the head. Furthermore it is recommended to improve, whenever possible, the legibility of the source documents.

The keyboard should be equipped with a support for the right hand or for the forearm.

Postural efforts at VDT workstations

161 VDT operators indicated pain and other impairments in the area of the neck, shoulders, arms and hands. The incidence of these physical impairments as well as the complaints about eye strain are shown in Figure 2.5. It is interesting to note the high incidence of pains in the groups of data entry terminal operators on the one side and the low figures in the control group of 'traditional office workers' on the other.

All operators of the four groups were also examined by a medical doctor. One result of the medical findings is reported in Figure 2.6, which shows the incidence of painful pressure points on tendons, joints and muscles in the area of the shoulders. The clinical symptoms in the shoulder

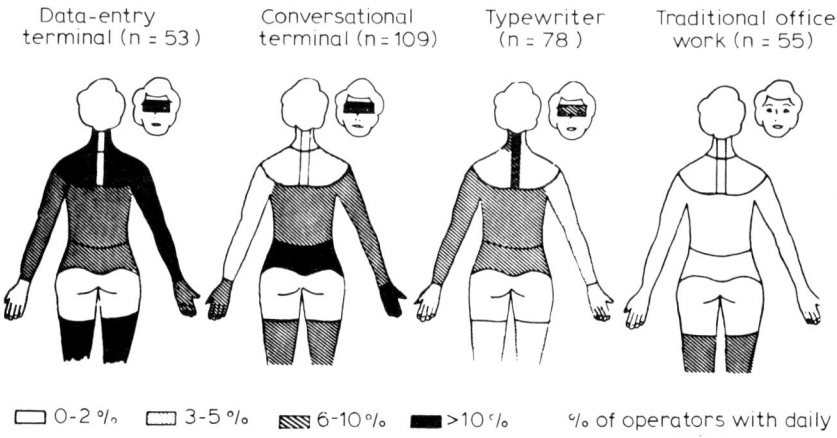

| Data-entry terminal (n = 53) | Conversational terminal (n = 109) | Typewriter (n = 78) | Traditional office work (n = 55) |

☐ 0-2 %   ☐ 3-5 %   ▨ 6-10 %   ■ >10 %   % of operators with daily pains

Figure 2.5 The incidence of 'daily' pains in the four groups of VDT operators and typists. The different shades indicate the percentage of operators and the localisation of their complaints

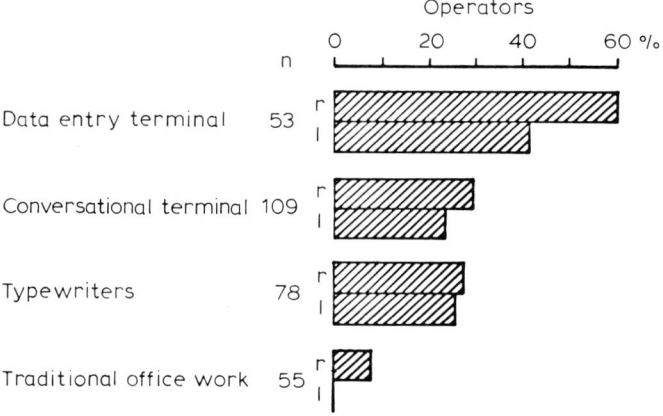

Figure 2.6 The incidence of medical findings: painful pressure points at tendons, joints and muscles in the area of shoulders. n = number of operators; r = right side; l = left side

area are frequent at data entry terminals and rare in the control group of traditional office work. The survey revealed that physical impairments in hands, arms, shoulders and neck are reported by some employees operating keyboards. In general, the complaints as well as the medical findings are more often observed in the group working on data entry terminals. Some of the symptoms can be considered as localised fatigue and are reversible. Other findings show more serious impairments, involving tendons and joints, which might have a more chronic character.

The results of the analysis of relationships between the incidence of impairments and the design of the workstations can be summarised as follows. The incidence of physical impairments is higher when forearms and hands are not rested on a support, when the keyboard height above desk exceeds 7 cm and when the level of source documents is low.

From theory to practice

The field study shows that the theory about the adverse effects of constrained postures due to static postural efforts is valid for at least one in four business machine operators. The results justify the following practical recommendations.

Separate devices to adjust independently the heights of desk level, the position of the source documents as well as the height of the terminal display are necessary.
Movable keyboards give greater flexibility, more space to rest hands and forearms and allow for one-handed operations to turn the keyboard anti-clockwise in order to decrease the ulnar deviation of the right hand.
All workplaces with keyboards should provide adequate opportunity to rest hands or forearms; this is especially indicated for jobs on conversational terminals characterised by frequent waiting times.

Adequate and adjustable supports for the source documents are indispensable; source documents lying on the desk always cause a postural effort in the neck and back.

Chairs with high backrests and adjustable inclination are recommended.

References

HÜNTING, W. *et al.* (1980a). 'Constrained posture in accounting machine operators', *Applied Ergonomics*, **11**, 145–149.

HÜNTING, W. *et al.* (1980b). 'Constrained postures of VDU operators' (in *Ergonomic Aspects of Visual Display Terminals*, GRANDJEAN, E. & VIGLIANI, E. (eds), p. 175), Taylor and Francis, London.

Läubli, Th. *et al.* (1980). '*Arbeitsbedingte cervicobrachiale Beschwerden bei Büroarbeiten*', *Zschr. Sozial- und Präventivmedizin*, **25**, 407–412.

Chapter 3

Prevention of fatigue amongst data entry operators

R. Kukkonen, T. Luopajärvi & V. Riihimäki

Introduction

The development of computers in recent years has resulted in their wide use in several commercial fields, such as banking and insurance; new professional classes, e.g., data entry operators, have evolved. The work of data entry operators demands concentration, eye–hand coordination and accuracy. The work imposes unilateral loads, mainly in the shoulder–hand region. These unilateral loads involve static strain in the arm, the repetition of tens of thousands of finger movements daily, and constant sitting in one position.

In some studies, symptoms of the neck and shoulder regions have been associated with this kind of static strain (Ferguson 1971; Komoike et al. 1969). The prevalence of tension neck syndrome in these studies appeared to have a broad range of 4–42% depending on the criteria used and the type of work of the population studied (Maeda 1977; Partridge 1968).

Several factors – incorrect dimensions of the workplace, incorrect placing of furniture and work equipment, poor physical environment, improper frequency and duration of breaks and an unfavourable way of working – can be considered to worsen the strain and precipitate the onset of symptoms (Onishi et al. 1976). However, the significance of any one of these factors with a view to designing an appropriate program of prevention measures has not been thoroughly studied.

The aim of this investigation was to study whether loading symptoms and signs in the regions of the neck, shoulder and arm can be prevented by an intervention program which encompasses ergonomic improvements, health education and physical activation of the workers.

Material and methods

The intervention program was carried out over a period of six months in the computer department of a bank. The study comprised 60 female data entry operators. Their average age was 27 years and the duration of their professional careers was 3.5 years. The first reference group consisted of 44

28

data entry operators who work at another bank. Their average age was 29 years and they had professional experience on average of six years. The second reference group comprised women with assignments in varying office tasks from a third workplace. Their average age was 31 years and average time of their employment was 4.9 years (Table 3.1). The interven-

Table 3.1 *The age and time of employment (in years) of the study persons*

Characteristics	Study group	Reference group (1)	Reference group (2)
Number	60	44	57
Age (mean)	27	29	31
Age (SD)	7.0	5.4	7.7
Employment (mean)	3.6	6.0	4.9

tion program involved several procedures designed to produce an ameliorating effect on the strain amongst operators. The subjective and objective statuses of health and well-being were assessed through a questionnaire and health examination.

Assessment of the effects of intervention

The effects of intervention were assessed through a health examination which comprised a questionnaire and a standardised clinical functional examination of the neck and upper limbs. The questionnaire requested information on the following items: the type of complaints, their localisation and the frequency of symptoms. After the functional examination, the physiotherapist checked the information given on the questionnaire by interviewing the examinee. The clinical functional examination was performed by a physiotherapist who did not know to which group the examinee belonged.

Intervention actions

Ergonomic survey

The intervention actions were begun with an ergonomic survey of the work. The survey included
  (1) assessment of the ergonomic characteristics of the work-desk and chair as well as the data processing equipment;
  (2) observation of the working posture, movements and working technique;
  (3) measurement of the illumination, temperature, draught and noise;
  (4) interview of the foremen and workers in order that the organisation of the work and the physical, mental and social environment at the workplace could be determined.

Results of the ergonomic survey

The structure and adjustability of the work-desks, chairs and data processing equipment corresponded well with ergonomic recommendations. However, the workers were not familiar enough with the adjustability of their equipment to carry out adjustments themselves. On the other hand, due to insufficient ergonomic information, the level of motivation was not the best possible. Consequently, many poor working positions which result in unfavourable loading of the neck and shoulders were noted; this included improper practices during the breaks, such as knitting, which tended to add to the load rather than to decrease it.

The load of these regions was further increased by high ambient temperature and improper illumination, which in this context means a general level of illumination which is too high as well as reflections from the screen and from wide window surfaces.

The interviews of the foremen revealed that data entry operators were taught to handle certain kinds of material. This speeded up the work but simultaneously increased monotony. The data entry operators themselves described their work as, at times, very pressing, monotonous and lacking physical variety.

Ergonomic improvements

Whenever necessary the desks, chairs and data processing equipment were adjusted individually to suit each worker, who was instructed to carry out the adjustments herself. One further way of improving the working posture and working movements was to design and construct supports for the documents that had previously been kept on the desk.

The general illumination was decreased to 300–500 lux and spot lighting was provided for those workers who did not have it. Reflections were also diminished by increasing the use of venetian blinds. In order to vary the work tasks, data entry operators were taught to feed documents of different sources into the computer.

Health education

In order to understand ergonomic principles in general better and to enhance the level of motivation with respect to preventive activities at one's own workstation, the study group was offered a short course of basic training on pertinent aspects of ergonomics. Four lectures were given to small groups, dealing with muscle physiology, the etiology and prevention of muscle strain, the significance of proper work habits including the systematic incorporation of 'minibreaks', methods of relaxation of muscle tension as well as the results of the health examination. In addition, four lessons on relaxation by means of exercises were given in order that the correct muscle tension could be felt and the ability to relax could be learned.

Physiotherapy

Physiotherapeutic treatment was given to those workers for whom the company doctor prescribed it. The treatment usually comprised ultrasound, massage and relaxation exercises. During the six month investigation, 17 operators from the study group and none from the first reference group had had physiotherapeutic treatments.

Results

At the first health examination prior to the execution of the intervention actions, the data entry operators (the study group and the first reference group) reported significantly more stiffness and pain in the neck and shoulders, numbness in the elbows and swelling of the ankles and feet than the second reference group of ordinary office workers (Table 3.2).

Table 3.2 *Percentage of study persons reporting subjective symptoms in different parts of the body in the first health examination*

Localisation of symptoms	Study group + reference group (1) N = 104 (%)	Reference group (2) N = 57 (%)	p
Neck and shoulders	58	37	<0.02
Elbows	20	6	<0.05
Back	45	32	n.s.
Lower limbs	50	14	<0.001

In the clinical functional examination of the neck, the shoulders and the upper limbs, a significantly higher prevalence of tender points and palpable hardenings was found in both the study group and the first reference group of data entry operators than in the second reference group (Table 3.3). Even the tension neck syndrome (Waris 1979) appeared significantly more often in data entry operators than in office workers (Table 3.4). The study group and the first reference group did not differ from each other with

Table 3.3 *Percentage of study persons who exhibit objective signs in the first clinical functional examination*

Signs	Study group + reference group (1) (%)	Reference group (2) (%)	p
Limitation of neck movement	32	28	n.s.
Tender points and hardenings in neck–shoulders	71	54	<0.05
Tender points and hardenings in elbows	23	16	n.s.

Table 3.4 *Percentage of subjects who present the following syndromes in first health examination*

Syndrome	Study group + reference group (1) (%)	Reference group (2) (%)	p
Tension neck	47	28	<0.02
Cervical syndrome	1	2	n.s.
Humeral tendinitis	1	1	n.s.

respect to the subjective symptoms and objective signs. The follow-up examination was performed by the same physiotherapist half a year later on the study group and the first reference group only. Prevalence of the neck–shoulder and back symptoms had decreased significantly in the study group (Figure 3.1). The same was true in the prevalence of tender points and hardenings of the neck and shoulders (Figure 3.2).

The prevalence of tension neck syndrome decreased in the study group from 54% to 16% whereas it remained at a similar level (43% and 45% respectively) in the first reference group. In all the statistical calculations for group differences, the chi-square test was used.

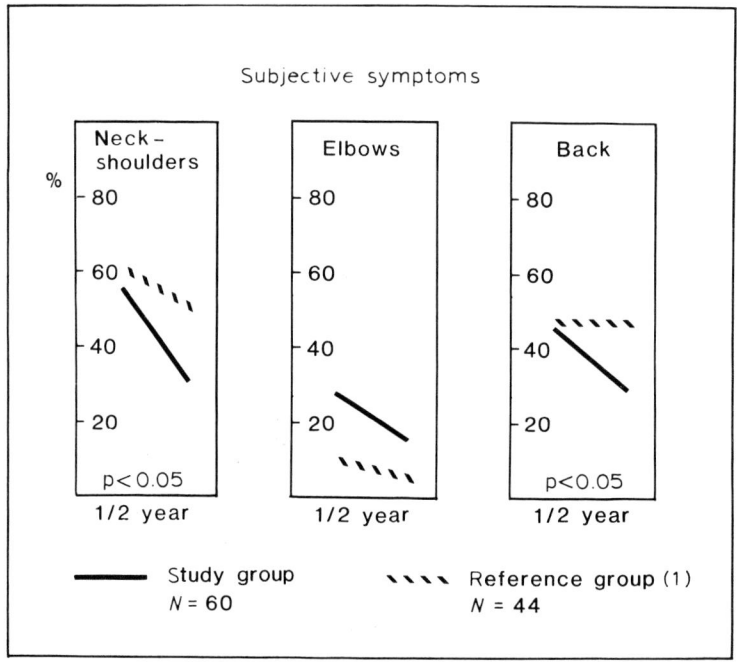

Figure 3.1 Symptoms experienced in different parts of the body in the study group and in the first reference group before and after intervention actions

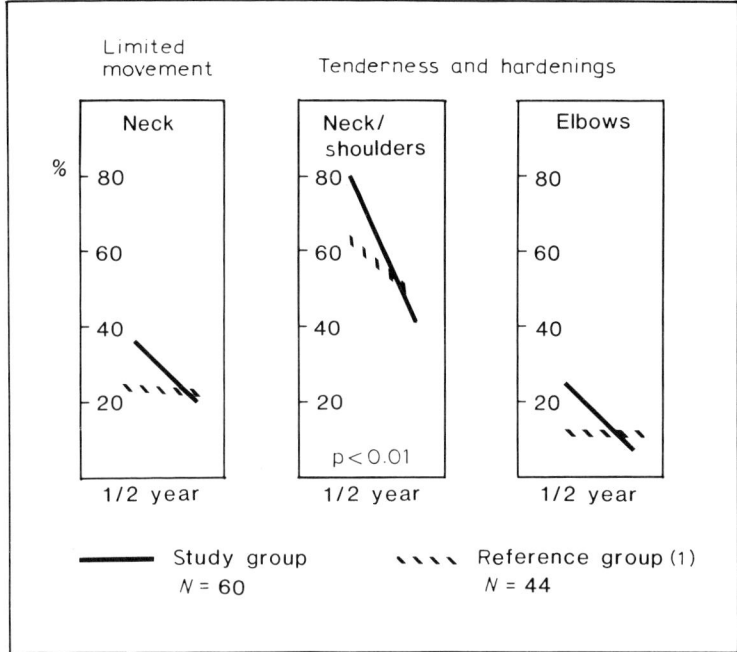

Figure 3.2 The objective signs in the study group and the first reference group before and after intervention action

Discussion

Since the causes of musculoskeletal diseases are little known, the intervention program was carried out on a wide basis. First it was considered important to eliminate all obvious ergonomic defects and second was the instruction of the worker to improve her working situation.

The overall effects of the intervention in our study were positive. The results show that improved ergonomic conditions and individual attention alleviate the symptoms of muscle strain and increase the well-being of data entry operators at work. A useful result of this investigation was the compilation of an instruction booklet for data entry operators. According to our experience, it is essential to train the workers to recognise the ergonomic problems of their workplace and to be able to use the proper work techniques. Negligence in this respect is likely to counteract the advantages which ergonomically well-planned facilities offer. Since it was also found to be difficult for workers to change their individual working habits, it may be concluded that information on ergonomics should be provided during vocational training. Later during the professional career, further instruction pertaining to everyday work situations should be given.

References

FERGUSON, E. (1971). 'An Australian study of telegraphists cramp', *Br. J. Indust. Med.*, **28**, No. 3, 280–285.

KOMOIKE, Y. *et al.* (1969). 'Health control on key punchers, typists and others', *The Sumimoto Bulletin of Industrial Health*, **5**, 82–112.

MAEDA, K. (1977). 'Occupational cervicobrachial disorder and its causative factor', *J. Human Ergol.*, **6**, 193–202.

ONISHI, N. *et al.* (1976). 'Shoulder muscle tenderness and physical features of female industrial workers', *J. Human Ergol.*, **5**, No. 2, 87–102.

PARTRIDGE, R. E. H. (1968). 'Rheumatism in dockers and civil servants', *Ann. Rheum. Dis.*, **27**, 559–568.

WARIS, P. (1979). 'Epidemiologic screening of occupational neck and upper limb disorders', *Scand. J. Work Environ. & Health*, **5**, Supp. 3, 25–38.

Chapter 4

The working environment of cleaners. Evaluation of physical strain in mopping and swabbing as a basis for job redesign

J. Winkel, B. Ekblom, M. Hagberg & B. Jonsson

Introduction

Cleaning work in public buildings and industrial plants in Sweden has developed into a full-time specialised occupation, engaging about 150 000 cleaners in 1980. The search for increased benefit at decreased cost has caused the introduction of new equipment and work methods. Cleaning work has been decomposed to such a degree that many cleaners carry out only a few work tasks. This causes not only a psychosocial impoverishment of the job but also a limitation of the physical load to fewer muscles and joints.

Work disability forced in one year 24 out of 240 cleaners at a hospital to change their job. In 17 cases it was due to shoulder–neck disorders (Olivecrona and Rosenberg 1979). It has been suggested that the work disabilities among cleaners might be due to medical conditions or low physical fitness rather than physical strain during work.

Figure 4.1 Swabbing of the floor by moving the cloth in S-shaped curves

The average heart rate during cleaning work for 60 cleaners was reported to be 109 min^{-1} (Petersson *et al.* 1975). According to Astrand and Rodahl (1977), the severity of this work load might be classified as 'moderate'. However, this is not consistent with a questionnaire study amongst 558 cleaners, in which 93% rated the work as heavy (Ahlstrand and Lidehäll 1981). In another questionnaire answered by 279 cleaners, 43% reported work-related complaints in the low back, 40% in the shoulders and 33% in the neck (Ahlstrand *et al.* 1978). The work task considered by the cleaners to be the heaviest physically was floor cleaning. This is usually performed either by mopping or swabbing. In mopping, a moist short-threaded cloth is used to wipe in S-shaped curves on the floor. Similarly a long-threaded wet cloth is used in swabbing (Figure 4.1). The latter is used when the dirt sticks to the floor and also for ordinary floor cleaning when mopping might be used as well.

The aim of the present study was to assess the work stress associated with mopping and swabbing in light of the reported complaints in shoulder and neck amongst cleaners as a basis for job redesign.

Material and methods

Kinematic analysis

The tool is moved with the left hand in a power grip round the middle of the broomstick and the right at the top, whilst the cleaner steps backwards slowly. The left hand pulls the tool to the left with an abduction – extension in the gleno-humeral joint combined with a retraction of the scapula and an extension of the elbow joint (Figure 4.2a, nos 6–9). Simultaneously the

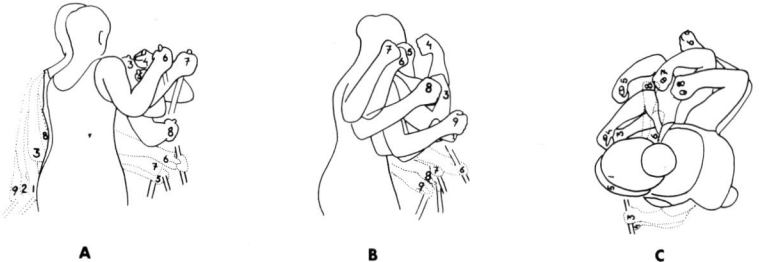

Figure 4.2 Body movements during a work cycle. The numbers 1–9 indicate the sequence of the movements which are seen from behind (a), from the right side (b) and from above (c)

right hand is counteracting a co-movement of the top of the broomstick with an abduction and inward rotation in the gleno-humeral joint and an extension in the elbow joint (Figure 4.2a, and b, nos 6–9). Whilst moving the cloth to the left the broomstick is rotated by the right hand with an extension – supination of the wrist. Completion of the work cycle by moving the cloth to the right is performed by the opposite movements in the above-mentioned joints. The cycle time is about 2 s.

Subjects

The subjects were six females with 2–12 years' (mean 4.7 years) experience as professional cleaners. All were right-handed, that is, worked with the right hand on top of the broomstick. Their average age was 26.2 years (range 20–41 years). A few days before the experiments a manual medical and anthropometric examination of the subjects was made. They were found to be free of complaints in the musculoskeletal system and to have ordinary body size and strength in the muscle groups relevant to the investigation.

Experimental procedure

The experimental task consisted of continuous swabbing and mopping of a 16 m^2 area for one hour respectively. The subjects were to maintain their normal, self-chosen work rate. The work rate was measured as the area cleaned per minute. Between the mopping and the swabbing one hour of rest was given.

Measurement of work stress

The circulatory strain was assessed from the heart rate monitored continuously during the experiments. Every fifth minute the overall level of rated perceived exertion (RPE) was assessed by the subjects on a numerical scale (Borg 1970). The muscular load was evaluated by vocational electromyography (EMG). After a pilot study of 12 different muscles in the shoulder girdle, four of these were selected for the main study. The location of the electrodes is shown in Figure 4.3. The myoelectric activity was recorded on tape by bipolar surface electrodes from the right- and left-descending part of the trapezius muscle and the left-middle part of the trapezius muscle, and by bipolar wire electrodes from the right supraspinate muscle. Test contractions gave the EMG–force relationship for the investigated muscles by simultaneous recording of myoelectric activity and force during a slowly increased submaximal contraction for shoulder elevation, retraction and abduction.

EMG data analysis

For muscular load evaluation, vocational electromyography offers the possibility to estimate the contraction levels of a muscle. However, in an occupational situation the contraction levels are rapidly fluctuating and for ergonomic evaluation it is necessary to get a measure of the distribution of contraction levels over a certain period of time. By estimating the amplitude probability distribution function (APDF), such a measure is offered, exposing the static, the median and the maximum contraction levels for the time studied (Hagberg 1979). The myoelectric and force signals were determined as root-mean square (RMS) values by computer-aided analysis from the tape recorder (Ericson and Hagberg 1978). By power function regression analysis of the EMG levels versus force levels during the test contractions, the EMG–force relationship was established.

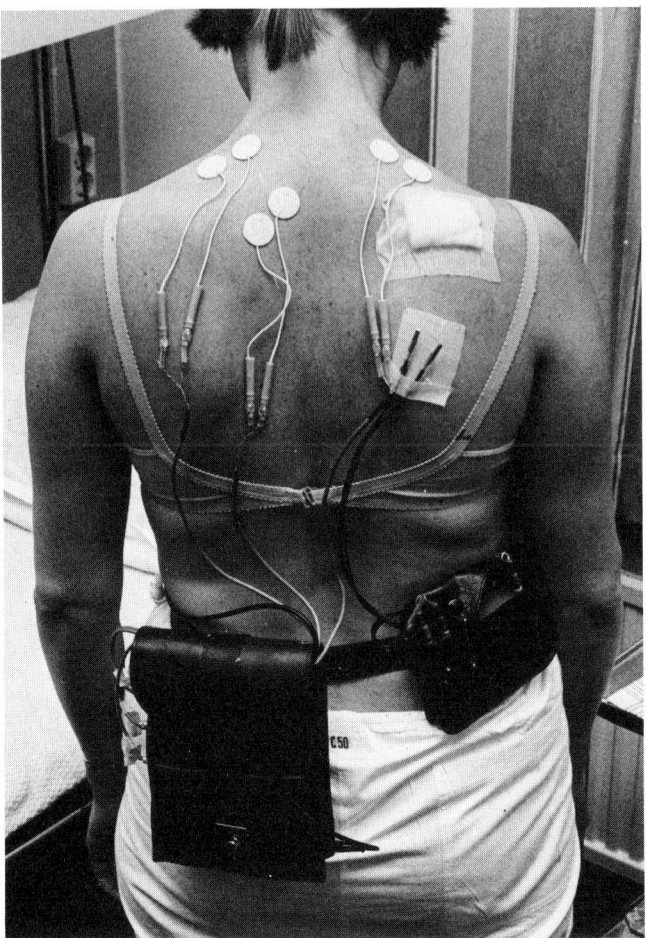

Figure 4.3 Location of the electrodes during the electromyographic study

Thus the APDF of the EMG signals during work could be transformed to an APDF of contraction levels for the different muscles. The distribution of load levels was evaluated for the first five minutes of each experiment to avoid influence of fatigue on myoelectric signal amplitudes. Muscular fatigue was evaluated by regression analysis of the EMG amplitude (RMS) and mean power frequency (MPF) versus time. The characteristic changes of the myoelectric signal as a result of muscular fatigue are (1) an increase in the RMS value, and (2) a decrease in the MPF (Kadefors *et al.* 1968).

Results and discussion

It was found that swabbing, on average, was performed at a rate 50% slower than mopping, although the ratings of perceived exertion were significantly higher in swabbing ($p<0.01$). This is in accordance with the significantly higher heart rate during swabbing compared to mopping ($p<0.025$) (Figure 4.4). In mopping neither work rate nor heart rate changed significantly during the experimental period. Thus the strain on the body apparently was too low to generate fatigue measured as increase in heart rate. In swabbing the increase in heart rate was highly significant ($p<0.001$). This might be due to the highly significant increase in work rate ($p<0.001$).

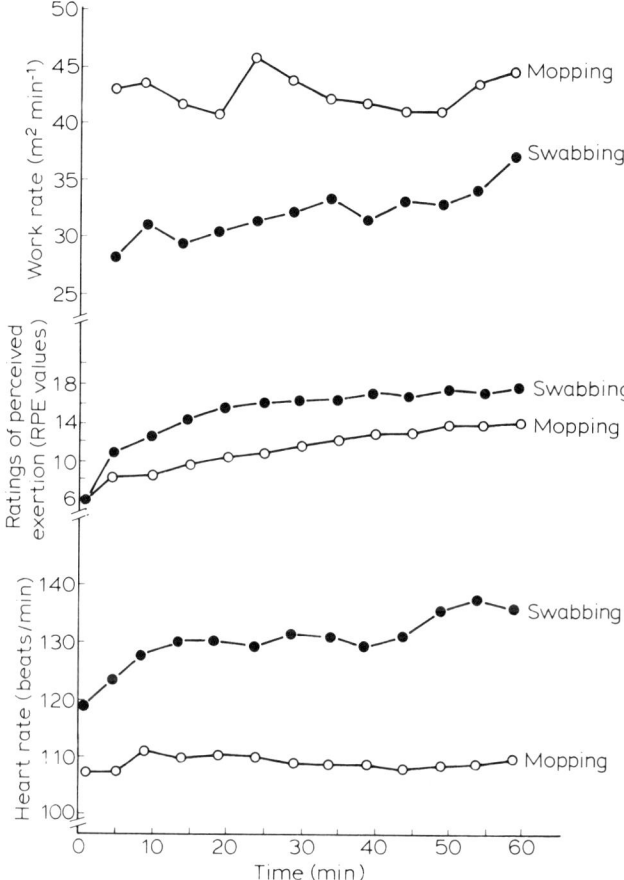

Figure 4.4 Work rate (top), ratings of perceived exertion (middle) and heart rate (bottom) during the experimental hour. Each dot represents the average of the six subjects

According to Pandolf (1978) an 'overall' RPE rating is determined by two prominent factors: a local muscular exertion and a central cardiopulmonary exertion. In the present study the average RPE values increased gradually during both mopping and swabbing without a corresponding increase in heart rate suggesting local strain as a dominant factor (Figure 4.5). This is further indicated by the high local muscular load shown in the

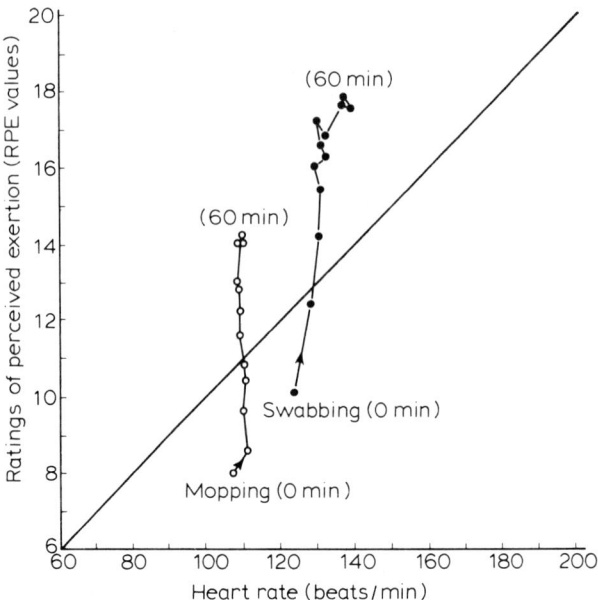

Figure 4.5 Changes in RPE values in relation to heart rate during
the experimental hour. The straight line indicates a one to ten
relation between RPE value and heart rate, which is sometimes
obtained for middle-aged people and for work loads of medium
intensity levels (Borg 1970)

electromyographic study (Figure 4.6). Jonsson (1978) has suggested
threshold limit values for 'long-lasting' work. These are illustrated in
Figure 4.6 and propose an overload first of all on the right-descending part
of the trapezius and the right supraspinate muscle during both mopping
and swabbing. Cleaners usually experience a heavier physical load on the
shoulders when swabbing compared with mopping. Accordingly the maximum load levels were significantly higher during swabbing compared with
mopping for three of the investigated muscles (the supraspinate muscle
showed no significant difference). However, none of the load peaks
exceeded the suggested threshold limit value. Neither the static nor the
median load levels showed any significant differences between the two
cleaning methods.

In spite of the high load levels for two of the investigated muscles no
clear electromyographic indication of fatigue could be shown. The fatigue
effects may have been masked by temperature increase (Petrofsky and
Lind 1980). A significant increase in RMS values for the right-descending
part of the trapezius and the right supraspinatus muscle could only be
shown during swabbing (seven muscles). However, these changes could
also be caused by the highly significant increase in work rate. Special
attention should be paid to the changes of MPF during the working hour.
An example is shown in Figure 4.7. No significant decrease in MPF
developed as might be expected in case of fatigue. However, a moving
window *t*-test on these data, comparing MPF during the working hour with

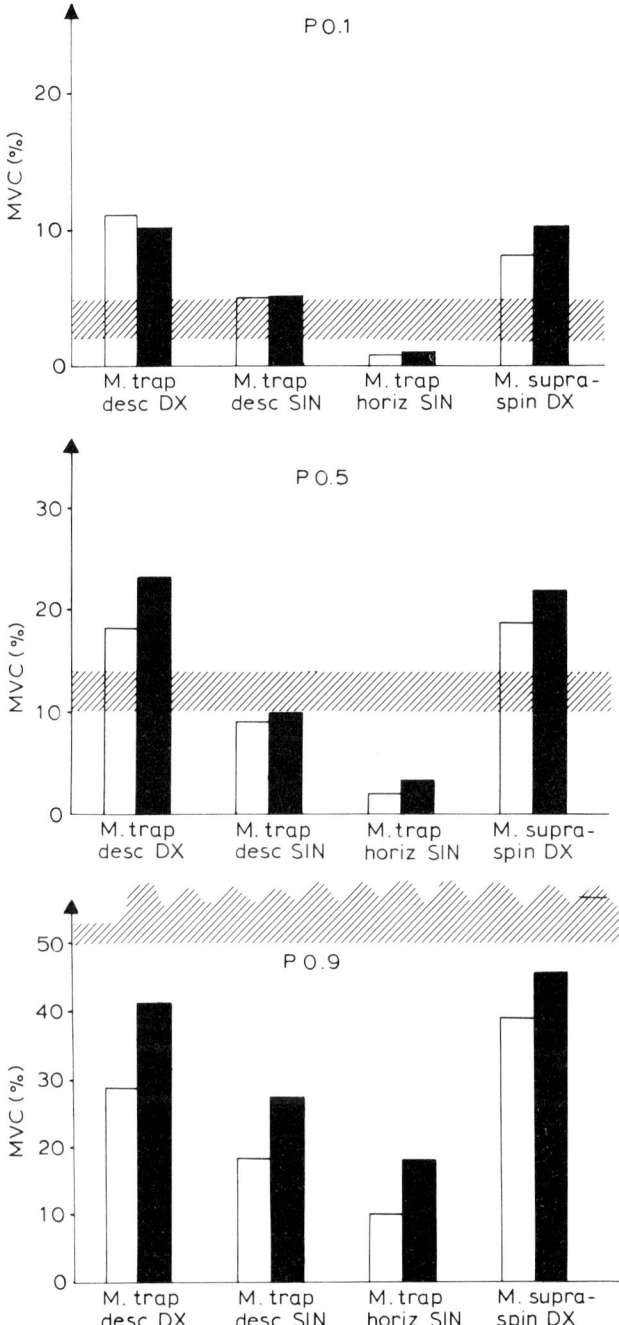

Figure 4.6 Muscular load levels during mopping (blank staples) and swabbing (black staples). P 0.1: static load level, P 0.5: median load level, P 0.9: maximum load level. Hatched areas: suggested threshold limit values according to Jonsson (1978)

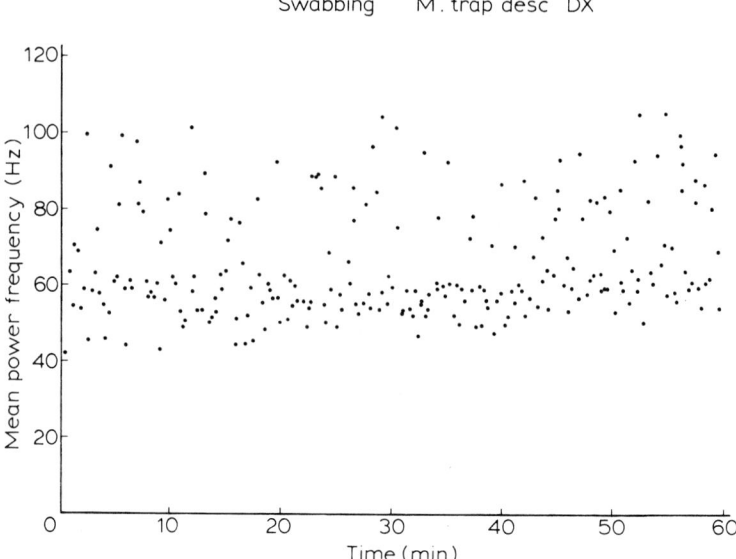

Figure 4.7 MPF for the right-descending part of the trapezius muscle during one hour of swabbing. One subject. One sample every 15 th second

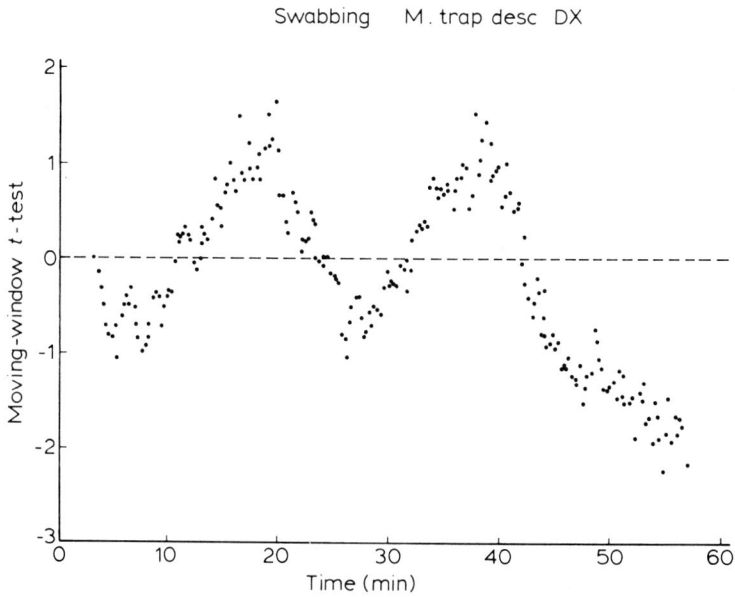

Figure 4.8 A moving window *t*-test on the data illustrated in Figure 4.7. The window was 25 samples (6 min of work) and moved over the 240 samples (60 min in one sample step)

the first six minutes of work, unveiled a cyclic change of the t- value (Figure 4.8). A positive and increasing t-value indicates an increasing probability of a decrease of MPF. In most cases all four muscles showed such a rhythmic pattern with a variable districtness, amplitude and frequency. An alternating recruitment of motor units due to a selective muscle fibre fatigue might be one possible explanation to the observed changes (Hagberg 1981a; Hagberg 1981b).

Olivecrona and Rosenberg (1979) have carried out a clinical examination of 17 cleaners with cervicobrachial disorders. These patients suffered from pain mainly correlated to the right-descending part of the trapezius muscle and the right superspinate muscle (or the corresponding muscles on the left side if they were left-handed). These findings are in agreement with the present electromyographic studies of muscular load levels.

Conclusion

The following practical implications of the study are suggested as a basis for job redesign.

(1) Whenever swabbing is interchangeable with mopping, the latter should be preferred.
(2) both mopping and swabbing should probably not be performed for an extended period of time without intermittent rest pauses.

Acknowledgement

This investigation was supported by grants from the Swedish Work Environment Fund.

References

AHLSTRAND, H. *et al.* (1978). '279 lokalvårdares synpunkter på sin arbetsmiljö' Technical Report 1978:01T, University of Luleå, Sweden [in Swedish].
AHLSTRAND, H. & LIDEHÄLL, P. (1981). *Working Environment, Division of Labour, Elimination – A Study of the Working Conditions of Cleaning Personnel*, Doctoral Dissertation 1981:8D, University of Luleå, Sweden [in Swedish with a summary in English].
ASTRAND, P-O. & RODAHL, K. (1977). *Textbook of Work Physiology*, McGraw-Hill Book Company, New York.
BORG, G. (1970). 'Perceived exertion as an indicator of somatic stress', *Scand. J. Rehab. Med.*, **2–3**, 92–98.
ERICSON, B-E. & HAGBERG, M. (1978). 'EMG signal level versus external force: a methodological study on computer aided analysis', in *Biomechanics*, Asmussen, E. & Jörgensen, K. (eds), VI-A, 251–255), University Park Press, Baltimore.
HAGBERG, M. (1979). 'The amplitude distribution of surface EMG in static and intermittent static muscular performance', *Eur. J. Appl. Physiol*, **40**, 265–272.
HAGBERG, M. (1981a). 'Electromyographic signs of shoulder muscular fatigue in two elevated arm positions', *Am. J. Phys. Med.*, **60**, 111–121. .
HAGBERG, M. (1981b). 'On evaluation of local muscular load and fatigue by electromyography', *Arbete och Hälsa*, **24**, 1–53. Arbetarskyddsstyrelsen, Sweden.

JONSSON, B. (1978). 'Kinesiology with special reference to electromyographic kinesiology', (in *Contemp. Clin. Neurophysiol.*, Cobb, W. A. & van Duijn, H. (eds), **34**, 417–428), Elsevier Scientific Publishing Company, Amsterdam.

KADEFORS, R. *et al.* (1968). 'Dynamic spectrum analysis of myopotentials with special reference to muscle fatigue', *Electromyogr.*, **8**, 39–74.

OLIVECRONA, E. & ROSENBERG, B. (1979). Lokalvårdarnas arbetsmiljö: Undersökning av en grupp lokalvårdare vid Region-sjukhuset i Umeå, Technical Report 1979:73T, University of Luleå, Sweden, [in Swedish].

PANDOLF, K. B. (1978). 'Influence of local and central factors in dominating rated perceived exertion during physical work', *Perceptual and Motor Skills*, **46**, 683–698.

PETERSSON, N. F. *et al.* (1975). 'Undersökning av lokalvårdares arbetsmiljö', *Undersökningsrapport AMA* 003/75, Arbetarskyddsstyrelsen, Sweden, [in Swedish].

PETROFSKY, J. S. & LIND, A. R. (1980). 'The influence of temperature on the amplitude and frequency components of the EMG during brief and sustained isometric contractions', *Eur. J. Appl. Physiol.*, **44**, 189–200.

Chapter 5

Improving visual inspection performance

E. D. Megaw, J. Powell & L. Bellamy

Introduction

The literature on industrial visual inspection reflects two broadly contrasting approaches. The first of these involves a form of checklist which summarises the many factors that have been investigated for their effects on the accuracy of inspection performance (Megaw 1979). Whilst checklists of this kind provide a convenient means of documenting the available literature, they do not encourage the practitioner to adopt a coherent method of investigation. Moreover the checklist often refers to laboratory-based studies, the relevance of which has not been established in field studies. One can cite the case of the time-on-task factor. Despite the enormous volume of literature on the vigilance decrement, there is still no conclusive evidence whether such a decrement exists on the shop-floor. Quite the contrary, the observation that inspectors frequently take very short unofficial rest pauses (Nachreiner 1977) would suggest that the vigilance data are not relevant.

The alternative approach has been to evolve models that enable the effects on performance of altering some of the inspection parameters to be predicted (Drury 1975; 1978). This approach parallels the development of search models for military tasks (Greening 1976). It is not unfair to say that these models are generally oversimplified in their underlying assumptions (Megaw and Bellamy 1979) and in the range of parameters they can accommodate. This is reflected in the finding that such models have been tested mainly with laboratory studies where simulated inspection material was used.

We have, therefore, a situation where the checklist approach is too vague and the modelling approach too constrained. Both suffer from the choice of factors or parameters for investigation being arbitrary, often reflecting the whim of the investigator. This has important repercussions since the selection of factors for investigation is likely to determine the solutions that an investigator proposes, and, for this reason, it is not surprising that there is a dismal absence of validation studies in ergonomics literature.

What follows is an outline of an alternative approach which enables the ergonomist to consider a wide range of factors and to embark on an investigation without pre-empting solutions. The approach is sufficiently robust to be applicable when numerous constraints are typically imposed by the company for whom the investigation is being undertaken. One obvious constraint is that both quality and training departments have a low priority within a company, which means that costs have to be kept to a minimum. A further constraint is that the investigation should cause as little disruption to production as possible. An essential feature of the approach is that the several activities contributing to the total project can be undertaken in parallel. With the many delays that are inevitable with industrial studies, the traditional systems approach (Singleton 1971), where the investigator is encouraged to work through a series of sequential steps, is often too cumbersome.

Outline of the approach

The mean features of the approach are shown in Figure 5.1. Quality standards should be established directly from the objectives of the study as proposed by the company. These standards are set alongside the tradition-al criteria which are familiar to the ergonomist but are usually considered by company personnel to be of secondary importance. They include health

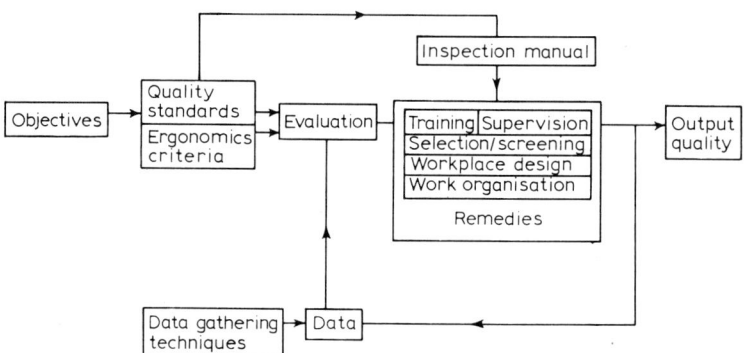

Figure 5.1 A summary of the approach outlines in the text

and safety at work, acceptable workloads, comfort, job satisfaction, acceptable rates of absenteeism and so on. During the course of the study, numerous data gathering techniques are employed in order to generate data. These data are evaluated against the prescribed standards so that the appropriate remedies can be selected. Naturally, this sequence of inves-tigation can be repeated to assess the success of any changes that are introduced. Although such an approach contains nothing profound or novel to the ergonomist, a brief description of the various stages follows.

Objectives

Although one of the more obvious objectives of any inspection process is to match output quality with customer specifications, managers often have more idiosyncratic goals. They may wish to reduce the cost and volume of scrap, reduce the cost of inspection labour, or increase the ease of detection of a particular defect type.

Quality standards

It is obvious that to achieve a meaningful evaluation of existing methods, the objectives of any study must be translated into quality standards. However, all our studies have shown that individual companies can rarely arrive at a consensus on standards. There is a conflict between those standards expressed by the corporate policy, the marketing department and the quality control (QC) managers, supervisors and line inspectors. Therefore, one of the main objectives of a majority of studies can be the setting of unequivocal objective standards. Although these can only be reached by company personnel, the ergonomist plays an important role in translating them into a format which enables them to be conveyed accurately to inspectors through training and on-line supervision. It is another matter that managers may wish to tighten or relax the standards depending on the state of the market. The point is that quality standards must be specified in as concrete a form as possible. Because the process of establishing these standards is usually a prolonged affair, the investigation must often proceed in their absence.

Data gathering techniques

Data gathering techniques are listed in Table 5.1. Most of them are commonly used by ergonomists although some are more specific to

Table 5.1 *Data gathering techniques*

Direct observation

Filming of	Photometry
inspection cycle	luminance, illuminance
eye movements	Anthropometry
Inspector performance	workplace dimensions and layout
monitor on-going inspection	Posture assessment
prepare special batches	questionnaire
introduce known faults into on-going	Vision testing
inspection	orthorater for acuity, phorias
Obtain quality records	Munsell for colour vision
customer returns	card-sorting task for peripheral vision
quality audit	laser optometer and questionnaire for fatigue
fault list	Organisation
standards	information on current work organisation
inspectors' fault records	job satisfaction questionnaire
Measure fault conspicuity	
use of questionnaire	
use of visibility meter	

inspection-like tasks. These include the recording of eye movements, the assessment of fault conspicuity and the use of test batches of items to measure inspection performance.

Data and evaluation

The data that can be generated from the various techniques are listed in Table 5.2. Particularly important are the performance measures, although in the absence of reliable quality standards they must be treated with

Table 5.2 *Data that can be obtained from techniques given in Table 5.1 and used for evaluating inspection methods and performance*

Cycle times	Fault list
Inspection times	Fault probabilities
Eye movement scanning strategies	Fault standards
Performance measures	Fault conspicuities
apparent fraction defective	Workplace dimensions and layout
hit probability	Fatigue measures (visual and postural)
correct accept probability	Visual profiles of inspectors
correct decision probability	Flow chart/work organisation
parametric and non-parametric measures of	Production rates
sensitivity and response bias	Standard inspection times
information theory measures of	Job descriptions
misclassification and grading errors	Payment systems
Bayesian measures	Job satisfaction

caution. The experience and knowledge of the ergonomist plays a critical role in the evaluation of data. The error taxonomy shown in Table 5.3 can help the evaluation and selection of remedies if appropriate performance data are available. Broadly, the taxonomy is based upon the assumption that performance error can occur with any one of four cognitive functions underlying the inspector's task. Table 5.3 indicates a fifth source of error

Table 5.3 *A taxonomy of errors in visual inspection*

(1) Cognitive function – SEARCH

Error	Causes	Remedies
Inexhaustive search	Insufficient viewing time	Re-set viewing time – training
Misses	Inappropriate standards	Training, standards
	Sequential effects – 'set'	Supervision
	Self-terminating strategy	Training
Exhaustive search, but inefficient	Random or systemic search?	Identify fault locations and range of fault conspicuities – training
Long search times	Peripheral acuity of inspectors	Selection, training

(2) Congitive function – DETECTION

Error	Causes	Remedies
Failure to detect	Poor visual skills	Selection and screening
Misses	Low fault conspicuity	Workplace design
	Physical fatigue	Workplace design,
and		work organisation
Detect 'noise' as 'signal'/*false alarms* (rare)	Vigilance and shift effects	Work organisation
	Inappropriate inspector 'set' (a) fault set (b) response bias	Standards, supervision

(3) Cognitive function – JUDGEMENT

Error	Causes	Remedies
Misses and *False alarms*	Misapplication of functional standards	Training, standards, supervision, aids – workplace design
	Misapplication of cosmetic standards	Training, standards, supervision, aids – workplace design
	Sensory adaptation, sequential effects	Standards, supervision, aids – workplace design

(4) Cognitive function – OUTPUT DECISION

Error	Causes	Remedies
Misclassification of faults and errors in grading	Lack of job and product knowledge	Training, supervision
Misses and false alarms	Social and departmental pressures	Work organisation
	Payment systems	Work organisation

(5) Other activities – HANDLING AND PACKAGING

Error	Causes	Remedies
Introduction of faults	Poor handling during inspection	Workplace design, training
	Inadequate transport and packaging	Work organisation, workplace design

which is outside the actual visual inspection task. Unfortunately, interpretation of error data should often be supplemented by other data, for example eye movement recordings, if the taxonomy is to be used effectively.

Remedies

If the setting of standards is excluded, Figure 5.1 and Table 5.3 suggest that there are bascially five areas to consider and these are set out in Table 5.4. To a large extent these five constitute a re-classification of the factors included in the checklist approach.

Table 5.4 *Major remedies for improving inspection methods and performance*

Training
    use inspection manual
    set inspection time
    set inspection method
    set search strategy
Supervision
    on-line feedback/feedforward to
        maintain standards
    increase sensitivity to faults
    adjust response bias
    provide motivation
Selection and screening
    for visual skills
    for trainability
	Workplace design
	    workplace layout
	    lighting
	    seating
	    inspection aids
	    data-logging methods
	Work organisation
	    reorganise job content and task
	        reallocation
	    improve information flow
	    payment systems
	    rest pauses
	    social interaction
	    methods of conveying items to and from
	        workplace

Inspection manual

In the flow chart of Figure 5.1 there is an important interface between quality standards and training which is referred to as an inspection manual, where training includes on-line training in the form of supervision. In a sense this manual represents a task analysis and should not be confused with a traditional manual. Such a manual should include information on the causes and effects of each defect type, the conspicuity and location of defects, their frequency of occurrence, the method for inspecting them and, of great importance, a clear representation of standards. The sequence in which the defects are listed in the manual may reflect the recommended search strategy rather than a classification based upon cause or effect.

A case study

Background to the project

In the following an account is given of the progress that has been made on one project over a period of 18 months. As well as the three authors, many students have made valuable contributions to the project. Except for one student, none of us has been stationed with the company for extended periods of time. As a consequence, we have not been involved directly with any re-organisation on the shop-floor that we may have requested, but have had to rely on managers successfully interpreting and executing our requests. This has led to difficulties during the course of the project. No financial assistance was provided by the company for the project. The company is experiencing the effects of the current recession and recently workers and managers have been made redundant. The firm in which the study is being conducted manufactures a variety of plastic components which are distributed either to factories within the company for assembly or to other customers. The components are either compression or injection moulded and in the latter case can be divided into thermo-setting and thermo-plastic mouldings.

The main reason for setting up the study was the concern of the QC department over the high level of scrap. However, it was soon evident that the assembly plant was dissatisfied with the quality of components they were receiving and the company was also keen to secure new customers. The study was to concentrate on the final 100% inspection task. Because of the overlap in the activities contributing to the project, each activity is described from the point of view of the data that were initially collected to evaluate the current inspection methods and the activities are sequenced in the order in which the data were obtained.

General flow chart

We were surprised to find that this kind of information was not readily available. Several visits were necessary for us to compile the chart shown in Figure 5.2. One reason for the delay was that the details of the flow chart depend on the particular component with which one is concerned.

During the course of the project, focus of attention changed from one component to another mainly at the request of the management. Not only were the production processes being continually modified, but the problems as perceived by the managers were changing. Their goals were short-term compared with ours and it was difficult for us not to be drawn into their problems.

The flow chart does highlight an important fact which is widely known on the shop-floor. The inspection personnel are responsible to the QC department and receive a fixed pay rate whilst the machine operators who are responsible to the production department, work on a piece rate. The piece rate system is based on volume of production and not quality. The result of this organisational conflict is likely to be one of the factors contributing to the high scrap rate.

Fault list

It was soon apparent that no quality standards were available. As a preliminary step to obtaining standards, fault lists were collected. These lists summarised the causes of the fault types and for any particular component, they included approximately 20 fault types. The problems with drawing up the lists were similar to those mentioned in relation to the flow charts.

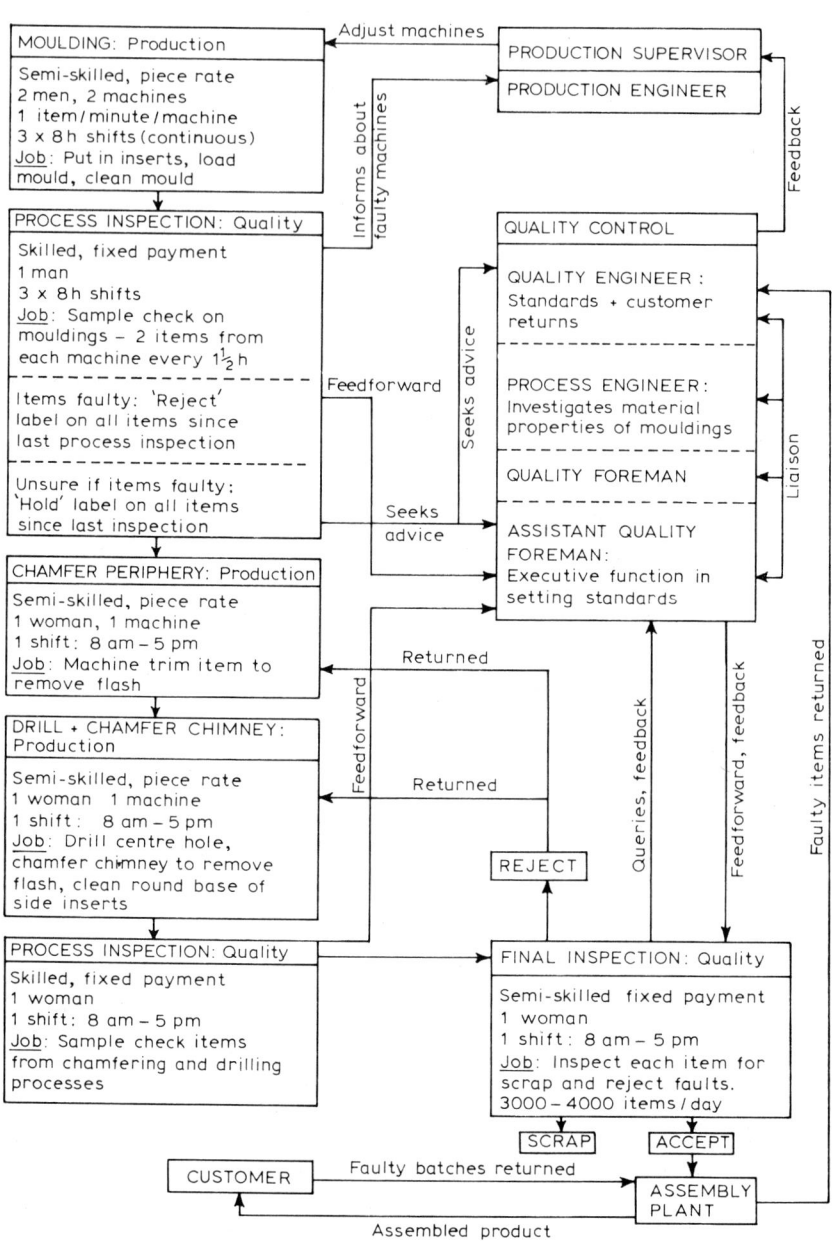

Figure 5.2 Example of a flow chart for the production and inspection of one component type

Performance data

Experience in compiling the fault lists suggested that specifying quality standards in a form suitable to include in an inspection manual and against which to evaluate performance was going to be an extremely protracted process. It was, therefore, decided to begin collecting performance data on two components chosen by QC management before obtaining quality standards. We adopted the method of using a pre-selected batch of components (Sinclair 1979) since we wished to make accurate comparisons between a number of inspectors and also to measure the reliability of each inspector. To have sampled the on-going inspection would have been of limited value since inspectors are often examining different components and quality fluctuates over the day.

The following account is restricted to one of the two selected components. A batch of 235 items was prepared by taking items that had been accepted by one of the line inspectors and adding certain defective items selected by the process engineer. These made up 17% of the batch. This batch was given to six inspectors on two separate occasions separated by one week. Although referred to as inspectors, the group included the QC manager and foreman. The components were inspected at the normal workplace and the inspectors were requested to adopt their usual method and speed of sorting the components into accept, scrap and reject.

Apart from the QC manager, all the inspectors worked at the normal daily rate for the component. The results of most interest are those regarding the scrap rate. Whilst all the inspectors showed a remarkable consistency over the two inspections, the differences between inspectors were enormous. At one extreme, an inspector scrapped 3.4% of the batch and at the other extreme, an inspector scrapped 46.8%. Taking the 12 decisions made in respect of each item, there were unanimous decisions to scrap 1.3% and to accept 33.2% of the batch. Although individual inspectors were consistent in their scrap rates, they did change their decisions from the first to the second inspections. For example, the mean probability of scrapping an item on the second inspection given it had been scrapped on the first inspection was 0.69.

To enable the main bulk of performance measures to be estimated, it was necessary to have the batch carefully sorted by someone whose decisions could be taken to reflect quality standards. Eventually, the QC manager from the plant where the components are assembled was persuaded to do this. This person was familiar with the functional testing of the components. Of the 116 components he found time to inspect in detail, he considered 10 should be scrapped. Performance measures were then established, based on the decisions made to the 116 components on both inspections. The results showed that the inspector with the highest hit rate (0.80) had the highest false alarm rate and the highest R:S score (probability of scrapping an item divided by the *a priori* fault probability). On the other hand the inspector with the lowest hit probability (0.25) had the lowest false alarm rate and R:S score. The sensitivities to the faults of the inspectors were evaluated using non-parametric and parametric measures. Estimates of d' (parametric measure) ranged from 0.66 to 1.90. However, it is important to point out that the ranking of the sensitivities of the inspectors is dependent upon the measure that is used.

Table 5.5 shows the correlation coefficients between the measures of sensitivty (d', Ag, A' and E) and the more traditional measures of hit probability, correct accept probability (1 − false alarm probability) and correct decision probability. Hit probability positively correlates with E (% improvement in quality due to inspection) and Ag (the most conservative measure of sensitivity). Correct accept probability positively correlates with correct decision probability and d'. In general these two groups of measures are negatively correlated. In other words an inspector with a low false alarm rate comes out favourably in terms of d' but poorly in terms of Ag. The picture is reversed for an inspector with a high hit probability. We have found this relationship between measures to be a feature of conditions where fault probability is low and inspectors have low sensitivities to faults.

Table 5.5 *Spearman rank correlation coefficients between various performance measures*

	Correct accept	Correct decisions	Ag	A'	d'	E
Hit	−0.60	−0.89*	0.89*	0.29	−0.26	1.00*
Correct accept	−	0.83*	−0.20	0.40	0.89*	−0.60
Correct decisions		−	−0.66	0.06	0.54	−0.89*
Ag			−	0.57	0.20	0.89*
A'				−	0.76	0.31
d'					−	−0.26

* Indicates the correlation is significant. $p<0.05$.

For the final part of the collection of performance data, a sub-batch of 35 components was chosen from the main batch on the grounds that inspectors had shown wide disagreement over them. On this occasion, the six inspectors were asked to tell the experimenter the reasons for making each of their output decisions. They were encouraged to say when they detected a potential fault but considered it acceptable. Analysis of the inspectors' protocols indicated that the inspectors had their own standards. For example, two inspectors never scrapped items on account of blisters, another inspector only scrapped items for large chips and another was particularly fussy over damage to the high tension (HT) chimney.

The overwhelming impression from the performance data is one of enormous variation in the standards of the inspectors. In relation to the error taxonomy, the errors could have originated from inspectors not giving the necessary visual coverage to the component, not adopting the correct 'fault set' and not making the appropriate judgements. The high false alarm rate shown by five of the inspectors suggests the latter is the most important cause. Naturally, the high false alarm rate is probably another reason for the concern originally expressed by the QC manager over the high scrap rate. On the whole, the faults are relatively conspicuous, although there was evidence that blisters and cracks were difficult to detect on certain areas of the components. This was one argument for re-designing the workplace.

Cycle times, inspection times, eye movements

A pilot study was conducted into the relationship between cycle times and eye movements. This was done on the shop-floor for one component and one inspector using video recordings of on-going inspection and of the accompanying eye movements. The technique that was used for the eye-movement recording has been described by Megaw and Richardson (1979). A mean cycle time of 2.97 s was obtained. Of this time, 1.80 s (SD = 0.67 s) was spent visually inspecting an item that was accepted, 1.33 s (SD = 0.71 s) on an item that was scrapped and 2.39 s (SD = 0.54 s) on an item that was rejected. The times to scrap an item were significantly less than those for accepting or rejecting items. One interpretation of these results is that the inspector was employing a self-terminating search strategy and was confident in deciding to scrap an item.

The distribution of eye fixations demonstrated that typically the first three or four fixations were directed to the bottom of the component, followed by one or two to the top and finally one or two to the rim of the component. During the first fixation the inspector orientated the component. The successive fixations on the bottom of the component were clustered closely together. During the fixations on the rim, the component was rotated by the inspector.

In the absence of quality standards for the component, we were again not in a position to evaluate the eye movement scanning strategy in terms of the total number of fixations, the distribution of fixations and their sequence. The daily rates that inspectors are expected to achieve for a particular component are governed by traditional practices although account is taken of the complexity of the component, the product cost and the customer's quality requirements. Certainly management was prepared to reduce daily rates if we proposed that this would bring major benefits.

Workplace data and design

Direct observations

The initial impression of the final inspection area was that it was cluttered and disorganised. Most of the components arrived for inspection in standard size cardboard boxes. There were six individual work benches. The benches had been designed on the 'sit or stand' principle, but in reality were too low for a comfortable standing posture and too high for a comfortable seated posture. All the inspectors worked from a seated position, but due to the height of the bench, this could hardly be considered comfortable.

The existing chairs are unsuitable for the task in almost every respect: the seat height is fixed, there is no provision for adjustment of the height or angle of the back-rest, the chair is made from a rigid plastic material which is uncomfortable for prolonged sitting, and there is no swivel facility to enable easy manœuvring. The clearance between the seat of the chair and the underside of the bench is inadequate for most of the inspectors who could be seen leaning forwards with their backs curved and their thighs crushed under the table. Another factor contributing towards poor postures is the need for inspectors to obtain the necessary lighting conditions to increase the conspicuity of certain fault types. No suitable foot-rests are available.

Other points we noted were that the inspectors did not have enough room on the bench surface to accommodate the boxes for the different categories of inspected items, ('accept', 'scrap' or 'reject'), and also that they tended to tip a number of components out of the box on to the work surface at one time before inspecting them.

A lighting survey revealed that the overhead fluorescent lights produced an uneven illuminance (between 800 and 1300 lux) on the working surfaces. Although the workplaces were equipped with supplementary fluorescent tubes, some of these had no glare shields, and all were positioned dangerously low. As a result, most of the lamps were not used.

Questionnaire data for existing workplace

Although we had suspected through our own observations and informal discussion that the inspectors may have many criticisms of the comfort and the general layout of their workplaces, we wished to quantify these complaints more formally before attempting to make any changes in the workplace design. We therefore designed three different questionnaires aimed at finding out, (1) inspectors' opinions about their existing workplaces, (2) in which body regions and to what extent they experienced postural discomfort and (3) whether any sumptoms of visual fatigue were present.

The workplace evaluation questionnaire was given to each of the eight final inspectors on one occasion, whereas the other two questionnaires were administered at three different times of the day so that we could get a picture of how any reported symptoms changed in severity over the course of the working day.

The factor associated with the workplace which received the worst ratings was the amount of available space. The inspectors were also generally dissatisfied with the existing arrangement for picking up and discarding items, the overall comfort of the workplace and the lighting.

It was no surprise to find that the greatest sources of physical discomfort were the back and buttocks regions. Some of the inspectors had previously mentioned that they suffered from backache and that the seat surface was uncomfortable. The severity of the reported symptoms increased markedly over the course of the day and there was even some discomfort reported at the very beginning of the day which seems to suggest that the symptoms did not necessarily dissipate completely after an evening's rest away from work. By the end of the day there was not a single region of the body where inspectors reported no discomfort.

The results from the visual comfort questionnaire confirmed the severe complaints of aches in the body in general and of the neck and shoulders in particular. How much of this is due to poor visual conditions at the existing workplace and how much is due to the layout of the work bench itself is difficult to establish. There was an increase over the course of the day in the desire to rub the eyes, headaches and giddiness. The amount of boredom and overall tiredness rose fairly sharply over the course of the day.

Design of the prototype workplace

The results from the previous two sections provide strong evidence for the need to completely re-design the existing workplace. The intitial prototype is illustrated in Figure 5.3. The work surface height has been lowered to 736 mm to enable inspectors to sit with their feet on the ground. The surface has been divided into a number of functional areas.

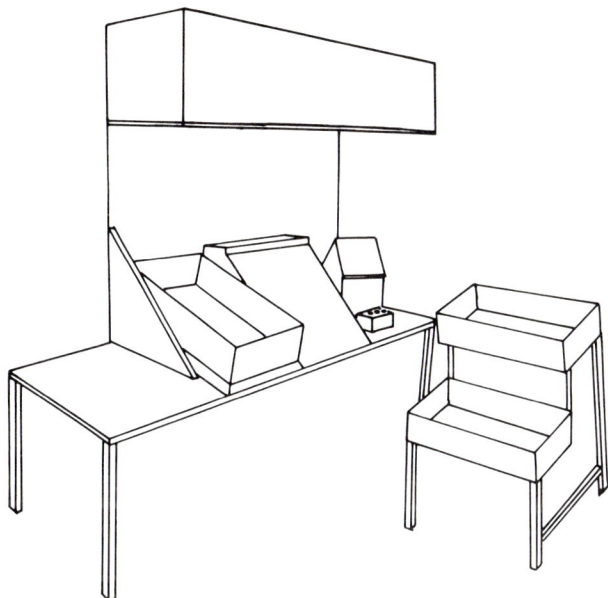

Figure 5.3 The main features of the prototype workplace

Directly in front of where the inspectors sit there is an angled viewing area at 45°. This is to encourage inspectors to adopt an upright posture, to bring the components closer to the light source and to prevent them from tipping the components on to the viewing area. To the left of the viewing area the box of components currently being inspected can be rested at one of two angles, the choice of angle depending on the size and weight of the components. Towards the extreme left there is a flat surface to support other boxes of incoming components.

To the right of the viewing area, there is a flat surface on which rests a small diffusion box and a compact keyboard. Both can be positioned to please the inspector. The diffusion box should be used to highlight certain defects which occur in various holes in the components. The luminance of the diffusion screen is 500 cd m^{-2}. The keyboard has been introduced mainly at the request of the production department who are anxious to have feedback on the relative scrap rates of four major classes of fault. The counters are electronic and, therefore, can be positioned remote from the workplace. Gauges can also be kept on this part of the work surface. A separate unit has been constructed to hold two other boxes, the top one for accepts and the lower one for scrapped components. This unit can be positioned anywhere to the right of the inspector. There is no need for a similar box for rejects since rejects are usually indicative of a missing operation in which case the incoming box of components is returned to the relevant production station.

Preliminary investigations had shown that the most suitable arrangement of lighting for a majority of the fault types was to have the light source located between the inspector and the task. The height of the source must be sufficient to prevent inspectors banging their heads and to avoid glare but, at the same time, must allow the appropriate task illuminance to be achieved. For economic reasons the company requested we used the existing twin 600 mm 20 W fluorescent fittings. To achieve the required illuminance, a ceiling lined with tin foil was constructed with a glare shield similarly lined with foil fitted around the ceiling. To avoid the inspectors being distracted, the area between the rear of the work surface and the ceiling was boarded up. The surface of this partition up to 65 cm above the work surface was painted matt grey and the remaining surface with white gloss. All the working surfaces were covered with matt grey vinyl. This arrangement provided an illuminance of 1500 lux at the mid-point of the viewing slope and a luminance level of $250 \, \text{cd m}^{-2}$. The luminance of the components depends on their colour and degree of specularity but ranged between $40-150 \, \text{cd m}^{-2}$.

We contacted over 50 manufacturers in an attempt to obtain a seat which satisfied our requirements. The results of this time-consuming exercise were disappointing. Only two manufacturers offered a suitable design and only one of these was in the price range acceptable to the company. It should be emphasised that the chair was in the secretarial range and had not been designed for use on the shop-floor.

Evaluation of the prototype workplace

For a variety of reasons beyond our control, only four inspectors could take place in the evaluation of the workplace on the shop-floor. Two of them were new to inspection and had not participated in the original assessment. Each inspector was given a brief introductory session to the workplace before being left to work at it for one week. Over the last day, the same three questionnaires were administered. Finally an informal meeting was arranged with all four inspectors together.

Many of the findings were discouraging. All the inspectors disliked the viewing slope on the grounds that it slowed them down. None of them liked the positioning of the incoming box of components to the immediate left of the viewing area. They commented that the new design meant it was difficult for them to converse with neighbouring workers and three of the inspectors found the grey colour of the workplace dreary. On the positive side, they all appreciated the new work height, the general lighting, the diffusion box, the use of the keyboard and the new chair design.

The questionnaires on postural and visual fatigue also provided conflict-
ing results. One of the two inspectors who had contributed to the
assessment of the original workplace showed a very marked decrease in
postural complaints but an increase in visual discomfort. For the other
inspector, the results were reversed. However, it was very noticeable that
these two inspectors were not using the workplace as they had been
instructed but were reverting to their original methods which were
completely inappropriate for the new design. In contrast to these results,
both the naïve inspectors showed a near total absence of postural and
visual complaints to the new workplace.

Modification to prototype

In response to the views expressed by the inspectors we have made a few
modifications which are illustrated in Figure 5.4. The viewing slope has
been lowered to 23° and can now be removed should the slope not be
suitable for the inspection of certain types of component. The box of
components under inspection can now be sunk into the work surface to
reduce the amount of static load when reaching for the components. The
viewing slope has been painted a darkish green and the surrounding
surfaces a lighter green. This gives luminance ratios between task, background and surround in the order of 1:3:10. We have had to lower the light

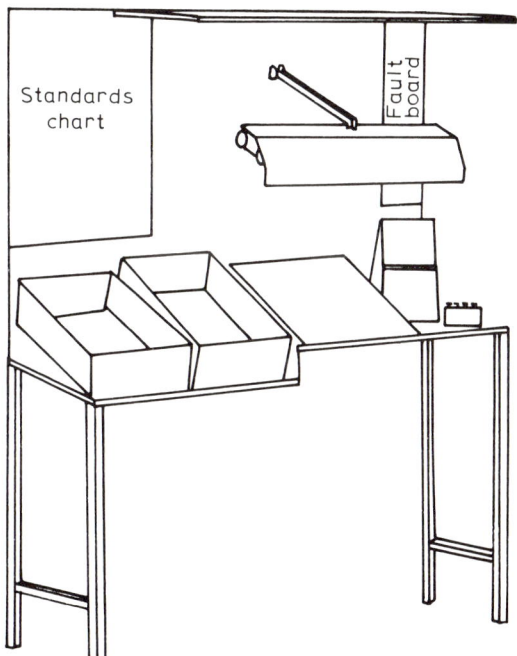

Figure 5.4 The modified prototype workplace

fitting to obtain the same illuminance as before and this has meant re-designing the reflector and glare shield. Two visual aids have been fixed to the rear partition, one providing examples of the major fault types, the other providing information on standards.

Although we have not evaluated the modified prototype, we have received favourable responses during the course of developing and validating a training programme for the inspectors.

Screening of inspectors

Visual profiles were obtained for all the final inspectors using the Bausch and Lomb orthorator. The results are confidential to the company.

We were interested in standardising a test we had developed in the laboratory to measure peripheral acuity. Normally tests of peripheral acuity are extremely time consuming to administer. However, we had devised a search task where the search time correlated very closely with a traditional measure of peripheral acuity. The search task requires subjects to sort packs of cards. Each card is filled with a background of equally spaced Xs where one of the Xs is replaced by one of the two target characters. The subject has to sort the cards into two piles according to the target character. For the student population, the mean time to sort the practice packs was 9 min 36 s (SD = 5 min 3 s). When we came to give the task to six experienced inspectors we were surprised to find that they all found the task extremely difficult to complete. They were often convinced the cards did not contain a target and, consequently, two of them failed to complete the practice runs. The mean sort times for the remaining inspectors was 18 min 20 s. If nothing else, this experience reminded us of the difficulties in extrapolating the results from laboratory to 'real' situations.

The design and validation of easily administered tasks for the selection of inspectors continues to elude researchers (Nelson and Barany 1969).

Quality standards, inspection manual

The collection of data on standards initially took place to provide information for the inspection manual. This was undertaken by a student who spent over one month with the company administering short questionnaires and conducting informal interviews with whoever could provide some relevant information. This was completed for two components. An example from one of the manuals is given in Table 5.6. The appearance of the fault is usually supplemented by a photograph or diagram.

Training programme

To a large extent the variation in standards displayed by the inspectors is a result of them never having received any training despite the fact that the company has an active central training department. In common with a majority of ergonomists we have had little experience with developing

Table 5.6 *Example of fault data from the inspection manual*

Fault type	Blisters
Location	Anywhere, more common on HT chimney
Lighting requirements	Overhead fluorescent source positioned between inspector and task
Appearance	Blister-like – a small area of high specular reflectivity surrounded by area of low reflectance
Cause	Moulding condition, e.g. trapped gas
Effect	Depends on location, could prevent sealing of components or may flake off leaving underlying plastic exposed to contamination
Occurrence	Usually a batch fault
Action	HT chimney – scrap LT chimney – scrap Skirt – scrap Sealing rim – scrap if >1 mm Outer part of upper rim – scrap if >3 mm Inner part of upper rim – scrap if >0.5 mm Edge – scrap if >3 mm Outside of sealing flange – scrap if >2 mm Inside – scrap if prevents insertion of core

training programmes. The design of the programme was, therefore, somewhat *ad hoc* but was intended to fulfil the aims of

(1) providing inspectors with essential product knowledge;
(2) familiarising them with the fault types and the range of severity they can expect for a particular fault type;
(3) demonstrating the visual aids to assist them maintain quality standards;
(4) introducing them to the new workplace;
(5) describing a method of visually scanning the components;
(6) providing a means of assessing the progress of the trainee.

The following summarises the stages of the programme we developed.

(a) Provide trainee with a handout outlining the programme and giving a labelled diagram of the component.
(b) Show a short video film illustrating the manufacturing and subsequent assembly stages for the component.
(c) A more detailed version of the above is given by means of a tape-slide show which can be interrupted by the trainee.
(d) Introduce trainee to the visual aids
  (i) common fault board
  (ii) standards chart.
(e) Introduce trainee to workplace.
(f) Suggest method of visually scanning the component.
(g) Trainee is given a sample of 20 components to examine. Each component is faulty. The trainee is 'cued' on the fault characteristics (Embrey 1979).

(h) Trainee given small sample of each of the main fault types. The faults vary in severity and the trainee is asked to rank them in terms of severity and to indicate the cut-off point (accept or scrap) by referring to the standards chart if necessary.

(i) Trainee given sample of 40 components to inspect and is given feedback after each decision.

(j) Trainee given a different sample of 40 components to inspect without feedback.

(k) The previous stage is repeated with the same sample.

The programme allows earlier stages to be repeated if the trainee fails to achieve satisfactory performance at any stage where objective criteria have been specified. The two visual aids are always available at the workplace. The standards chart is a two-way classification of faults. Along the horizontal, the fault types (blister, crack, chip, etc.) are listed and on the vertical the fault locations (HT chimney, LT chimney, skirt, etc.). The entries in the cells indicate whether a particular combination of fault type and location can exist and, if so, what are the critical dimensions. These data were modified from the inspection manual.

While we experienced some problems with the programme, the preliminary results have been encouraging. After completing the programme two student subjects were more sensitive to the faults than any of the experienced inspectors. These results applied to measures based on Ag as well as d'. We have had the opportunity to train only one of the company's inspectors. Because this inspector was not in the original group of six, she was given the batch used in the final stages of the programme to inspect before receiving training.

Comparing before and after performance, her hit rate increased and false alarm decreased as a result of training. There was an increase in d from 1.15 to 2.57. Using the data from the last two stages of the programme, her performance was more reliable than that of any of the original group of inspectors. In contrast to these favourable results, the training programme did cause a very substantial increase in cycle times. This was probably due to the over-elaborate instructions the trainees were given on the method of scanning.

The most neglected aspect of this whole project is establishing recommended viewing times. To this end, we have begun to collect data on the conspicuities of the faults by administering questionnaires and using a modified visibility meter (O'Donnell et al. 1976). When this work is completed we hope to specify a more economical way of scanning the components and introduce a speed criteria into the programme. However, it is worthwhile pointing out that the increase in cycle times due to the training did not result in an increase in false alarm rate which might have been predicted if the training programme had been ineffective (Drury 1973).

Conclusions

Progress on the project has often been slow and frequently interrupted. The contrast in payment systems for production and quality operators and the absence of objective quality standards have been identified as the two main causes of the high scrap rate and of the other complaints regarding the final outgoing quality. We do not know to what extent the quality of production can be improved with the existing moulding machines. Although the inspection methods and procedures that we have proposed have not yet been implemented by the company on a permanent basis, several aspects of the proposed methods have received a degree of validation. We feel we have been successful in designing an inspection workplace, in establishing objective quality standards and methods of representing them and in the basic development of a training programme. Further work is needed before the ideal viewing time can be defined for a component. On concentrating our effort on the task of the final inspectors we have neglected the role of the quality supervisors and foremen. Before attempting to define how feedforward and feedback information should be provided to final inspection, it is recommended that supervisors and foremen should receive training on the same lines as those developed for the inspectors.

What became apparent during the course of the project was that several of the more refined techniques that were applied did not yield data which were immediately useful in evaluating the inspection methods. For example, although eye movement recordings give the investigator a very clear indication of how the components are visually scanned, this information does not by itself demonstrate whether or not the eye movement strategy is satisfactory. The data only become useful when information on quality standards including information on fault locations, conspicuities, frequencies and importance is available. In addition the introduction of refined performance measures, contrary to expectation, sometimes confused matters. This was reflected in the strong negative correlations that were obtained between different measures of the sensitivity of the inspectors to the faults. Certainly, the case study has emphasised the need for the further development of ergonomics techniques which take into account the accuracy and level of measurement that are found in manufacturing organisations.

Acknowledgements

We are extremely grateful for the facilities and cooperation given by the company in which the study was conducted, particularly by the Quality Control Department personnel.

This work was partly funded by a Science Research Council grant, GR/A 92979.

References

DRURY, C. G. (1973). 'The effect of speed of working on industrial inspection', *Applied Ergonomics*, **4**, 2–7.
DRURY, C. G. (1975). 'The inspection of sheet materials – model and data', *Human Factors*, **17**, 257–265.

DRURY, C. G. (1978). 'Integrating human factors models into statistical quality control', *Human Factors*, **20**, 561–572.

EMBREY, D. E. (1979). 'Approaches to training for industrial inspection', *Applied Ergonomics*, **10**, 139–144.

GREENING, C. P. (1976). 'Mathematical modelling of air-to-ground target acquisition', *Human Factors*, **18**, 111–148.

MEGAW, E. D. (1979). 'Factors affecting visual inspection accuracy', *Applied Ergonomics*, **10**, 27–32.

MEGAW, E. D. & BELLAMY, L. (1979). 'Eye movements and visual search', (in *Search and the Human Observer*, Clare, J. N. & Sinclair, M. A., (eds), p. 65), Taylor and Francis, London.

MEGAW, D. & RICHARDSON, J. (1979). 'Eye movements and industrial inspection', *Applied Ergonomics*, **10**, 145–154.

NACHREINER, F. (1977). 'Experiments on the validity of vigilance experiments', (in *Vigilance: Theory, Operational Performance and Physiological Correlates*, Mackie R. R., (ed), Plenum, New York.

NELSON, J. B. & BARANY, J. W. (1969). 'A dynamic visual recognition test', *AIIE Transactions*, **1**, 327–332.

O'DONNELL, R. M. *et al.* (1976). 'Sector disc visibility comparator', *Lighting Research and Technology*, **8**, 113–114.

SINCLAIR, M. A. (1979). 'The use of performance measures on individual examiners in inspection schemes', *Applied Ergonomics*, **10**, 17–25.

SINGLETON, W. T. (1971). 'The systems prototype and his design problems', (in *The Human Operator in Complex Systems*, Singleton, W. T., Easterby, R. S. & Whitfield, W., (eds), p. 20), Taylor and Francis, London.

Chapter 6

A practical methodology for the investigation of materials handling problems

J. E. Ridd

Introduction

The manual handling of materials in industry is often fraught with problems, many of which have, in the past, been accepted as occupational risks. The unfortunate consequence of many of these activities is the onset of back pain, and Shepherd (1970) found that 53% of the manual handling accidents surveyed resulted in injuries involving the spine and trunk. Ayoub *et al.* (1979) argued that the major proportion of the 400 000 back injuries suffered in the USA each year are the result of lifting loads which are too heavy. The problem has been summarised by Stubbs and Nicholson (1979) who state that 'Low back pain is a common ailment in most modern societies and back injuries are a constant and undiminishing hazard of the industrial environment'.

The most recent figures available from the Department of Health and Social Security show there to have been 26.4 million days of certified incapacity due to back pain in Great Britain for the year 1978/79 (Wilde 1980). Clearly, apart from personal suffering, the resulting costs to industry of replacement, retraining and of lost production are enormous and reinforce the case for improved methods of accident prevention in manual materials handling activities.

Many industries have, for a number of years, been holding training courses in the principles of kinetic lifting, following the recommendations of McClurg Anderson (1970). Although some organisations have been able to demonstrate a reduction in the number of handling accidents and a consequential fall in the amount of sickness absence since the introduction of such courses, Brown (1978) could find no significant reduction in the overall number of injuries due to lifting and handling over the past 30 years.

Many authors (Glover 1961; La Rocca and McNab 1969; Chaffin 1976; Snook *et al.* 1978; Ridd and Stubbs 1980) have discussed various methods by which the incidence of manual handling accidents, and in particular the occurrence of back injuries, may be reduced in labour-intensive industries.

These methods appear to fall into three distinct categories as described by Snook, namely

(1) careful selection of workers;
(2) good training in safe lifting:
(3) designing the job to fit the worker (ergonomics).

He suggests that the only, albeit partially, effective method for the control of low back injuries is the third method – the ergonomic redesign of the task. The available evidence suggests that the first two methods, as practised at present, are less successful, although new approaches in both areas have shown promising results in the preliminary studies (Porter *et al.* 1978; Hooper 1980).

Indeed there is now a growing school of thought which states that training can be far more effective if it is more closely related to the actual occupation of the trainee and to specific problems which he will encounter in his daily activities.

For several years, since its inception in 1972, the Materials Handling Research Unit (MHRU) has been adopting many of these ergonomic theories and applying them to practical industrial problems with the aim of reducing industrial manual handling accidents. The Unit has developed an analytical method which can identify those areas where the risk of accident and injury is greatest and hence indicate priority occupations requiring investigation. The physical stress on the back, incurred during the potentially hazardous activities, can then be measured and if it is found to be above safe levels, alternative procedures are tested and, where an acceptable method is found which reduces the truncal stress, this is recommended for adoption.

The implementation of this methodology and potential benefits to be derived are perhaps best explained by describing a case study of a cable manufacturing plant in Norway.

The first stage of any investigation is the collection of epidemiological data for statistical analysis; however, in this study the industry had themselves carried out such a survey as part of the brief of the newly established Work Environment Organisation (Aarås and Westgaard 1980). This has been set up within Standard Telefon og Kabelfabrik A/S (STK) to monitor new and existing work situations.

The analysis of the morbidity data had identified a particular department within the Company with a significantly high incidence of musculoskeletal problems. This department was the cable manufacturing plant where 600 of the Company's 3500 staff were employed. The available records for this group showed that the occurrence of musculoskeletal disease equated with that of infections and bronchial complaints and also that the average work absence resulting from musculoskeletal problems was, by far, the longest of all causes of work absence. A further, and most important, finding of the survey was that cable drum handling was implicated in 30% of these accidents and injuries (Figure 6.1).

It was in the light of this evidence that the MHRU was asked by the Work Environment Organisation to carry out a study of the materials handling problems within the cable manufacturing plant, and in particular, to investigate cable drum handling. At the end of the study the Unit hoped

Figure 6.1 Use of drum lever to start drum rolling

to present recommendations to the Company which should help to alleviate the stresses induced by those identifiably hazardous activities and so reduce the level of work absence resulting from musculoskeletal problems.

Method

The investigation was carried out in two stages. The first was to observe both the known high-risk materials handling activities and also any other potentially stressful manual task. The second stage was to quantify the handling stress by use of a radio pressure pill. This device records intra-abdominal pressure (IAP) which has been shown to be an indirect measure of truncal stress. The technique makes use of the observation that when heavy loads are lifted there is an increase in the IAP caused by the simultaneous contraction of abdominal and associated musculature and that these pressure rises are proportional to the magnitudes of the forces acting on the lower spine (Davis 1956; Morris *et al.* 1961; Eie and Wehn 1962).

In a detailed study of manual handling hazards in the British building and construction industry, Stubbs (1975) and Davis and Stubbs (1978) found that peak IAPs in excess of 13.3 kPa were frequently induced with model tasks from occupations with significantly higher incidences of back injuries. Thus there appears to be an increased liability of back injury in those working in the construction industry who sustain repeated, frequent high stresses which induce peak IAPs above 13.3 kPa. Nicholson *et al.* (1981) found similar results in their study of British telecommunications engineers and Stubbs (1980) indicates that the critical stress value appears to be valid not only for the construction industry, but also for other industries where manual materials handling takes place.

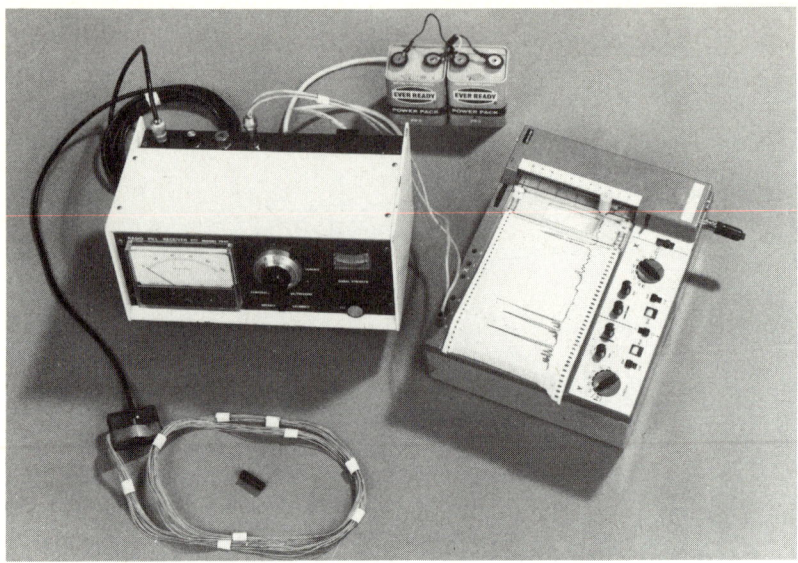

Figure 6.2 Portable equipment for monitoring the radio pressure pill

In order to measure IAP, a pressure-sensitive radio pill was swallowed by the subject (Davis *et al*. 1977) and the signal picked up by an aerial, worn around the waist, which was connected to a portable receiver and chart recorder (Figure 6.2). Thus any manual activity giving rise to IAP measurements which are equal to or in excess of 12 kPa can be identified and examined to assess whether the stress can be reduced. (For safety in practical investigations a 10% reduction in the critical pressure value is made.)

Subjects

Three volunteers (aged 26, 45 and 62 years), each from a different department within the plant, were employed in this study. The youngest had suffered from back problems for many years, however, he found no difficulty with the tasks presented to him and experienced no pain whilst

Table 6.1 *Anthropometry*

Measurements	Subjects 1	2	3	Mean	SD	British industry subjects
Age (years)	45	26	62	44.3	18.0	36.7
Weight (kg)	90	106	78	91.3	14.0	78.6
Stature (cm)	183	188	176	182.3	6.0	178.7
Acromial height (cm)	152	153	147	150.7	3.2	145.3
Grip span (cm)	159	161	158	159.3	1.5	156.9

$n = 233$

being monitored. The second, middle-aged and final older subjects had no history of skeletal disorder. However, the older man had undergone a hernia operation in recent years. Before carrying out the routine tasks a limited number of anthropometric measurements were made and are shown in Table 6.1. The results are contained in Tables 6.1–6.3.

Discussion

Anthropometry

The subject data were compared with that obtained from British male industrial workers, as no similar data were available for the STK workforce as a whole, nor indeed for the Norwegian male population.

The comparison shows a 2%–3% difference in stature for the two sample populations and a difference between the mean weights of 14%. In both cases the Norwegian sample was the greater, and should the anthropometry of these volunteers be found to be larger than the mean for

Table 6.2 *Comparisons of intra-abdominal pressure values (kPa) for two drum handling postures and various activities.*

Drum handling activity using both techniques: Arms (A) Legs (L) and percentage reduction in pressure (%)	Drum material, weight (kg) and diameter (m)										
	Metal 710/1.2	Wood 2100/1.8	Wood 2100/1.8	Wood ? /2.0	Metal 3000/1.5	Wood 3000/2.0	Wood 3600/2.4	Wood 4000/2.0	Wood 4000/2.2	Wood 4000/2.6	Metal 6500/2.6
Pushing drum on level surface A			8.8			6.9		12.4	8.6	10.0	21.3
L			3.1			2.8		2.3	2.8	1.5	13.4
%			65			59		82	67	85	37
Pushing drum up an incline A					10.4		7.5				
L					4.8		6.0				
%					54		20				
Pushing drum on to slide A			10.8			8.4	9.6		*		
L			7.6			6.5	4.3		3.6		
%			30			23	55				
Pushing drum along on slide A			8.8								
L			3.9								
%			56								
Twist drum on ground A	8.7				11.6						
L	6.3				4.3						
%	28				63						
Rocking/pushing drum on uneven ground A		9.2									
L		7.2									
%		22									

The mean percentage reduction in the pressure level when using the legs as the pushing force is 50%

* For this manoeuvre with this drum the subject failed when using the 'arms' technique, but was able to complete the task when pushing with his legs

Table 6.3 *Intra-abdominal pressure measurements when handling* (1) small cable drums, and (2) sacks of raw material

(1) Small cable drums

Size (diameter) and weight	Activity		Pressure (kPa)	
			Restricted	Clear
40 cm 40 kg	Lifting from ground to various rack levels with restricted and clear access	Top		13.4
		Middle	10.1	5.4
		Bottom	6.0	4.6
40 cm 135 kg	Lifting to and from the bottom rack level	Lift up	17.2	15.0
		Lift down	13.4	9.2
40 cm 100 kg	Lifting from ground to payoff stand		9.5 (SD = 0.6)	
	Dragging stand plus drum		6.7 (SD = 1.4)	
	Lifting drum off stand		5.1 (SD = 0.7)	

(2) Sack handling

Weight (kg)	Activity	Pressure (kPa)
25	Lifting various sacks	9.2 (SD = 1.4)
35	from ground to	12.9 (SD = 0.3)
50	wooden pallet	17.0 (SD = 1.4)
25	Emptying sacks into	6.4 (SD = 1.4)
50	storage hoppers	11.7 (SD = 2.8)

Critical intra-abdominal pressure = 12 kPa (90 mmHg)
(1 kPa = 7.5 mmHg; 100 mmHg = 13.3 kPa)

the whole STK workforce, then the mean peak pressures recorded, and hence the induced stress, must be considered as low for the activities observed.

Radio pressure pill measurements

Large cable drums

Handling operations involving 27 different drums were monitored and where possible the subjects carried out up to six manoeuvres with each, making an approximate total of 160 monitored activities per subject.

The series of manoeuvres repeated with each drum comprised

pushing drum on horizontal surface;
pushing drum up incline;
pushing drum onto drum slide*;
pushing drum along on drum slide*;
turning drum on turntable;
turning drum on ground.

* Drum slide – this apparatus enables drums to be manoeuvred at right angles to their normal direction of travel.

The subjects were allowed to adopt their preferred posture for each of these tasks; invariably this proved to be pushing forwards with the arms used to exert the force (Figure 6.3). In some cases, where this occurred, the subject was asked to repeat the manoeuvre but using a different technique. This new, prescribed technique was to lean with his back against the drum with flexed knees, grip the drum sides with his hands and to push the drum along using his legs as the driving force (Figure 6.4).

Figure 6.3 Posture usually adopted when manoeuvring cable drums

Figure 6.4 Recommended posture for drum manoeuvring

In those situations where both postures were adopted it was found that, without exception, the prescribed technique was far less stressful (as measured by IAP). The results of these measurements are given in Table 6.2, where it can be seen that the percentage reduction in peak IAP when adopting the prescribed technique ranged from 22%–85% (mean 50%). It is also noteworthy that for some manoeuvres with particular drums the 'arms technique' (as in Figure 6.5) was found to be unsuccessful, or to induce multiple high peak stresses. However, a controlled push with the subject's back against the drum completed the operation successfully in the same time with far less stress.

Figure 6.5 Subject being monitored while pushing drum

Clearly the prescribed technique (as in Figure 6.4) would reduce back stress in situations where it could be safely applied and the adoption of this technique as the standard procedure for moving all but the smaller range of drums* was strongly recommended.

It was suggested that pushing with the back against the drum and thus facing backwards, prevented the subject from seeing where he was going. However, our observations suggest that the benefits of increased control and reduced stress when adopting the prescribed technique, far outweigh the apparent hazard of reduced vision, particularly when a single worker pushing a large drum using the 'arms technique' has no greater view forward as, invariably, his head is down and positioned centrally between the drum rims. Should the lack of forward vision prove hazardous, however, then it was suggested that two people be employed in moving the drum.

Where it was possible to reduce the stress in the above manoeuvres the cause must primarily be postural and hence it can be postulated that specific training would ameliorate the problem.

* Small drums are those with a diameter of 1 m or less.

However, bad posture was by no means the only cause of high truncal stress. Where the subjects used the same drum for different activities, any increase in back stress must have been a function of the activity. For example, the table below shows the mean peak pressures for manoeuvring the same five cable drums in three different situations

Pushing drums on horizontal surface	2.7 kPa (SD = 1.3)
Pushing drums up incline	8.7 kPa (SD = 2.4)
Pushing drums onto a drum slide	8.3 kPa (SD = 2.5)

These figures show that the trunk stress when manoeuvring drums other than on a level surface is over three times that when pushing the same drums on flat ground.

These results demonstrate that the environment, the task and the posture adopted are all critical factors in determining the level of induced truncal stress and that the size and weight of the cable drum, although important, should not be the only consideration when assessing the difficulty of a drum handling manoeuvre.

It is evident from the data presented so far, that there is no single answer to the manual handling problems of this company whose working methods are in no way atypical. There is an obvious requirement for specific training concerning the handling of the many and various cable drums, but there is also a need to ensure that the extensive manual handling of drums, as carried out at present, is reduced to a minimum and clearly this requires task redesign in order that the worker can operate the system more efficiently.

In some departments many drums were held 'ready for use' but, with the limited storage space, easy handling was prevented and often no mechanical aids could be used. Better handling techniques could have been adopted if there had been a rationalisation of the storage areas with the drum flow controlled according to actual, rather than predicted, requirements. Often as here, redesign of the management of a work system can alleviate many of the physical stresses involved in an activity.

The external drum storage areas demonstrate some of the benefits to be gained by effecting changes to the work environment. The existing area was fully, but not efficiently, occupied and was on uneven ground which often resulted in the movement of a number of drums in order to gain access to the required one. As can be seen from Table 6.2, the reduced back stress to be gained by improved posture for this activity is small (22%); thus the recommendation was that the area should be levelled to reduce truncal stress and that there should be more order in the distribution of the drums to reduce the unnecessarily high frequency of handling.

Small cable drums

It was not only the large diameter cable drums which posed the manual handling problems, indeed the smaller drums (40 cm diameter) often caused greater concern because of the increased frequency of handling. High pressures were recorded when replacing 40 kg drums of copper wire (Figure 6.6) in the top and middle layers of a three-tiered metal rack, and also when handling heavier drums (135 kg) on the bottom layer. The mean

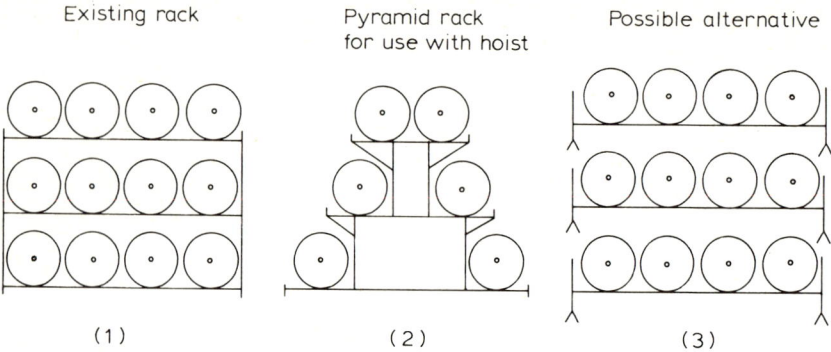

Existing rack   Pyramid rack   Possible alternative
                     for use with hoist

(1)   (2)   (3)

Figure 6.6 Rack storage of small cable drums

pressures for these activities are shown in Table 6.3. By simulating a situation where each layer was not obstructed by the one above – as with the 'pyramid rack' (Figure 6.6) – we were able to show greatly reduced handling stresses, although the storage capacity for these racks is less. A possible alternative is also shown in Figure 6.6 where a three-piece rack is used in conjunction with a hand-operated electric hoist which would lift both drums and rack sections as required and so reduce the level of manual labour.

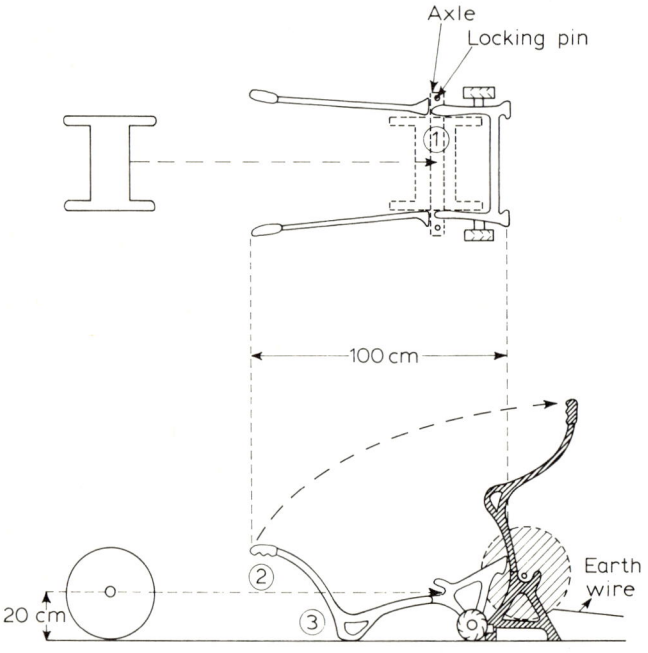

Axle
Locking pin

100 cm

20 cm

Earth
wire

Figure 6.7 Drum barrow. To use this mechanical aid the drum is rolled to position (1) where an axle is fitted and locked in place; the handles (2) can then be lifted for transportation or raised further until the secondary handles (3) can be reached to assist in standing the frame upright

A further hazard with the small cable drums was identified in a department where 100 kg drums of earth wire were manually loaded on to payoff stands (allowing a drum to revolve as wire is removed), which were then dragged across the floor into position. Both of these activities were potentially hazardous because of the weight involved and the postures adopted to accommodate the environmental constraints. However, the provision of a special stand (Figure 6.7) based on the design of the sack barrow could remove the stressful activities from the task, and this was recommended to STK, although no tests have been conducted to assess the benefits of such a mechanical aid.

Sacks of raw materials

As a result of previous concern STK derived a policy of only manually handling sacks weighing up to 25 kg and had, in fact, requested that suppliers conform to this wherever possible.

However, high IAPs were still recorded for some sack handling activities (Table 6.3) indicating the need for specific handling training in this area. It is worth noting that despite the considerable time spent, and willingness of the subjects to persevere with learning the correct sack handling procedure, it was not possible to reduce the stresses to acceptable levels when manually handling either the 50 kg or 35 kg sacks.

Conclusions

Many techniques for manual materials handling were suggested for those stressful activities monitored at STK; however, the potential stress implicit

Figure 6.8 Electric truck for the smaller cable drums

Figure 6.9 Cable drum waggon

in many other operations could only be alleviated by the provision of mechanical aids and indeed these are now being used at the cable manufacturing plant (Figures 6.8 and 6.9).

It is not always necessary, however, to remove the manual labour element from the task in order to ameliorate the handling problem. This study demonstrated that a considerable reduction in manual handling stress and therefore, also in the risk of injury can be achieved without high capital expenditure. The most significant reduction in physical stress was brought about by a simple change in the posture when manoeuvring the large cable drums – namely to use the prescribed technique (see Figure 6.4).

This investigation also serves as an illustration of the problems incurred when moving from the laboratory to the field situation. Despite the considerable level of success that we experienced, due largely to the cooperation of the STK management and workforce alike, the experimental design drawn up in the laboratory was used only for reference once on site. We found that our work was necessarily controlled by the availability of personnel, of equipment and of the departments, and that materials available one day had been used by the next.

Until ergonomics is accepted by all concerned as a contributor to the overall efficiency of the plant, the human factors consultant will only be called in to rectify problems which manifest themselves when the plant begins operation; at which time it is often either very expensive or impossible to introduce the ideal ergonomic answer to the problem. The constraints of the existing system must inevitably impinge on the acceptable solution which invariably results in a compromise between task redesign, training of personnel and personnel selection – the three major approaches to the prevention of low back injury.

References

AARÅS, A. & WESTGAARD, R. H. (1980). 'The organisation and execution of work environmental projects in a Norwegeian industrial company', *Ergonomics*, **23**, 707–726.

AYOUB, M. M. *et al.* (1979). 'Predicting lifting capacity', *Am. Ind. Hygiene Ass. J.*, **40**, 1075–1084.

BROWN, J. R. (1978). *Manual Lifting and Related Fields, an Annotated Bibliography*, Ontario Ministry of Labour.

CHAFFIN, D. B. *et al.* (1976). *Pre-employment Strength Testing in Selecting Workers for Manual Handling Jobs*, US Department of Health, Education and Welfare, CDC 99–74–62.

DAVIS, P. R. (1956). 'Variations of intra-abdominal pressure during weight lifting in various postures', *J. Anatomy*, **90**, 601.

DAVIS, P. R. & STUBBS, D. A. (1978). *A Method of Establishing Safe Handling Forces in Working Situations*, US Department of Health, Education and Welfare, NIOSH 78–185.

DAVIS, P. R. *et al.* (1977). 'Radio pills: their use in monitoring back stress', *J. Med. Eng. Technol.*, **1**, 209–212.

EIE, N. & WEHN, P. (1962). 'Measurement of the intra-abdominal pressure in relation to weight bearing of the lumbosacral spine', *J. Oslo City Hospital*, **12**, 205–217.

GLOVER, J. R. (1961). 'Manual handling and lifting', *J. Industrial Nursing*, **13**, 289–300.

HOOPER, E. G. (1980). 'Kinetic handling – have we got it right?', *Occ. Safety and Health J.*, Oct., 21–22.

LA ROCCA, J. & McNAB, I. (1969). 'Value of pre-employment radiographic assessment of the lumbar spine', *J. Can. Med. Ass.*, **101**, 49–54.

McCLURG ANDERSON, T. (1970). 'Human kinetics in strain prevention', *Br. J. Occ. Safety*, **8**, 248–250.

MORRIS, J. M. *et al.* (1961). 'Role of the trunk in stability of the spine', *J. Bone and Joint Surgery*, **43A**, 327–386.

NICHOLSON, A. S. *et al.* (1981). 'The magnitude and distribution of trunk stresses in telecommunication engineers', *Br. J. Ind. Med.*, **38**, 364–371.

PORTER, R. W. *et al.* (1978). 'Measurement of the spinal canal by diagnostic ultrasound', *J. Bone and Joint Surgery*, **60**, 481–484.

RIDD, J. E. & STUBBS, D. A. (1980). 'Industrial accidents: a preventative approach', *Int. Environment and Safety J.*, Aug. p. 41.

SHEPHERD, P. M. (1970). Unpublished observations.

SNOOK, S. H. *et al.* (1978). 'The study of three preventative approaches to low back injury', *J. Occ. Med.*, **20**, 478–481.

STUBBS, D. A. (1975). *'Trunk Stresses in Construction Workers'*, Ph.D. Thesis, University of Surrey, England.

STUBBS, D. A. (1980). *'Back Pain in Industry'*, Conference proceedings, NAIDEX '80, 45–54.

STUBBS, D. A. & NICHOLSON, A. S. (1979). 'Manual handling and back injuries in the construction industry: an investigation', *J. Occ. Accidents*, **2**, 179–190.

WILDE, M. V. (1980). Personal communication (Department of Health and Social Security).

Chapter 7

Ergonomics in intensive care. Applying human factors data to the design and evaluation of patient monitoring systems

I. A. R. Galer & B. L. Yap

Introduction

Diagnosis and treatment

The diagnosis and treatment of the sick call for a wide range of skills and capacities. A clincian combines extensive medical and scientific knowledge with the care and compassion in which his profession is rooted. The diagnostic process involves the recognition of patterns of symptoms, the testing of hypotheses about the reason for these, and the discounting and weighting of individual symptoms. The process is complicated by the fact that two patients with the same injury or disease may generate different patterns of symptoms. The treatment process calls for the selection and administration of medication and noting the resulting changes in patterns of symptoms. These tasks may be descriptive, empirical or intuitive but above all, they are complex.

The intensive care of hospital patients presents, in many respects, a major challenge to the clinician. The unstable condition of many such patients calls for unreserved devotion by hospital staff. Of particular important is the detection and recognition of a change in the condition of the patient; unless this done rapidly and unless corrective action is taken equally rapidly, the patient may be in mortal danger. For example, mortality rates due to head injury have been shown to be directly related to the length of the delay between the first sign of a deteriorating conscious level and surgical evacuation of the clot. 'The mean delay in patients who died was 15.7 h, whilst in good quality survivors, the mean delay was 1.9 h. It is obvious that the earlier the deteriorating conscious level is recognised, the shorter is the delay.' (Cranswick *et al.* 1979). As with diagnosis and treatment, patient monitoring is a complex task since as many as 60 parameters of the patient may need to be recorded at intervals as short as 15 min. It is necessary also to be able to infer the state of the patient over a given period of time in the form of trends and summary indices; and to communicate to another clinician the condition of the patient unambiguously. These functions of data acquisition, data recording and communication are vital if life-threatening complications in the patient are to be detected.

Current methods

In the intensive care unit studied, these acquisition, recording and communications functions are at present performed with the aid of hand-completed charts. Seven such charts are required for each patient. The variables recorded include drugs administered, physiological parameters, perceptual-motor parameters and various aspects of 'conscious level' such as alertness, response to commands, the efficiency of speech and emotional response. Fifty-seven of these variables are required.

Chart-keeping is not only a time-consuming and tedious job, it is also susceptible to human error. At present the nurse is required to record values, plot graphs and to sum the 'Conscious level' value mentally to give a combined 'neuroscore' value. (The neuroscore, which has a maximum value of 50, has been shown to be a valuable index for the detection of deterioration in a patient (Price *et al.* 1976; Cranswick *et al.* 1979).) Clinicians refer to these ward charts to make diagnostic decisions, and make cross-references amongst the charts. Chart-keeping also places severe restrictions on the further evaluation of data in terms of trend analysis and other statistical calculations (Stalhammar *et al.* 1979); such types of analysis are considered to be a crucial factor in intensive care, especially in the measurement of intracranial pressure (Takizawa and Sugiura 1979). Error may, therefore, occur both at the recording stage and at the diagnostic stage, and may be compounded by the use on the chart of subjective terms such as 'semi-coma', 'stupor' and 'unconscious', which mean different things to different people. Where speed and accuracy are the essence in intensive care, the microprocessor may be a useful tool to aid diagnostic management.

The use of microprocessors

The doctor in clinical decision making needs data – usually in summary and presented clearly (Byford 1979). The nurse, already stressed by poor doctor/patient ratios (Martin and Norman 1973) has to deal with the continuous observation of patients, the occasional emergency, and with her other duties. There is some sense in identifying simple, repetitive and tedious functions of which doctors and nurses might be relieved, and in providing them with information rapidly and accurately which aids them in the duties for which they are best suited.

Computers play a controversial role in medical practice: terms such as the 'electronic doctor' and 'computer diagnosis' have enjoyed some popular currency and suggest a kind of mechanical medicine. This prospect has, rightly, met with considerable resistance on the part of many clinicians who express the fear that computer usage is dehumanising and thus has no place in medicine. An ergonomist ignores this attitude at his peril, because the successful implementation of any computer system, in medicine as with other areas, will depend directly upon the participation of the eventual user. In putting ergonomics principles into action, the ergonomist must assume the role of analyst, designer, educator and persuader; he must not only design the system with sensitivity and thoroughness, but must demonstrate its value to the user by showing how and under what circumstances it may be used to greatest effect.

Previous development work and its evaluation

The need to record clinical data and communicate it unambiguously had been recognised by the hospital studied for some time, and a prototype of a computer interface unit had been developed.

The input controls consisted entirely of thumbwheel switches as alpha-numeric keyboards had proved to be unworkable in similar systems adopted by other hospitals (Price 1979; Martin and Norman 1973). The system would provide for one interface unit per patient, located on the wall beside the patient's bed. The interface unit would eliminate the use of ward charts. The present project was originally intended as an evaluation of this prototype, with recommendations for possible display and panel improvements.

The ergonomics literature was studied for information about thumb-wheel switches and panel design. The following drawbacks of the interface unit were identified.

(1) Using thumbwheel switches for 57 variables may be confusing and could cause lengthy search times.

(2) The panel was visually complicated due to combinations of switches in the array. For example, a one-digit variable required one switch whilst a three-digit variable would need three switches linked together.

(3) The 57 switches, although grouped, were not colour coded, adding to confusion.

(4) The numbers on the switches provided visual feedback, but their perspex covers obscured them by reflecting the light.

(5) The size of the panel was $540 \times 500\,mm$, giving a visual and attentional field too large for the task (Krais 1976). In addition, the reach envelope necessary for using the unit would cause difficulties for tall and short people. There were considerable parallax prob-lems, due principally to the convex surface of the switches.

(6) To enter three-digit values via thumbwheels may tax the short-term memory of the nurse, due to interference and disruption (Conrad 1958). Plath and Kolesnik (1966) examined the use of thumbwheel switches for entering navigational coordinates in an aircraft. Entries took approximately 2.75 s per wheel setting; thus a three-digit setting could take 8.25 s. The length of time to input a value and the lack of 'preview' on the switches was considered a threat to short-term memory along the lines of the 'decay theory' suggested by Broadbent (1963).

(7) Except for the 'neuroscore' display the mode of interaction with the unit was one of data input only. Whilst the system allowed for displays at the central nurses' station in the ward, observations and link analysis revealed the need for constant man-man and man-machine interactions simultaneously at the bedside.

(8) Thumbwheel switches could not provide the required system flex-ibility. For example, the system in the form studied could record only the amount of fluid excreted by a patient, and could not distinguish whether it was urine, vomit, or drained fluid.

(9) The unit was designed to be wall-hung. This was not necessarily the best method as the spaces between beds were often cluttered with life-support machines, chairs and miscellany. However, the size and design of the unit made alternative placements, or more important-ly the choice of a range of locations, very difficult.

(10) Thumbwheels in the quantity used would be expensive and the unit lacked the aesthetic appearance that could be designed into equip-ment of this nature.

It was therefore concluded that the thumbwheel unit was unlikely to be acceptable for the tasks it was meant to perform. The problems identified presented such major difficulties that it was thought impossible to recom-mend detail changes that would make the system efficient and acceptable. A completely new approach was needed and was effected by the design and evaluation of a new interface unit.

New interface unit: design, development and evaluation

The design and development of the unit may be described in five main stages

(1) feasibility and exploratory studies;
(2) developing the design concept;
(3) construction and evaluation of a mock-up;
(4) final specification and construction of a prototype;
(5) evaluation of the prototype.

Feasibility and exploratory studies

A number of visits were made to the intensive care ward, with the following aims.

(1) To gather information about the social and technical environment in which the equipment would be used, by discussion with nurses and doctors about their needs, medical constraints and the spatial characteristics of the ward.

(2) To introduce the nature of the project to the users. It was planned that such an introduction 'could contribute much to promoting users' development and the ensuring of subsequent and adequate "task fit" between user needs and the service provided when the computer is installed' (Eason et al. 1974). If users are systematically exposed to plans for computerisation, are involved in the development process and are persuaded that the computer is an aid to their work and not a replacement, their resistance to change may be reduced and the final system stands a greater chance of being accepted.

Developing the design concept

Based on the feasibility studies, the design concept was developed on the following principles.

(1) *Ease of use.* Clinicians were treated as 'naïve computer users'. Eason *et al.* (1974) report that one of the most conclusive findings, particularly amongst naïve users, was that it was their difficulty in using the computer system which restricted their use of it. Even when they felt the system might be able to help them, they tended not to use it because of the effort and time it would take them. In the light of this, 'effort to use' factors were regarded as vitally important.

(2) *Training.* Closely related to ease of use was the objective that clincians would require little training for the system. In an environment where acceptance of the system can easily become a major problem, and where staff already bear high workloads, lengthy training times and the maintenance of skill by rehearsal and retraining would undoubtedly create difficulties.

(3) *Consequences for the clinician's job.* It was important that the system and the interface unit would maintain and if possible enhance job satisfaction. Whilst ease of use is important, it has been argued that oversimplification of the interface to cater for the lowest level of ability is likely to be inefficient (Hillix and Coburn 1961). At the same time, however, operation of the unit (the secondary socio-technical system) should not impair the interaction between clinician and patient (the primary system). Consequently an attempt was made to strike a compromise: whilst being easy to use, operation of the system would be a challenge and an interest to the clinician.

(4) *Flexibility.* In the interests of cost and acceptability, it was considered important to design the system with capacity for accommodating further functions and tasks. This approach permits the improvement of the system as scientific and technological knowledge advances.

The design concept was of a keyboard unit with an integral display, mounted on a movable arm at the bedside. Operation of the keyboard is effected by pressing a parameter selection key, and then a numeric key. Careful consideration was given to the idea of using a standard QWERTY keyboard arrangement. Whilst this arrangement has led to good results for speed and accuracy in touch typing, and whilst it is probably the most familiar even for non-typists, it was nevertheless rejected. Clinicians would enter data intermittently between observations of the patient and so rapid and continuous data entry skill is not required. When the clinician needs to enter a measurement, however, he should be able to do it quickly. To select a parameter, it is necessary with a conventional keyboard to type either the full name of the parameter or some mnemonic or acronymic substitute for it. In the former case, the unskilled typist may well incur time and error penalties; in the latter case, whilst entry time for a known parameter may be reduced, the clinician must have learned and remembered the appropriate code, or must be able to refer to an index of such codes; total entry time is likely to increase, therefore, if we include in the operation the time taken to recall or look up the correct code. With one key per parameter, however, these problems are avoided since the clinician has only to select and press one key; the system is then ready to accept numeric data for that parameter.

A potential problem lies in the fact that with this arrangement the clinician would have to search for one amongst 57 parameter keys, However, Lockhead and Klemmer (1959) demonstrated that subjects can operate successfully when 137 keys are used and if these findings are applicable to the present situation, then 57 keys is well within the maximum cited. The problem was further reduced by grouping and coding the keys as an aid to visual scanning. Those parameters which are medically related and which are usually recorded as a set were grouped together, with the most frequently used groups closest to the numeric keyset. Figure 7.1 shows the proposed keyboard layout and Figure 7.2 illustrates one of the parameter key groupings in detail.

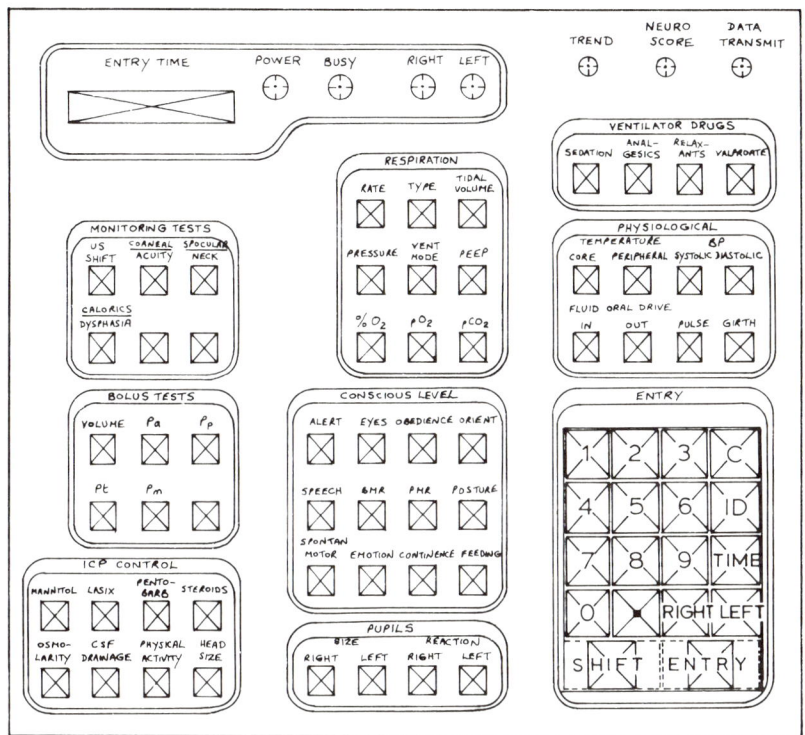

Figure 7.1 Proposed keyboard layout: keyboard unit

A task analysis showed that clinicians did not record the parameters within a group in a fixed order. It was, however, thought desirable that some such structure should be encouraged, to avoid errors of omission in data entry. The design does this but remains flexible: the clinician can, for example, take the measurements a row at a time, moving from left to right or from right to left; or a column at a time, moving from top to bottom or vice versa. Any such strategy can be used; the clinician need only select a strategy and use it consistently. As Figures 7.1 and 7.2 show, key groups are further identified by the use of border lines.

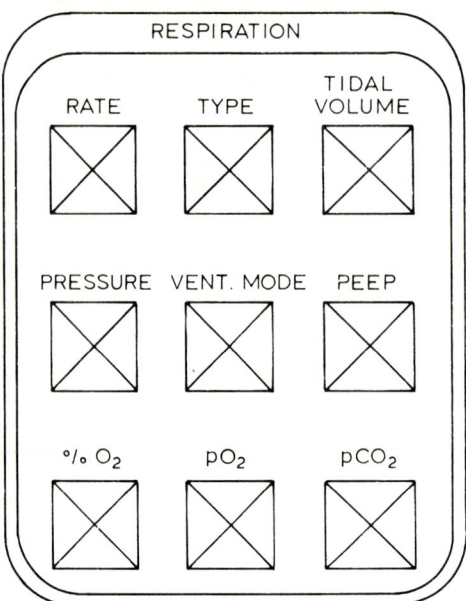

Figure 7.2 Example of parameter key groupings:
keyboard unit

Colour coding and labelling were also employed. Whilst several authors (McCormick 1976) have indicated that people can identify up to nine colours, it was felt that the use of a different colour for each group of keys would visually complicate the keyboard. In addition, it is difficult to obtain key tops in more than three or four colours. Three colours – red, grey and blue – were therefore selected, covering respectively three, two and three groups of keys. This supra-grouping was made on the grounds that groups sharing the same colour code had more in common than groups with different colour codes. All parameters, groupings, numeric and display keys were fully labelled.

The unit provides four main displays. These are shown in Figure 7.3.

The 'neuroscore', described previously, can be called up by pressing a single key. The trend display, called up similarly but after having selected a parameter, will show the readings taken of that parameter over the

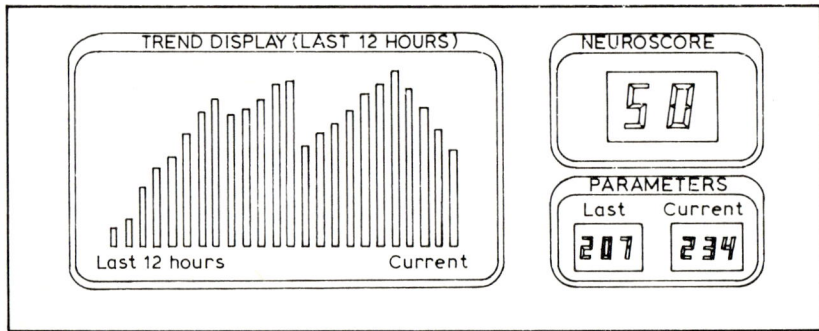

Figure 7.3 Proposed displays: keyboard unit

previous 12 h, in the form of a histogram. The parameter displays perform the dual function of showing the immediate status of the patient, as well as providing visual feedback of numeric values entered. Before any values are entered, this display shows both the the value last recorded for the parameter selected (the 'current' value) as well as the one before that (the 'last' value). When a new value is entered, the 'current' value is displaced to the 'last' display and the previous 'last' value is stored permanently. If the new value is judged correct by the clinician, pressing the 'enter' key causes it to be registered. Thus the unit provides a window of values in the stream of data input to the system. If the new value is incorrect it can be cleared by pressing the 'C' (clear) key and then re-entered.

Some initial hardware specifications were made at this stage, based on published literature. These specifications covered the following features.

(1) Keyboard angle and display panel angle. The keyboard angle was set at 17.5° from the horizontal (Scales and Chapanis 1954; Cooper 1976). The display panel angle was set at 45° from the horizontal, whilst its perspex cover was at 60° to reduce the incidence of glare and reflected light.

(2) Key size and key spacing. The parameter selection keys are 12.7 mm square with a displacement of 1 mm, and provide tactile feedback via a 'snap' when fully depressed. The distance between key centres is 20 mm for horizontal spacing and 25 mm for vertical spacing. The numerical keys are 19.05 mm square with a displacement of 2.5 mm (Stewart 1976; Deininger 1960). The numerical keys are arranged in the TEL layout, that is a $3 \times 3 + 1$ matrix with 1, 2 and 3 on the top row (Lutz and Chapanis 1955; Conrad and Hull 1968).

Early in the development of the design concept, two drawings, showing a possible keyboard layout, and an impression of the unit in use at a patient's bedside, were presented for discussion to the clinicians in the ward. The exchange of opinions that resulted between users, engineer and designer raised some useful points for later project development. The main purpose was to involve all parties in the design of the unit and to get an understanding of their reactions to the new concept.

Later, in the development of the design concept, full-scale drawings of the unit were again presented for discussion. Major alterations and additions were made even at this stage: for example, an additional group of six parameters keys was included, necessitating a complete redesign of the layout. The order of keys within parameter groups was also changed several times.

Construction and evaluation of a mock-up

Whilst drawings provide vastly more information than verbal descriptions, they are not capable of conveying fully the nature of the product being designed. They can, in addition, provide only partial information to the designer who may need to work out some of the more subtle configurations of the product in three dimensions rather than two. Accordingly a cardboard mock-up of the interface unit was constructed and an interim evaluation of it was made to reduce the chances of major deficiencies becoming 'frozen' in the design. Figure 7.4 shows this mock-up. Six nurses took part in the evaluation. After an explanation of how the unit worked and a demonstration of how data would be entered, each nurse was instructed to enter a number of parameter/value combinations, by pressing

Figure 7.4 Cardboard mock-up of keyboard unit

the colour patches that represented the keys, She was then asked a number of questions about the ease of use of the unit; any difficulties foreseen; the layout of the keys and their labelling; key size and key spacing; keyboard angle; and any improvements that might be made. The responses received led to some minor changes to the design; no major problems were identified.

Final specification and construction of a prototype

On the basis of the three stages described so far, final detailed drawings and specifications for the interface unit were made and a working prototype was built. The one feature of the unit that could not be incorporated into the prototype within the time available was the trend display: problems were encountered at that stage in finding a suitable type. It was resolved to pursue the development of the unit without this facility although provision was made for it to be fitted into the unit when the problems of availability were resolved. The prototype is shown in Figure 7.5.

Figure 7.5 Prototype keyboard unit

Using ergonomic principles and data in design is in many ways a predictive process. The ergonomist must first anticipate the user population and its characteristics – its capacities and limitations in psychological, anatomical and biomechanical terms. He must secondly anticipate how the product will be used – at what times, under what circumstances, and under what conditions of abuse. He must then refer to the ergonomic data as a source for hardware and software specifications. Rarely are these data completely suited to his needs: they will usually have been collected in a different context, in relation to different pieces of equipment, using different criteria of efficiency, safety and acceptability, and with different user populations in mind. Thus the design of keyboards for clinicians unskilled at data entry may borrow from the literature relating to telephone usage (amongst students of psychology!), the skilled typing of textual material and the errors incurred in data entry under stressful battlefield conditions. Faced with this information the ergonomist must select a set of specifications relevant to his understanding of his present design problem, and that of the work reported. Compromises will be made as the ergonomist passes through a subtle process of weighting priorities and discounting factors. The result will be some recommendations that the ergonomist *anticipates* will meet the requirements of his problem.

The ergonomist who manages to avoid such predictions, who finds that his information is perfectly accurate and is based on a complete knowledge of the user population and the conditions of use, is either mistaken or is uniquely lucky. In virtually every case, references and predictions will have been made under some uncertainty. If there is no uncertainty, an evaluation of the product is superfluous as its results would add nothing to the design. If, however, there is some uncertainty then an evaluation of the product is necessary to test the assumptions made in the design process. Such an evaluation was made in the present case.

Evaluation of the prototype

Aims. The evaluations was designed as a test of the speed and accuracy of data entry and of users' preference for the interface unit. The original thumbwheel prototype was compared in these terms with the keyboard prototype.

Experimental design and dependent variables. A repeated measures design was used, such that each clinician operated both interface units. Half the subjects used the thumbwheel unit first, and half the keyboard unit. Error was defined as the proportion of entries transmitted by the clinician which contained one or more undetected errors. Time per entry was calculated as the mean time between activation of the first key and activation of the 'data transmit' key. User preferences were measured in two ways: after using the first interface unit the clinician completed a set of nine seven-point rating scales on various aspects of its use. These scales were administered again after using the second unit, and will be called the Absolute Rating Scale (ARS). In addition, the clinician completed a further nine scales at the end of the whole experiment, in which the keyboard and thumbwheel units were compared directly, and in one of which the keyboard was compared with the traditional ward charts. This set of scales will be called the Relative Rating Scales (RRS).

Apparatus and materials. Data entered via the two interface units were collected automatically by electromechanical logging systems. The keyboard unit was linked to a Commodore Pet computer, which measured the time taken to enter a data point. The data were displayed on a VDU and were checed for accuracy by the experimenter. The thumbwheel unit was linked to a PDP-11 computer and the data entered by the clinician were recorded via a teleprinter and checked for accuracy by the experimenter. Data entry times in this case were recorded with a stopwatch.

The units were placed in separate rooms. The keyboard unit was mounted with the keyset at a height of 1000 mm (approximate elbow height); the thumbwheel unit was mounted with the centre of the panel at a height of 1450 mm (approximate eye height).

Data to be entered via the interface units were drawn from the charts of an intensive care patient. Two sets of data were prepared, one for each unit. The individual data points within each set were printed on cards, and the cards were randomly ordered. This made the task slightly more difficult than it would be in the real case, where groups of parameters would be entered in a set sequence.

Owing to small variations in the prototypes each nurse entered 37 parameters into the keyboard unit and each doctor, 17; these numbers were 36 and 14 respectively for the thumbwheel unit.

Subjects. Twelve nurses and four doctors took part in the experiment. The nurses ranged in age from 19 years to 47 years, with a mean age of 26.5 years. Their nursing experience ranged from 8 months to 33 years with a mean of 8.6 years. The three doctors who disclosed their ages and clinical experience were 27, 29 and 33 years, with experience of 6, 3 and 6 years respectively.

Procedure. Subjects were tested individually. After being told by the experimenter the function and method of operation of the interface unit they were to use, the experimenter made three demonstration entries. The subject then made five trial entries, working from data cards similar to those described above. He was then told to enter the data from the test set of cards, working as quickly and accurately as possible, and having been told how to clear an incorrect data point and re-enter it. Questionnaires were completed after using each of the interface units, and at the end of the whole experiment as described above.

Results. The numeric keys on the keyboard unit did not allow subjects to enter data as fast as they might wish, due to a time delay of approximately 0.5s in the circuitry. This factor is considered to have increased the entry time for this unit and although a correction could be made, this has not been done as the results in their present form are unequivocal. The time delay was due to a simplification made in the prototype and can easily be eliminated in later models.

Table 7.1 shows the mean and standard deviation of error rate and time per entry for both unit, for doctors and nurses. A Wilcoxon matched pairs signed-ranks test of the nurses' error data showed that the keyboard unit produced significantly less error than the thumbwheel unit ($T = 7.5$; $p<0.05$). A t test on the nurses' entry time showed that the mean time for the keyboard was significantly less than that for the thumbwheel unit ($t = 8.15$; $p<0.001$).

Statistical tests were not carried out on the doctors' data as the sample size was very small. It is of interest, however, to note that error rates were

Table 7.1 *Error rates ane entry times for each interface unit.*

	% error		Time per entry (s)	
	mean	SD	mean	SD
Nurses ($N = 12$)				
Keyboard	0.7	0.25	7.1	1.4
Thumbwheel	2.3	1.53	9.7	1.4
Doctors ($N = 4$)				
Keyboard	0	0	7.1	0.3
Thumbwheel	0	0	8.8	0.9

zero for both units (reflecting, perhaps, greater skill or care); entry times were consistent with those of the nurses.

Questionnaire data for nurses and doctors are presented together, as a preliminary analysis revealed no systematic differences in opinion between the two groups. The questionnaire data led to the conclusion that the keyboard unit was superior to the thumbwheel unit, to a greater or lesser extent, on all the ARS used

clinicians liking for working with the unit;
ease of searching for the correct key/switch;
ease of entering three-digit numbers;
forgetting numbers when making entries;
glare and reflections from the surface of the unit;
ease of reading numbers on the keys/switches;
size of the unit;
appearance of the unit;
tolerance to use of the unit for varying periods of time.

Data for the RRS showed that 15 of the 16 clinicians preferred the keyboard unit to the thumbwheel unit overall; 14 thought parameter search was easier; 14 found the thumbwheel unit more difficult to use; eight found they forgot numbers more frequently with the thumbwheel unit, compared to only one with the keyboard; 13 said that numbers were easier to read on the keyboard; six said that glare was more of a problem with the thumbwheel unit than with the keyboard (the rest were indifferent); four would rather use ward charts than the thumbwheel unit whilst only two would rather use charts than the keyboard; and, most significantly, 14 would like to see the keyboard unit installed in the ward, whilst only one preferred to see the thumbwheel unit installed.

Discussion

The results showed that, in terms of those functions evaluated, the keyboard unit is superior to the thumbwheel unit in entry time, error rates and personal preference. In addition, the evaluation process suggested that the keyboard unit was easy to learn: five minutes' experience with it was sufficient to prepare the clinician to use the unit effectively.

It should be remembered, however, that the evaluation was not perfect. It was compromised by time, money, technical resources and many of the practical obstacles that arise in applied research but which are rarely recognised by writers of textbooks. Not all the features of the keyboard unit were studied; for example, use of the neuroscore facility and the trend display, entering patient identification numbers, and perhaps most important, the learning and use of numerical values of each parameter. The experimental design was not ideal, in that subjects used the interface units successively, slightly different data recording methods were used for the units, and numbers entered were read from cards rather than from direct observation of the patient. And the sample, whilst representing four-fifths of the whole population, comprised only 16 people. In spite of this the results were encouraging and point clearly to areas where further research and development are needed.

This project offered nothing revolutionary in either the theory or practice of ergonomics. Theory and general principles were drawn from two main areas: the literature on the human use of computer systems and the involvement of users in their design; and the extensive information on panel and display design. In addition, some aspects of the systems approach to equipment design were used, in that system objectives and functions were considered; tasks were allocated to man and machine; the interface was designed in the light of the needs and skills of the users; training principles, whilst not studied in detail, were so concerned as to require minimal effort and investment of time; and the system was evaluated. Perhaps the most important aspect of the project from the point of view of theory and practice is that one was successfully translated into the other. Not only was it possible to develop the interface unit to prototype form on the basis of existing knowledge in approximately four months, but also the initial reluctance of users to accommodate the system was transformed to something approaching enthusiasm by the time the project had finished.

We regard the key to this success as lying in two areas. First, the sensible use of ergonomics, together with imaginative industrial design, can produce equipment appropriate to the needs of users, which is easy and efficient to operate, rugged and reliable in use, and pleasing to look at. Second, clinicians at the hospital were fully involved in all stages of the design and evaluation process. They provided the basic functional specifications and pointed out operational and environmental constraints. They commented vigorously on proposals, drawings, mock-ups and the prototype, knowing that the design process would be sensitive to their comments. They were the experimental subjects in the evaluation; and following the completion of the project each clinician in the ward received a written summary of the work that had been done. It may well be that in contexts less controversial than that of computers and medicine, such intimate contact between researcher and user may not be as important. In the present case, however, the investment of time and effort needed for such contact was fully vindicated.

It would be as much of a mistake to halt the work at this stage as it would have been to exclude users from the design process. However accurate an idea the ergonomist may have of the environment in which a piece of equipment is to be used, he cannot be sure of its performance without some data over a time period longer than the prototype evaluation. In the present case there is still a great deal to be done. Further work is taking place in three main areas. First, additional evaluation of the interface unit is being made in comparison with ward charts and in relation to users with varying amounts of clinical experience. Secondly, the work area around the intensive care bed is being studied in detail, for the efficient organisation of work including the use of the interface unit. Thirdly, training and monitoring procedures are being devised for the operation of the unit and for the change of operation from ward charts to the unit. Of particular importance here is the need to maintain, for a limited period at least and perhaps permanently, the skill required to use ward charts. In the event of a computer system failure such skills could become vital to the survival of the patient.

Acknowledgements

The authors wish to thank Mr D. Price, Consultant Neurosurgeon, and Mr J. Mason, Medical Physicist, of Pinderfields Hospital, Wakefield, for their great interest and assistance in this project.

References

BROADBENT, D. E. (1963). 'Flow of information within the organism', *J. Verbal Learning & Verbal Behaviour*, **2**, 34–39.

BYFORD, G. (1979). 'Data acquisition in intensive care', *Colloquium on Instrumentation and Control in Intensive Care*, London.

CONRAD, R. (1958). 'Accuracy of recall using keyset and telephone dial, and the effect of a prefix digit', *J. Appl. Psychol.*, **42**, 285–288.

CONRAD, R. & HULL, A. J. (1968). 'The preferred layout for numerical data-entry keysets', *Ergonomics*, **11**, 165–173.

COOPER, M. B. (1976). 'The effect of keypad angle of a table keyphone on keying performance', *Ergonomics*, **17**, 205–211.

CRANSWICK, T. *et al*. (1979). *Selection of a Coma Scale of Optimum Sensitivity*, Research Report, Pinderfields Hospital, Wakefield, UK.

DEININGER, R. L. (1960). 'Human factors engineering studies of the design and use of pushbutton telephone sets', *Bell Syst. Techn. J.*, **39**, 995–1012.

EASON, K. D. *et al*. (1974). *A Survey of Man-Computer Interactions in Commercial Applications*, Department of Human Sciences, Loughborough University of Technology, LUTERG No. 144.

HILLIX, W. A. & COBURN, R. (1961). *Human Factors in Keyset Design*, US Navy Electronics Laboratory, San Diego, California, Research Report No. 1023.

KRAISS, K. F. (1976). 'Vision and visual displays', (in *Introduction to Human Engineering*, Kraiss, K. F. & Moraal, J. (eds)), Verlag TUV Rheinland GmbH.

LOCKHEAD, G. R. & KLEMMER, E. T. (1959). *An Evaluation of an 8-Keyword Writing Typewriter*, IBM Research Report, RC-180.

LUTZ, M. C. & CHAPANIS, A. (1955). 'Expected location of digits and letters on ten-button keysets', *J. Appl. Psychol.*, **39**, 314–317.

McCORMICK, E. J. (1976). *Human Factors in Engineering and Design*, McGraw-Hill, New York.

MARTIN, J. & NORMAN, R. D. (1973). *The Computerised Society*, Penguin Books, England.

PLATH, D. W. & KOLESNIK, P. E. (1966). 'Readability and operability of three types of digital switches', *J. Engineering Psychol.*, **5**, 47–53.

PRICE, D. (1979). Private communication.

PRICE, D. *et al*. (1976). 'Analogue to digital conversion of consciousness', *J. Neurology, Neurosurgery and Psychiatry*, **39**, 919.

SCALES, E. M. & CHAPANIS, A. (1954). 'The effect on performance of tilting the toll-operator's keyset', *J. Appl. Psychol.*, **38**, 452–456.

STALHAMMAR, D. *et al*. (1979). *Intercranial Pressure Registration Administered by a Microprocessor*, Paper presented to the 4th International Conference in Intensive Care, Washington, USA.

STEWART, T. F. M. (1976). 'Displays and the software interface', *Appl. Ergonomics*, **7**, 137–146.

TAKIZAWA, H. & SUGIURA, K. (1979). *A Combination of Bedside ICP Recordings: Histogram, Trend, Graph and Digital Prints*, Paper presented to the 4th International Conference in Intensive Care, Washington, USA.

Chapter 8

Ergonomic systems design in two maintenance departments. Theory and practice

J. A. Landeweerd & D. P. Rookmaaker

Introduction

In ergonomics the 'Systems approach' has been explicitly introduced during the last 10 years. In 1967 Singleton used the expression 'systems ergonomics' to refer to ergonomic involvement in the design of man-machine systems (Singleton 1967). To speak about 'systems ergonomics' in this respect, however, is somewhat misleading in that all of ergonomics is related to systems (i.e. man-machine systems). We prefer to talk about 'ergonomic systems design' to refer to the process of designing man-machine systems from an ergonomic point of view.

In this paper we shall deal with two projects, both in maintenance departments of the Netherlands Railways, where an ergonomic approach to the (re)design has been carried out. The first project took place in the roller-bearing department (1977) and the second one in a department for the maintenance of trains doors (1978). Both provided interesting opportunities to test the ergonomic systems design model in practice.

The projects were set up as a cooperative effort between the department of Industrial Engineering of the Eindhoven University of Technology and the Central Ergonomics Group of the Netherlands Railways. The main parts of the investigations were carried out by two students of the department of Industrial Engineering under the supervision of members of the IE Department (the first author) and the Central Ergonomics Group of the Netherlands Railways (the second author). Also, at the departments involved, project groups were formed. Under the leadership of a member of the local management the course of the project was evaluated periodically with the investigators, personnel representatives and some technical specialists. Decisions were taken by a specially appointed technical project-leader.

Ergonomic systems design phases

In Figure 8.1 a schematic overview is given of the various phases in the ergonomic systems design process.

93

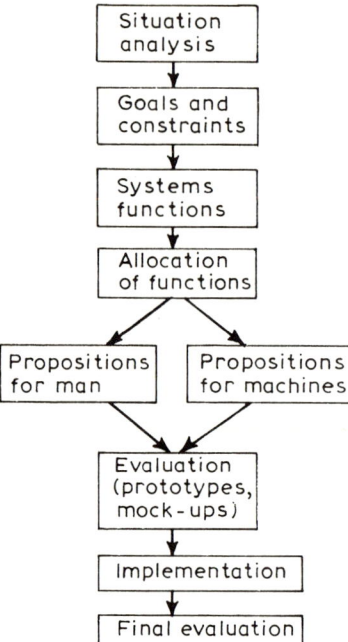

Figure 8.1 Ergonomic systems design

Situation analysis

The design of man-machine systems almost never starts from scratch, but is nearly always a matter of *redesigning* in a more or less radical way an already existing system. So in most projects it is necessary to carry out some preliminary analyses in the existing situation. In our view the most important analyses are as follows.

(1) *Process analysis.* One cannot start a stystems (re)design before having performed an analysis of the process in terms of inputs, transformation processes and outputs.

(2) *Ergonomic analysis.* For example an ergonomic workstation analysis by means of an ergonomic checklist.

(3) *Task analysis.* An analysis of tasks that are performed by the personnel involved. A suitable task analysis method has to be chosen.

(4) *Opinion analysis.* By which is meant any analysis of subjective feelings, attitudes and opinions of the personnel involved about aspects of their jobs.

Goals and constraints

A formulation of the goals of the system to be (re)designed need to be made. It is very important, that there is unanimity about goals and constraints between the groups involved (workers, management, research team); if not, problems in one or more of the groups involved may arise during the design process or the implementation. Also constraints should be formulated, although during the process changes may be made, e.g., more financial support may be given than originally foreseen).

Systems functions

Systems functions are those functions that have to be performed to fulfil the system's goal; in this phase they are formulated and broken down in operational terms, without expressing who or what performs them or how they should be performed. Often one proceeds from a global description to a more detailed level of description.

Allocation of functions

In this phase each systems function is analysed as to whether it should be allocated to man or to machine.

Criteria traditionally are the relative capacities and limitations of man and machine (which performs better?), costs (which costs more?) and motivational considerations (does the allocation lead to interesting and integrated tasks?). In such cases where there are conflicts between the criteria, problems may arise and a compromise should be reached. Systems tasks that are to be allocated to man should be evaluated as to whether they may be grouped to meaningful jobs and whether appropriate workers may be selected and trained. If not, perhaps the allocation should be re-evaluated.

Prototypes, mock-ups

The system to be (re)designed or parts of it may be evaluated by means of prototypes, mock-ups or simulators. It offers an excellent opportunity for user comments and user participation.

Implementation and final evaluation

The implementation phase will not be the great bottle-neck of systems design – as it is often depicted in traditional systems design – if in the phases described effective user participation has been organised and human (i.e. ergonomic) considerations taken into account. Nevertheless the final evaluation will show whether the original aims have been met.

General description of the two departments

The roller-bearing department

In the roller-bearing department of the Netherlands Railways the maintenance of wheel sets takes place. The wheel sets belong to the wagons that are revised once in every four years. In the roller-bearing department the axle boxes and bearings are removed from the wheel sets (about 30 every day) and they are cleaned and inspected. A wagon normally has two or four wheel sets, each consisting of an axle having wheels, bearings and axle boxes at both ends (see Figure 8.2).

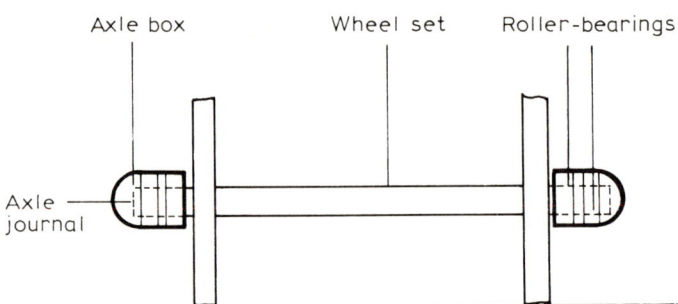

Figure 8.2 A wheel set (schematic)

In a small number of wheel sets only the axle boxes are removed; the other operations are identical to the wheel sets of which the bearings are removed as well. Axle boxes and gearings exist in various types.

The operations in the department are

(1) *transport* of wheel sets, axle boxes and bearings; the wheel sets are often pushed manually to the next destination. In other instances cranes may be used. The transport of axle boxes and bearings is done with various aids;

(2) *dismantling and assembling* of axle boxes and bearings; this takes place in work-pits of about 30 cm depth, located on both sides of the rails. A wheel set is never turned around;

(3) *cleaning and inspection* of axle boxes and bearings; cleaning mostly is done by the 'hydromaticus' (a cleaning machine). Also a lot of scouring and inspection has to be done.

In the department the personnel consists of eight people doing the roller-bearing maintenance; the work may be called rather heavy, monotonous and dirty.

The door department

Train doors at certain times need maintenance. There are many types of door but generally speaking, two main types may be distinguished

outer doors, mostly made of aluminium (40–70 kg) or of polyester (25–44 kg);
inner doors, almost always made of wood (13–27 kg).

Train door maintenance was always done in different departments, the reason for the project being the decision to centralise all the maintenance activities of doors in one department.

Basic operations here are transportation, dismantling and assembling of parts, revision, painting, etc.

The use of various types of handtool causes problems of noise, gases, dust, working posture, etc. In the various departments about 30 people occupy themselves with the maintenance of the doors.

As in the roller-bearing department it was decided to start a cooperative project between the Central Ergonomic Group of the Netherlands Railways and the Ergonomic Group of the department of the Eindhoven University of Technology to advise in the (re)design from a systems ergonomic point of view.

The design process

Situation analysis

The roller-bearing department. The ergonomic analysis of the roller-bearing department revealed various problems.

> *Static workload* may be observed in the manual pushing of the wheel sets etc.
> *Bad controls*, for example the grip of the tackle.
> *Heavy loads*, the axle boxes for example weigh from 27–44 kg.
> *Slippery floors* because of the grease.

The door department. Analysis of important problems in the existing situation was carried out by means of an ergonomic checklist analysis; by questionnaires to the personnel involved, asking about work attitudes and subjective feelings of load and by collecting accident records. A number of shortcoming was revealed, for example handling and transportation of doors exceeded acceptable limits of workload. Also problems concerning the use of handtools were revealed.

Goals

Goal of the roller-bearing department. In general terms the goal of the department is the maintenance of roller-bearings in such a way, that they are in the desired state. There are time and quality norms.

Goal of the door department. The goal is to deliver revised doors, meeting the quality norms within the time constraints (time depending on types of operations to be performed).

Constraints

In both situations a number of constraints have been formulated. Here are some of them.

(1) The capacity of the new door department must be equal to the sum of the capacities of the existing (dispersed) workstations where maintenance operations are performed on doors.
(2) Workers who in the existing situation spend more than 75% of their time on doors may be transferred to the new department.
(3) The number of workers in the new roller-bearing department may not exceed the number in the existing situation. An eventual small reduction is possible because of internal replacement possibilities.
(4) There are constraints of location: in both situations the department must be projected in the assigned halls.

Description of system functions

According to the procedure described by, for example, Singleton (1974), and Coburn (1973) the system functions are described, first in rather general terms, but then in more detail and more operationally. Although there are examples of criteria to use in deciding the level of detail in the analysis (for example, Annett and Duncan 1960, their analysis being especially suited to human task analysis for training), common sense still dictates much here.

The roller-bearing department. The system functions to be performed may be distinguished as follows (see Figure 8.3).

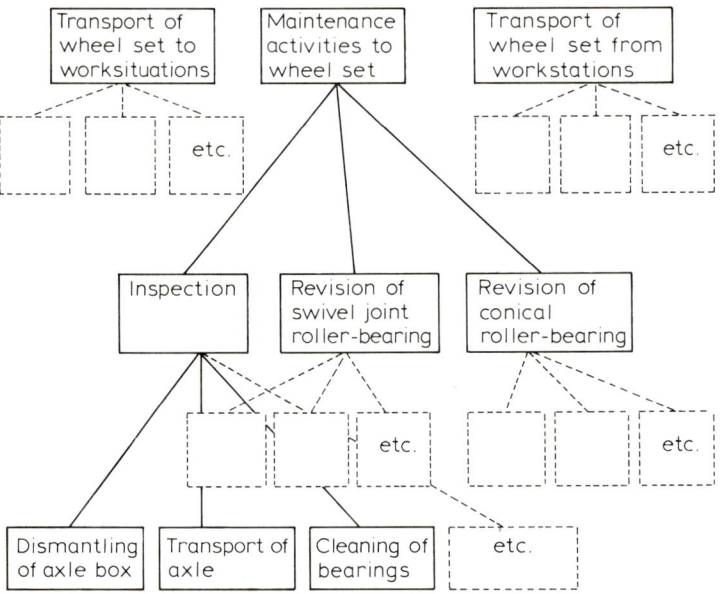

Figure 8.3 System functions and progressive redescription in the roller-bearing department

The door department. The basic system functions in the door department are as follows (see Figure 8.4).

Allocation of functions

The roller-bearing department. The allocation principles in the roller-bearing department led to a great number of propositions. One example; the systems function of 'transport of wheel set' has been allocated to the machine (heavy work), as well as to the transport of the axle box, for example. In the first case a mechanised system was designed that transports the wheel sets on rails in the floor. In the second case, a roller conveyer has been chosen as a solution.

The door department. The transport of outer doors in the existing situation caused a heavy *static load* in the back and the arms. This function then should be allocated to the machine (see *Propositions* on p. 100).

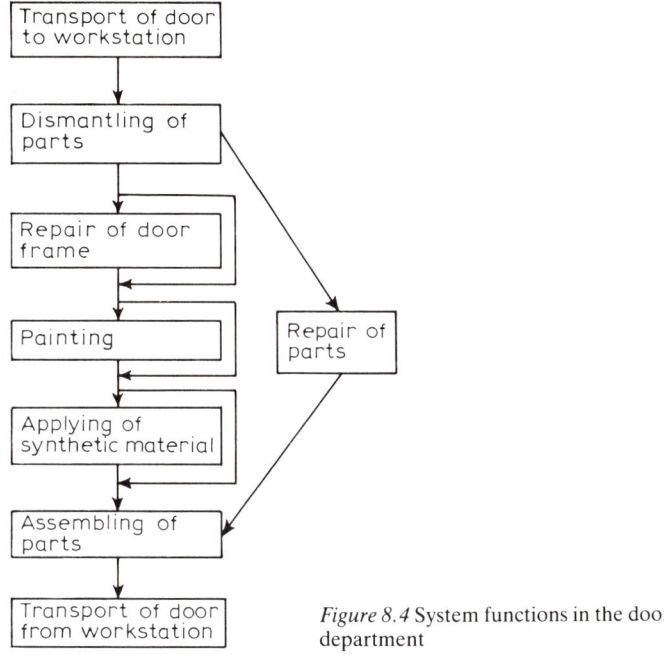

Figure 8.4 System functions in the door department

To conform to *motivational considerations*, for example the system functions having to do with outer doors have been combined in one job. Also it was tried to let the workers perform a greater number of operations on one object, to provide for task integration.

Propositions

After allocating system functions to man or machine, proposals have to be made concerning the actual realisations. Proposals concerning the design or purchase of machines and methods of work have to be formulated. Also the selection, training and job composition of the human components in the systems have to be taken into account.

Propositions for the roller-bearing department; an example. Frequent pushing, pulling and lifting of heavy parts, such as the axle boxes, present problems of static load. Each wheel set consists of two axle boxes (27–44 kg), that have to be manipulated rather carefully during assembly. The capacity amounts to about 30 wheel sets per day. The task in fact is too heavy, so that it had to be mechanised.

Two solutions were developed, i.e., releasing the axle box by vibration and releasing the axle box by hydraulic aids. In this way pulling becomes superfluous. Another improvement consisted of the transportation of the released axle box by means of an additional flexible construction.

The (often pneumatic) tools were adjusted to spring balances close to the dismantling working place. In this way in principle the work may be performed in a sitting position. It was decided to build a mock-up to test the two alternatives (*Mock-ups* p. 100). The hydraulic system proved to be constructively more favourable. The transport system had to be improved because of some mechanical weaknesses and user problems.

Propositions for the door department; an example. Manipulation of outerdoors proved to be a problem because of the weight (25–70 kg) and the dimensions (2 × 0.9 m^2). The problems arose during transportation, lifting to the working bench and taking it off. The work had to be divided between man and machine in such a way that these problems would be removed as far as possible.

The solution was to build a construction that could combine the function of 'transportation aid' and (in horizontal position) the function of a supportive frame for the door to be operated upon. The transportation problem as well as the lifting problem at the working bench could be solved at the same time. Rollers on this 'transportation chart' made it possible to transport a door rather easily to and from a stock, the floor of which consists of rollers having the same height. Two prototypes have been built and tested.

Scale models; mock-ups

Mock-ups, prototypes and scale models are well-known aids in evaluating design proposals. The following describes two examples from the roller-bearing department.

Scale models. Already in rather early phases of the design process scale models have been constructed of the six workstations involved (scale 1:50). They were made of maquette materials.

Also the resulting proposed overall layout of the new department has been set up in maquette form (scale 1:50). Interviews and talks with management, experts and the personnel involved led to a number of alterations during the process. Also task structures were discussed with the aid of the maquettes.

Mock-ups. A scale model 1:1 is called a mock-up. A mock-up allows one to make dynamic simulations (role-playing of actual working conditions). In the roller-bearing department a mock-up was made of the workstation for the dismantling and assembling of the axle boxes. It has been built in a working pit; the axles may be of various heights and and nearly all handtools to be used are present. Two subjects, differing in height (1.61 m (= 2.5 th percentile) and 1.91 m (= 97.5 th percentile)) simulated the work to be done.

The following techniques have been used in the evaluations.

Interview – the workers involved were asked about their subjective opinions.

Observation – especially working posture and working methods were observed. For example, reachability of handtools, reachability and controllability of controls, working posture whilse carrying out the tasks, sitting posture, and static and dynamic load.

Implementation

The roller-bearing department. The rebuilding of the department is almost finished, conforming generally to the guidelines resulting from the ergonomic systems design method.

Although the demands have been raised since the investigation, it is expected that the proposed system may meet them. It appeared that the project groups for the rebuilding and installation needed the active support of the ergonomist, to give advice in the phase of realisation.

The door department. The new department has been in operation for some time now. The transportation chart has been very successful. At the moment 15 of them are in use, although at the beginning eight were thought to be enough. One year after the installation a systematic evaluation is planned.

Some concluding remarks

(1) Because systems design more often than not is systems *re*design the design process should start with phase 0: the analysis of the existing situation. In most cases such an analysis will consist at least of the next partial analyses: process analysis, task analysis, ergonomic workstation analysis and worker opinion analysis. The distinction between curative and preventive ergonomics in our view should not be seen as a fundamental one but as a rather gradual transition from one to the other.

(2) Not only the goals of the system to be (re)designed should be formulated, but also the constraints. These constraints concern

(i) personnel considerations: it should be clear, for example, whether personnel may be transferred;

(ii) cost considerations: economic considerations may constrain the alternative possibilities in the (re)design;

(iii) time considerations: it should be clear, for example, what the life-expectancy is of the system to be (re)designed.

(3) Worker participation is an essential part of the design process. Its integration should be decided upon as soon as possible. Ergonomic system design in this way is in line with modern concepts of the design of work.

(4) Mock-ups, scale models, etc. play an important role in the design process. Firstly, because they allow for evaluation of design proposals. Secondly, they have the important function of letting the different groups involved participate in the design. More explicit rules, however, about *how* to carry out the evaluations with mock-ups are necessary.

(5) Deciding that a systems function is allocated to the machine is only the first step to specifying the form and function of the machine part. If you decide for example that the transportation function should be carried out by machine, the next question immediately arises, what machine? The same goes for the human tasks in the system.

(6) University and industry may both benefit by carrying out projects in mutual cooperation, in that theoretical or abstract considerations may be tested out in the field and industry may benefit from new insights.

References

ANNETT, J. & DUNCAN, K. D. (1960). *Task Analysis*, HMSO, London.

CANTON, P. (1978). Systeemergonomisch ontwerp van een afdeling voor de revisie van treindeuren, (*Ergonomic Systems Design for a Department of Train Door Maintenance* – in Dutch), M.Sc. Thesis, Eindhoven University of Technology.

COBURN, R. (1973). *Human Engineering Guide to Ship System Development*, Naval Electronics Laboratory Center, San Diego.

SINGLETON, W. T. (1967). 'The systems prototype and its design problems', (in *The Human Operator in Complex Systems*, Singleton, W. T., Eaterby, R. S. & Whitfield, D. C. (eds)), Taylor & Francis Ltd, London.

SINGLETON, W. T. (1974). *Man-machine Systems*, Penguin Books, London.

VOSKAMP, P. (1977). Ergonomisch ontwerp van een rollager-afdeling, (*Ergonomic Design of a Roller-Bearing Department* – in Dutch), Internal Report Netherlands Railways.

Chapter 9

Industrial workplace layout and engineering anthropology

B. Das & R. M. Grady

Introduction

The ideal industrial workplace layout should be compatible with not only systems performance requirements but also with the user. The ideal design should bear the performance capability and limitations of the user in mind and should ensure that the operator is able to see the working area clearly. Posture must be adequate and comfortable, and controls must be within reach to minimise error. To accomplish this, the designer must take into consideration the physiological, psychological, environmental and dimensional factors, which will affect operator performance and well-being. The overall design will no doubt be dependent on the interaction among the stated factors.

To keep the operator comfortable, an optimum industrial workplace layout must provide adequate postural support, proper distribution of body/limb weight, natural body/limb positions and should require little demand to use maximum reach or force. The user acceptance and operator motivation are the main psychological objectives of an industrial workplace layout and they can be achieved if the workplace is simple, convenient, well organised, attractive, reliable and safe. Due consideration must be given to environmental factors, i.e., illumination, temperature, ventilation, noise and vibration. Workplace dimensions should be compatible with anthropometric characteristics of the anticipated user. The following operator-related dimensional factors that influence industrial workplace layout should be considered.

(1) Postural control and distribution of body weight.
(2) Reach envelope of hands.
(3) Eye position with regard to display area (Hertzberg 1972).

Workstation design concepts have evolved mainly from the following areas

(a) industrial engineering;
(b) ergonomics or human factors engineering;
(c) industrial hygiene and safety engineering;

(d) industrial relations;
(e) behavioural science;
(f) industrial psychology.

In the context of industrial workplace layout, these disciplines have one or more of the following objectives

(i)   measure and improve worker productivity;
(ii) enhance worker satisfaction and job attitudes;
(iii) reduce operator fatigue;
(iv) improve working environments;
(v)   minimise worker safety hazards.

Industrial engineering involves plant layout, work methods and measurement. Plant layout is not concerned only with overall facilities but also with the arrangement of the work area. The designer can improve operator efficiency and reduce fatigue in manual work by following the principles of motion economy as related to the arrangement and conditions of the workplace. Determining time standards is a necessary step in the systematic procedure of developing new workplaces and improving methods related to existing work centres.

Ergonomics deals with anthropometry, biomechanics, kinesiology and work physiology. The discipline is especially concerned with the workplace dimensions and the tool and equipment arrangement. The anthropometric data consist of worker's body dimensions, ranges of motions for body extremities, and muscle strength capabilities. Advantage must be taken of the available anthropometric data to determine workplace dimensions, so that the operator is able to perform his or her work with maximum efficiency at minimum human cost.

Biomechanics is basically the mechanics of biological systems, especially the human body. The biomechanical approach to industrial workplace layout design gives due consideration to operator's capabilities, task demands and equipment in an integrated manner. Kinesiology deals with the study of human movement in terms of functional anatomy. The principles of kinesiology should be employed in the design of industrial workplace layout so as to avoid incompatible movements.

Work physiology is concerned with the determination of the worker's physiological reactions to his or her job demand and the maintenance of worker physiological cost within safe limits. It recognises that the workers vary in terms of their age, sex, background, physical and mental characteristics and health. These factors must be given due consideration in workplace layout design, so that a higher worker productivity can be maintained over a period of time during which different workers will be engaged to perform the required job or task.

Industrial hygiene and safety engineering aim to ensure that the environment and workplace do not pose adverse health and safety hazards to the worker. The impact of the Occupational Safety and Health Act, or OSHA, of 1970 is considerable with regard to setting safety standards and enforcing them at the workplace through periodic inspection process. Behavioural science, industrial relations and industrial psychology are all interested in improving work organisation and job design with a view to improving worker motivation, satisfaction and job attitudes. Such improvement will no doubt have a positive impact on workplace layout itself.

This chapter is primarily concerned with dimensional factors affecting workplace design through the application of engineering anthropology.

Development of industrial workplace layout design

Industrial workers are generally confined to a small working area of the plant – the workplace. Often the terms *workplace* and *work environment* are used interchangeably and include regular and protective clothing, lighting, climate, chairs, machines, tools and the actual product. In other words, everything except the worker. In designing the industrial workplace, the physical relationship in terms of distances and other linear dimensions, is often of major importance, especially from the viewpoint of production efficiency and operator physical and mental well-being. Small changes in workplace dimension can have considerable impact on productivity and occupational safety and health (Tichauer 1975).

For a seated operator at a fixed workstation, a minimum overall workspace envelope of about 76 cm long × 76 cm width × 146 cm height, is often suggested (Van Cott and Kinkade 1972). It is important to place the controls, switches, tools, equipment or objects upon which work is to be done within easy reach and in the most appropriate spatial position relative to the worker.

Maynard (1934) proposed two general concepts of industrial workplace layout design. The first concept was to reduce all motions used in the performance of the task to the lowest possible class. The five general classes of motion are

(1) finger;
(2) finger and wrist;
(3) finger, wrist and forearm;
(4) finger, wrist, forearm and upper arm;
(5) finger, wrist, forearm, upper arm and body.

The use of purely finger motions is seldom practical. In most workplace layouts, the main objectives are to eliminate all body movements, to reduce fourth-class motions to third-class and to reduce the length of all motion paths. The second concept was of normal and maximum work areas in the horizontal and vertical planes. It is logical that the working area should be kept at a minimum, so that the class of motion which must be used can be kept in the lower classifications.

For the purpose of developing the workplace layout, Maynard assumed that the operator was comfortably seated at or standing by the worktable or bench at the correct height. The normal working area in the horizontal plane of the right hand was determined by an arc drawn with a sweep of the arm. Only the forearm was extended, and the upper arm hung at the side of the body in a natural position until it tended to swing away as the arm moved toward the outer part of the workplace. Similarly, the normal working area in the horizontal plane for the left hand was determined. The overlapping area in front of the operator constituted a zone for two-handed

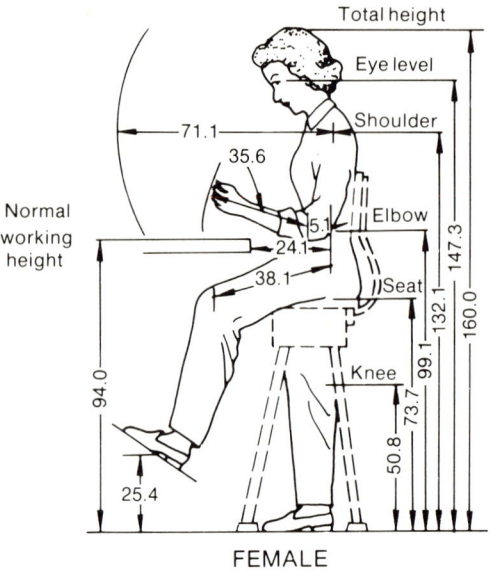

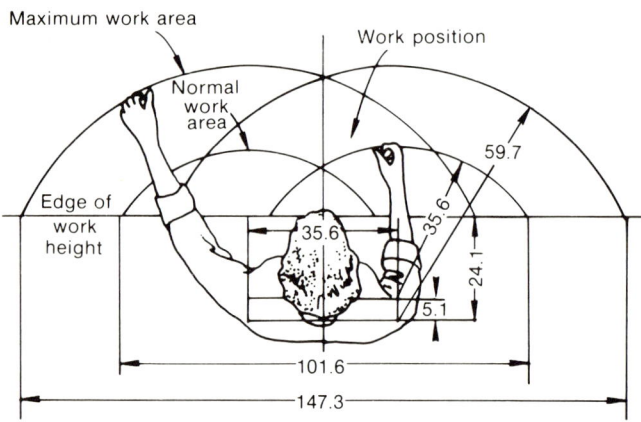

ALL DIMENSIONS IN CENTIMETRES

Figure 9.1 Normal and maximum working areas in the horizontal and vertical planes for female operator (Farley 1955)

work. The normal working area in the vertical plane of the right hand included the area made by the lower arm in an upright position hinged at the elbow moving in an arc. The normal working area in the vertical plane for the left hand was determined in a similar manner. The maximum working area was determined by drawing arcs with the arms fully extended. Both the horizontal and vertical planes were considered, as was the case with the normal working area.

The workplace layouts provided by Maynard were, however, dimensionless and therefore provided negligible guidelines to a designer. Barnes (1940) gave dimensions to Maynard's layouts, based on the data generated

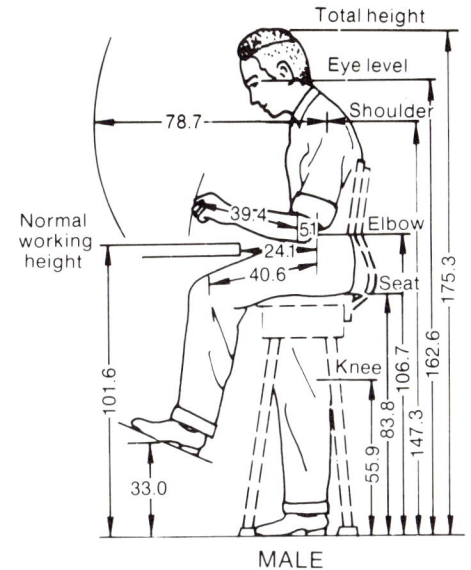

MALE

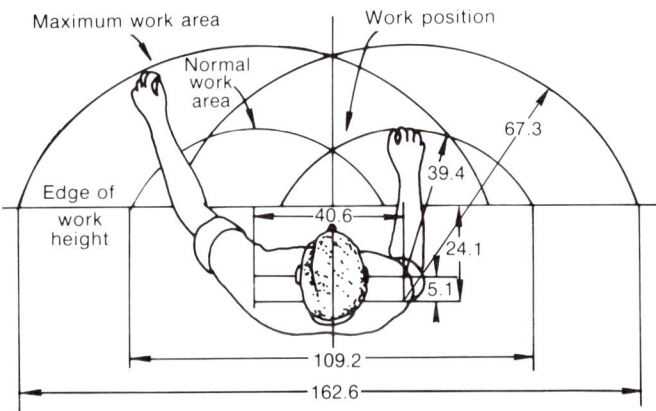

ALL DIMENSIONS IN CENTIMETRES

Figure 9.2 Normal and maximum working areas in the horizontal and
vertical planes for male operator (Farley 1955)

by Asa (1942). Subsequently, Barnes (1958) cited a study by Farley (1955)
and gave new dimensions to the layouts developed by Maynard (Figures
9.1 and 9.2). It should be pointed out that Farley gave only one work area
for male operators and one for female operators, based on the average
physical dimensions of men and women. He determined the normal
working area as being equal to the volume circumscribed by the horizontal
forearm pivoting about a relaxed vertical upper arm. He determined the
maximum working area as being equal to the volume circumscribed by the
movement of the fully extended arm pivoting about the shoulder pivot
point.

The results reported by Farley are probably those most widely used by designers of industrial workplace layout. However, according to Squires (1956), it is not correct to represent the normal working area in the horizontal plane by two intersecting semi-circles. He recognised that the arm does not move in a regular circular path. Squires pointed out that the elbow does not stay at a fixed point but moves out and away from the body as the forearm pivots. Squires' work described only the normal working area in the horizontal plane and did not include the maximum working area in the horizontal plane or the normal and maximum working areas in the vertical plane. The design of the normal working area in the horizontal plane as proposed by Squires was based on the existing anthropometric data for the 10th percentile male. His recommendations for the normal working area in the horizontal plane for the male operator are shown in Figure 9.3.

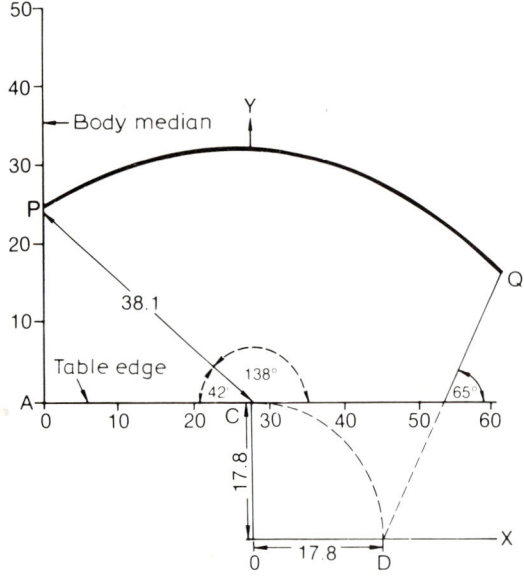

All dimensions in centimetres

Figure 9.3 Normal working area in the horizontal plane for male operator (Squires 1956)

On the basis of his analysis of the arm movement, he indicated that the path described by the hand when the forearm moved about a relaxed upper arm would be a prolate epicycloid (arc PQ). The coordinates of the arc PQ can be determined by the parametric equations

$$X = S \cos \theta + J \cos [65 + (73/90)\theta] \qquad (9.1)$$
$$Y = S \sin \theta + J \sin [65 + (73/90)\theta] \qquad (9.2)$$

where S = distance OC = elbow to shoulder projection distance, J = distance CP = distance from elbow to end of thumb, and θ = angle given at any instant by the radius which sweeps out the arc CD, degrees. For the coefficients S (distance OC) and J (distance CP), Squires used 17.8 cm and 38.1 cm, respectively. Also, he gave the distance AC, one-half the shoulder to shoulder distance, the value of 28.4 cm. By employing Squires' basic concept, Konz and Goel (1969) proposed a normal working area in the horizontal plane for the 5 th, 50 th and 95 th percentiles of the male and female US population. They pointed out that one standard work area is not satisfactory for everyone and recommended that more emphasis should be given to placement of objects straight ahead of the operator. Positions 50.8 cm or more from the body median should be de-emphasised.

A direct measure of the maximum functional reach envelope was developed by Kennedy (1964) and Chaffee and Emanuel (1964) for the male population only, for use in highly specialised workstations in military aircraft. Special workplaces were constructed for the specific purpose of measuring arm reach, which is a significant departure from the previous practice of deriving arm-reach curves from the dimensions of various body members.

The posture adopted by the subjects in the Kennedy study was not typical of the posture used by the industrial operators because of the tilt of the seat. Consequently, the data cannot be readily employed in the design of industrial workplace layouts. Also, in the Chaffee and Emanuel study, extreme postures were adopted by the subjects to maximise reach and therefore the data are not applicable in industrial workplace layout design.

Faulkner and Day (1970) conducted a study to determine the maximum reach envelope for the 5 th percentile female operator. The study was based on the measurements of a sample of 137 female operators performing a task at a seated workplace. They concluded that their results were different in several important aspects from the previous results or recommendations. Roth *et al.* (1977) while studying the reach profiles of the seated operator concluded that static measurement of reach is frequently inaccurate for design purposes. They proposed reach profiles based on the 5 th, 50 th and 95 th percentile body dimensions taken from a sample of 25 males and 24 females while they were seated.

In designing the industrial workplace, Woodson and Conover (1964) recommended that the dimensions of the larger worker should be used for determining clearances, whilst those of the smaller worker should be used to determine limits of reach. Additionally, they cautioned the designer to be mindful of the consequences of clothing, which add to the clearance requirements and also the possible restriction of movement.

Apart from considering static and dynamic measurements in developing an industrial workplace, a designer should take into account the height of the workstation. In recommending the optimum height, Barnes (1940) recommended that the hand be allowed to work 2.5–7.6 cm lower than the elbow. Since Barnes did not cite any evidence for his recommendations, Konz (1967) conducted an experiment to investigate the effects of work surface height on performance. Konz concluded that the best working height for a standing operator is about 2.5 cm below the elbow; nevertheless the working height can vary several centimetres up or down without any significant effect on performance. For determining proper workplace height, Konz (1979) has recommended three basic approaches

(1) make available several workplace or work surface heights;
(2) adjust the operator's elbow rather than the height of the workplace. This can be accomplished by utilising an adjustable chair or providing a platform to stand on if necessary;
(3) adjust the height of the work on the workbench.

For a successful industrial workplace layout design Khalil (1972) encouraged the designers to follow four basic design rules.

(a) Recognise that the operator is the centre of the design and therefore consider the operator's anatomical structure and obtain accurate anthropometric dimensions to fit the job to the operator.
(b) Utilise the principles of kinesiology in the design and avoid incompatible movements.
(c) Observe the physiological capacity of the operator and utilise physiological responses as criteria for the design.
(d) Apply psychological principles for improving morale and satisfaction.

Tichauer (1975) maintained that the previously developed guidelines for industrial workplace layouts are limited in application as they neglect necessary anthropometric considerations due to different ethnic compositions of the diverse working populations. To obtain maximum operator efficiency and physical well-being from an industrial workplace layout design, Tichauer recommends the following guidelines for the purpose of determining workplace dimensions.

(i)   Consider body measurement as well as range and strength of movement of the kinetic elements involved in a task.
(ii) Take account of the full range of body measurements of the specific working population involved in the task performance.
(iii) Recognise the differences of sex, ethnic groups and educational or social back ground because they affect specific types of manipulative skills.
(iv) Ascertain by biomechanical analysis the optimal position of operator with regard to equipment controls.
(v)   Provide maximum postural freedom in task design, especially for repetitive work situations.
(vi) Avoid standing on the toes and torsion or sideways bending of the trunk.
(vii) Avoid performing a task on a strip 7.6 cm wide from the border of the bench which is closest to the operator.

It must be recognised that designing the workplace to fit the average person is a serious error because it ignores the fact that no-one is average in all respects (Hertzberg 1972). For the purpose of designing the individual workplace, Hertzberg suggests that the designer should pay special attention to what the operator must see, hear, reach and manipulate and also to the body clearance.

It must be recognised that industrial workplace layout design parameters or dimensions must be compatible with the anthropometric considerations of the anticipated user. This will ensure greater productivity by maximising efficiency at a minimum human cost. Poorly designed workplaces are still commonplace in industry, a fact which is aggravated by the non-availability of usable design parameters.

A particular workplace layout may be used by one or more male operators, one or more female operators, or a combination of both male and female operators. Obviously, it is not always feasible or practical to change the design parameters of a workplace in industry every day or each work shift to suit the individual operator's anthropometric characteristics. However, an optimum industrial workplace layout should be designed with a view to accommodating the anthropometric characteristics of the user population.

Research was conducted to determine design parameters or dimensions for industrial workplace layout for various operating positions and operators through the use of the existing anthropometric data, so that they can be readily employed by a designer. Below, the methodology pursued in this research to determine industrial workplace layout design parameters or dimensions is highlighted. More details concerning this research were presented elsewhere (Grady 1979).

Engineering anthropology and its use in industrial workplace layout design

Anthropometry is the technology of measuring various human physical traits, primarily such factors as size, mobility, and strength. Engineering anthropology is the effort in applying such data to workplace, equipment and clothing design to enhance the efficiency, safety and comfort of the operator (Hertzberg 1972). Here, our main concern is to use engineering anthropology to develop design parameters or dimensions for individual industrial workplace layouts.

In the layout of any industrial workplace, a primary requirement is that all controls or tasks which require manual operation be located where they can be reached and operated efficiently. This can be achieved by selecting a representative sample, determining their functional arm reaches and defining a workspace envelope which specifies both the normal and maximum permissible areas or limits, so that all the necessary work-related items such as controls, tools and equipment can be placed within the workspace. This ideal procedure is seldom followed in real life or an industrial work situation. However, the problem can be alleviated by using relevant anthropometric data to develop industrial workplace layout design guidelines.

The existing anthropometric data were used in the present research to determine industrial workplace layout dimensions for performing indust-rial tasks whilst sitting or standing or a combination of both, using an individual male or female and a combination of male and female operators for the 5 th, 50 th and 95 th percentiles. The normal and maximum reach dimensions were based on the most commonly used industrial operations, which require a grasping movement or thumb and forefinger manipulation. However, appropriate allowances were provided to adjust the reach dimensions for other types of industrial operation. The normal and maximum horizontal and vertical clearances, as well as reference points for the horizontal and vertical clearances were established to facilitate the design of the industrial workplace. To describe the workspace envelope for the individual operator, the concepts developed by Farley (1955) and Squires (1956) were used. For determining the limits of reach and clearance requirements, the dimensions of smaller (5 th percentile) and larger (95 th percentile) operators were used, respectively. For the purpose of this research, it was necessary to adjust the existing anthropometric data and this was accomplished in the following manner.

Adjustment of existing anthropometric data

The anthropometric measurements that were used to determine design parameters or dimensions are stated below:

(A) Total height – the vertical distance from the floor to the top of the head.

(B) Body height (sitting) – the vertical distance from the sitting surface to the top of the head.

(C) Eye height (standing) – the vertical distance from the floor to the inner corner of the eye.

(D) Eye height (sitting) – the vertical distance from the sitting surface to the inner corner of the eye.

(E) Shoulder height (standing) – the vertical distance from the floor to the upper-most point on the lateral edge of the shoulder with the operator standing erect.

(F) Shoulder height (sitting) – the vertical distance from the sitting surface to the upper-most point on the lateral edge of the shoulder with the subject sitting erect.

(G) Body depth – the maximum horizontal distance between the vertical planes passing through the most anterior and posterior points on the trunk.

(H) Elbow-to-elbow breadth – the maximum horizontal distance across the lateral surface of the elbows.

(I) Thigh clearance – the vertical distance from the sitting surface to the top of the thigh at its intersection with the abdomen.

(J) Forearm length – the horizontal distance from the tip of the elbow to the tip of the longest finger.

(K) Arm reach – the horizontal distance from the posterior surface of the shoulder to the tip of the extended middle finger.

(L) Elbow height (standing) – the vertical distance from the floor to the depression at the elbow between the bones of the upper arm and forearm.

(M) Elbow height (sitting) – the vertical distance from the sitting surface to the bottom of the elbow.

(N) Popliteal height (sitting) – the vertical distance from the floor to the underside of the thigh immediately behind the knee.

The existing anthropometric data for the standing height, sitting height and eye height were based on erect standing and sitting positions. The industrial worker seldom assumes erect positions at work or at rest.

Consequently, the data were adjusted, in the following manner, to account for the 'slump' posture involved in the 'normal' standing and sitting positions.

Total or standing height (item A) and standing eye height (item C), subtract 1.9 cm.
Body or sitting height (item B) and sitting eye height (item D), subtract 4.4 cm (Hertzberg 1972).

With regard to forearm length (item J), the following adjustments were made for

(1) fingertip manipulation of controls, subtract 1.3 cm for flip and 2.5 cm for push;
(2) manipulation by thumb and forefinger, subtract 7.6 cm;
(3) grasp by the whole hand, subtract 12.7 cm.

Similar adjustments were made for fingertip, thumb and forefinger and hand manipulation, with regard to arm reach (item K). The essential

Table 9.1 *Existing antropometric measurements* (Hertzberg 1972)

Sex	Item	Body feature	Percentiles (cm)		
			5 th	50 th	95 th
Male	A	Total height	165.6	175.5	185.7
	B	Body height (sitting)	85.9	91.4	96.5
	C	Eye height	154.4	164.3	174.2
	D	Eye height (sitting)	74.7	80.0	85.1
	E	Shoulder height	134.1	143.8	152.9
	F	Shoulder height (sitting)	54.1	59.2	63.8
	G	Body depth	25.7	29.2	33.0
	H	Elbow-to-elbow	38.6	43.7	50.3
	I	Thigh clearance	12.2	14.2	16.5
	J	Forearm length	44.7	48.0	51.3
	K	Arm length	81.0	87.9	94.7
	L	Elbow height	103.1	110.5	117.9
	M	Elbow height (sitting)	18.8	23.1	27.4
	N	Popliteal height (sitting)	39.9	43.2	46.2
Female	A	Total height	153.2	162.6	173.2
	B	Body height (sitting)	82.3	86.6	90.9
	C	Eye height	143.0	152.9	162.8
	D	Eye height (sitting)	72.4	76.2	80.3
	E	Shoulder height	124.0	133.6	142.7
	F	Shoulder height (sitting)	51.6	56.6	61.2
	G	Body depth	20.8	23.6	26.7
	H	Elbow-to-elbow	34.3	37.8	42.4
	I	Thigh clearance	10.4	12.4	14.5
	J	Forearm length	40.1	44.2	48.3
	K	Arm length	72.9	78.7	85.1
	L	Elbow height	96.5	102.6	108.7
	M	Elbow height (sitting)	18.8	23.1	27.4
	N	Popliteal height (sitting)	34.8	38.1	41.1

Note: Dimensions based on US military population

anthropometric measurements were obtained for the 5 th, 50 th and 95 th percentiles for both male and female as shown in Table 9.1. It should be noted that the existing anthropometric data were derived on the basis of measurements from nude subjects (Hertzberg 1972). Therefore, the data were duly adjusted for clothing, shoe and other allowances, which were added or subtracted to the various measurements shown in Table 9.2 (Hertzberg 1972).

Table 9.2 *Clothing, shoe and other allowances or adjustments* (Hertzberg 1972)

Item	Body feature	Allowances or adjustments
A	Total height	Add 2.5 cm for men's and women's shoes
		Subtract 1.9 cm for slump posture
B	Body height (sitting)	Add 0.6 cm for clothing under the buttocks
		Subtract 4.4 cm for slump posture
C	Eye height	Add 2.5 cm for men's and women's shoes
		Subtract 1.9 cm for slump posture
D	Eye height (sitting)	Add 0.6 cm for clothing under the buttocks
		Subtract 4.4 cm for slump posture
E	Shoulder height	Add 2.5 cm for men's and women's shoes
		and 1.4 cm for clothing
F	Shoulder height (sitting)	Add 0.6 cm for clothing under the buttocks
G	Body depth	Add 1.0 cm for clothing
H	Elbow-to-elbow	Add 1.4 cm for clothing
I	Thigh clearance	Add 2.0 cm for clothing
J	Forearm length	Subtract 7.6 cm for thumb and forefinger manipulation
K	Arm length	Subtract 5.1 cm for measurement from the back of the shoulder
		Subtract 7.6 cm for thumb and forefinger manipulation
L	Elbow height	Add 2.5 cm for men's and women's shoes
M	Elbow height (sitting)	No allowance
N	Popliteal height (sitting)	Add 2.5 cm for men's and women's shoes

To allow for the grasping movement or thumb and forefinger manipulation, a subtraction of 7.6 cm from the given anthropometric data (Table 9.1) for the forearm length was made, for the purpose of determining the normal working area in the horizontal and vertical planes. It should be recognised that the anthropometric data for the arm reach (item K) are based on the measurements from the posterior surface of the shoulder. Consequently, to determine the proper arm reach from the shoulder pivot point for the purpose of establishing the maximum working area in the horizontal and vertical planes, it was necessary to subtract 5.1 cm from the given anthropometric data for the arm reach (item K), to allow for the distance from the back of the shoulder to the pivot point. An additional subtraction of 7.6 cm was made from the overall arm reach length, to compensate for the thumb and forefinger manipulation. The corrected or adjusted anthropometric measurements for clothing, shoe and other allowances or adjustments are shown in Table 9.3. These measurements were used subsequently to generate mathematically the normal and maximum working areas and other pertinent design dimensions of industrial workplace layout.

Table 9.3 *Corrected anthropometric measurements to account for shoe, clothing, and other allowances or adjustments*

Sex	Item	Body feature	Percentiles (cm)		
			5 th	50 th	95 th
	A	Total height (slump)	166.2	176.1	186.3
	B	Body height (sitting, slump)	82.1	87.6	92.7
	C	Eye height (slump)	160.0	164.9	174.8
	D	Eye height (sitting, slump)	70.9	76.2	81.3
	E	Shoulder height	138.0	147.7	156.8
	F	Shoulder height (sitting)	54.7	59.8	64.4
	G	Body depth	26.7	30.2	34.0
Male	H	Elbow-to-elbow	40.0	45.1	51.7
	I	Thigh clearance	14.2	16.2	18.5
	J	Forearm length	37.1	40.4	43.7
	K	Arm length	68.3	75.2	82.0
	L	Elbow height	105.6	113.0	120.4
	M	Elbow height (sitting)	18.8	23.1	27.4
	N	Popliteal height (sitting)	42.4	45.7	48.7
	A	Total height (slump)	153.8	163.2	173.8
	B	Body height (sitting, slump)	78.5	82.8	87.1
	C	Eye height (slump)	143.6	153.5	163.4
	D	Eye height (sitting, slump)	68.6	72.4	76.5
	E	Shoulder height	127.9	137.5	146.6
	F	Shoulder height (sitting)	52.2	57.2	61.8
	G	Body depth	21.8	24.6	27.6
Female	H	Elbow-to-elbow	35.7	38.2	43.8
	I	Thigh clearance	12.4	14.4	16.5
	J	Forearm length	32.5	36.6	40.7
	K	Arm length	60.2	66.0	72.4
	L	Elbow height	99.0	105.1	111.2
	M	Elbow height (sitting)	18.8	23.1	27.4
	N	Popliteal height (sitting)	37.3	40.6	43.6

Note: Dimensions based on US military population

Design of industrial workplace layout for the seated operator

An industrial operation should preferably be designed to permit the operator to perform the task or job in a seated position for the purpose of improving worker productivity by maximising effective motions, reducing operator fatigue and increasing operator stability and equilibrium. In designing seated operator workplaces, due consideration should be given to the variety of operators who will be working at the particular workstation, the chair, the foot rest and the workbench or worktable.

An adjustable-height chair is most desirable in an industrial work situation. With the provision of such a chair, the designer will be able to specify a standard workbench height, which of course is dependent on the nature of the work. The chair should be so adjusted that the optimum work height can be maintained. The work height should be indicated in terms of elbow height instead of the distance from the floor. The recommended work bench height is about 2.5 cm below the elbow (Konz 1979) and this criterion should be used if possible in developing industrial workplace layouts. The bench height can vary up or down from the elbow considerably without affecting work performance.

Determination of workspace dimensions for the seated operator

The working area in the horizontal plane for a seated male or female operator is shown in Figure 9.4 (the same figure will also represent the

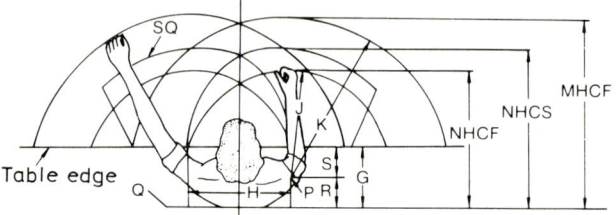

Figure 9.4 Normal and maximum working areas and clearances in the horizontal plane for a seated (also for standing and sit-stand) male or female operator

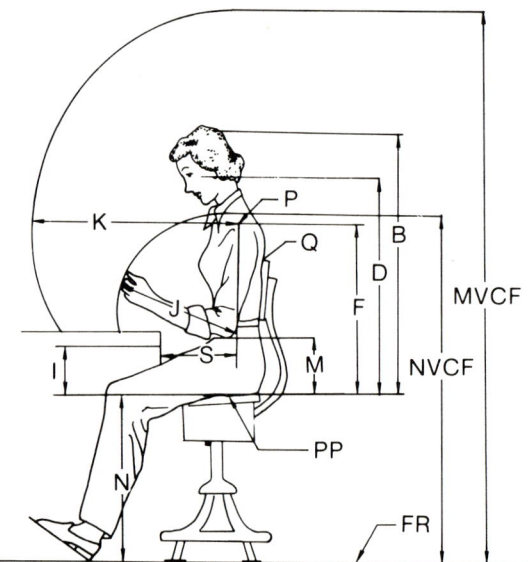

Figure 9.5 Normal and maximum working areas and clearances in the vertical plane for a seated (male or female) operator

standing and sit-stand male or female operator), whilst Figure 9.5 shows the working area in the vertical plane for a seated male or female operator. The normal and maximum working areas in both the horizontal and vertical planes were projected from the shoulder pivot point P. The pivot point in the horizontal plane was located from a reference point Q or where the operator's back made the contact with the chair back. The 95 th percentile body depth measurement (or item G) was used to determine the location of the reference point Q. For designing industrial workplace layout for general male operators (as an example), the 95 th percentile value of 34.0 cm would be used (see Table 9.3). The distance R or distance between P and Q was equal to one-half the body depth. The length S represented the distance from the shoulder pivot point to the edge of the workbench in both the horizontal and vertical planes and the lengths S and R would be equal.

The shoulder pivot point P in the vertical plane was located from a reference point PP or the sitting surface. The 95 th percentile thigh clearance (item I) was used to locate the point PP. Also, the elbow height (or item M), the popliteal height (item N) and the body height (item B) were based on the 95 th percentile measurements. To design industrial workplace layout for general male operators, the 95 th percentile values of 18.5 cm, 48.7 cm and 92.7 cm would be used for thigh clearance, popliteal height and body height respectively (Table 9.3). Once the distance between the bottom of the workbench and the seat of the chair was established, the vertical location of the shoulder pivot point could be determined. In order that the smaller operator reaches and properly views the work, the shoulder height (item F) and eye level (item D) were based on the 5 th percentile measurements. For the general male operator, the 5 th percentile values for shoulder height and eye level were 54.7 cm and 70.9 cm, respectively. The workbench or elbow height (item M) was based on the 95 th percentile measurement and this value was 27.4 cm for general male operator.

The normal and maximum working areas in the horizontal and vertical planes were determined from the 5 th percentile values of the forearm length (item J), the arm reach (item K) and the elbow-to-elbow breadth. (item H). For general male operators, the 5th percentile values for items J, K, and H would be 37.1 cm, 68.3 cm and 40.0 cm, respectively. With the above reach dimensions, it was possible to determine the normal and maximum working areas in the horizontal and vertical planes by using Farley's concept.

To apply Squires' concept of the normal working area in the horizontal plane, it was necessary to use the distance between the elbow and the shoulder projection (item S) and this distance was equal to one-half of body depth (item R). With these distances it would be possible to determine the normal working area (arc SQ) in the horizontal plane, according to Squires' concept, by finding the X and Y axis values from the shoulder pivot point P by varying the θ value in the parametric equations (9.1) and (9.2) stated earlier.

Although the manner in which the pertinent design dimensions were determined for general male operators was indicated above, the same procedure was basically followed to establish other design dimensions for workplace layouts for the seated operator. Table 9.4 summarises the pertinent design parameters, duly adjusted for clothing, shoe and other allowances.

Once the design dimensions and working areas were specified, it was possible to determine the normal and maximum horizontal and vertical

Table 9.4 *Dimensions for workplace layouts for seated male and female operators*

Item	Body feature	General male (cm)	General female (cm)	Combination of male and female (cm)	Individual male, percentiles (cm)			Individual female, percentiles (cm)		
					5th	50th	95th	5th	50th	95th
B	Body height (sitting, slump)	92.7	87.1	92.7	82.1	87.6	92.7	78.5	82.8	87.1
D	Eye height (sitting, slump)	70.9	68.6	68.6	70.9	76.2	81.3	68.6	72.4	76.5
E	Shoulder height (sitting)	54.7	52.2	52.2	54.7	59.8	64.4	52.2	57.2	61.8
G	Body depth	34.0	27.6	34.0	26.7	30.2	34.0	21.8	24.6	27.6
H	Elbow-to-elbow	40.0	35.7	35.7	40.0	45.1	51.7	35.7	38.2	43.8
I	Thigh clearance	18.5	16.5	18.5	14.2	16.2	18.5	12.4	14.4	16.5
J	Forearm length	37.1	32.5	32.5	37.1	40.4	43.7	32.5	36.6	40.7
K	Arm reach	68.3	60.2	60.2	68.3	75.2	82.0	60.2	66.0	72.4
M	Elbow height (sitting)	27.4	27.4	27.4	18.8	23.1	27.4	18.8	23.1	27.4
N	Popliteal height (sitting)	48.7	43.6	48.7	42.4	45.7	48.7	37.3	40.6	43.6

Note: (1) All dimensions based on US military population (2) Normal and maximum reach based on thumb and forefinger manipulation (items J and K) (3) Adjust items J and K values for: end-of-fingertip add 7.6 cm, flip add 6.4 cm and grip subtract 5.1 cm clearance dimensions. To determine the normal horizontal clearance (NHCF) dimension based on Farley's concept, it would be necessary to subtract the distance from the shoulder pivot point to the edge of the workbench (item S) from the forearm length (item J) and then add the body depth (item G). The maximum horizontal clearance (MHCF) dimension could be determined by subtracting the distance from the shoulder pivot point to the edge of the workbench (item S) from the arm reach (item K) and then adding the body depth (item G). To illustrate the above calculations, the dimensions of the seated general male operators would be used. Items J, K, G and S would be equal to 37.1 cm, 68.3 cm, 34.0 cm and 17.0 cm, respectively (Table 9.4). Thus, NHCF would be equal to: $(37.1 - 17.0) + 34.0 = 54.1$ cm and the MHCF would be equal to: $(68.3 - 17.0) + 34.0 = 85.3$ cm. To determine the normal horizontal clearance (NHCS) based on Squires' concept, it would be necessary to find iteratively the optimum Y axis value or the distance from the shoulder pivot point P to the arc SQ, by varying the θ value in the parametric equation (9.2) and then add the distance between the shoulder pivot point P and the back of the chair (Q) or item R. Thus, for the stated example, the NHCS would be equal to: $(48.9 + 17.0) = 65.9$ cm. The normal vertical clearance (NVCF) dimension would be equal to the popliteal height, sitting (item N) plus the elbow height, sitting (item M) plus the forearm length (item J). The maximum vertical clearance (MVCF) dimension would be equal to the popliteal height, sitting (item N) plus the shoulder height, sitting (item F) plus the arm reach (item K). To illustrate the above calculations, the dimensions of the seated general male operator would be used. Items N, M, J, F and K would be equal to 48.7 cm, 27.4 cm, 37.1 cm, 54.7 cm and 68.3 cm, respectively (Table 9.4). Thus, NVCF would be equal to: $(48.7 + 27.4 + 37.1) = 113.2$ cm and MVCF would be equal to: $(48.7 + 54.7 + 68.3) = 171.7$ cm. The horizontal and vertical clearance dimensions for workplace layouts for seated operators are summarised in Table 9.5.

Table 9.5 *Normal and maximum horizontal and vertical clearance dimensions for workplace layouts for seated male and female operators*

Population	Horizontal clearance (cm)			Vertical clearance (cm)	
	Normal, Farley (NHCF)	Normal, Squires (NHCS)	Maximum, Farley (MHCF)	Normal, Farley (NVCF)	Maximum, Farley (MVCF)
General male	54.1	65.9	85.3	113.2	171.7
General female	46.3	55.7	74.0	103.2	156.0
Combination of male and female	49.5	61.6	77.2	108.6	161.1
5th percentile male	50.4	59.3	81.3	98.3	165.4
50th percentile male	55.5	65.6	90.3	109.2	180.7
95th percentile male	60.7	72.1	99.0	119.8	195.1
5th percentile female	43.4	50.6	71.1	88.6	149.7
50th percentile female	48.9	57.0	78.3	100.3	163.8
95th percentile female	54.5	63.6	86.2	111.7	177.8

Note: (1) Reference points for horizontal and vertical clearances are chair back (Q) and floor (FR), respectively (2) Normal and maximum reach based on thumb and forefinger manipulation

Design of industrial workplace layout for the standing operator

The standing workplace is probably the least desirable, since the operator will be required to stand for long periods of time. This will make the operator tired earlier and cause a decrease in productivity. Nevertheless, standing workplaces are often necessary in industry and the designer is required to specify the design parameters.

The designer should give special attention to the height of the workbench in designing industrial workplace layout for the standing operator. An adjustable workbench would be ideal since the entire workplace population could be accommodated. However, in an industrial situation the same workbench would be used by a variety of workers and this would require continuous adjustment of the workbench height. To alleviate this problem Konz (1979) suggested three approaches. The first is to provide an adjustable workbench – this would be impractical when a variety of workers use the same workbench over a relatively short time period. The second is to adjust the operator's elbow, rather than the height of the workbench. This can be accomplished by raising or lowering the platform on which the operator stands. The platform can be made of several pieces of rug piled on top of each other; rugs help in reducing fatigue to the feet, as well as to the back. The third approach is to adjust the work on the workbench. For the purpose of this investigation, the second approach would be used.

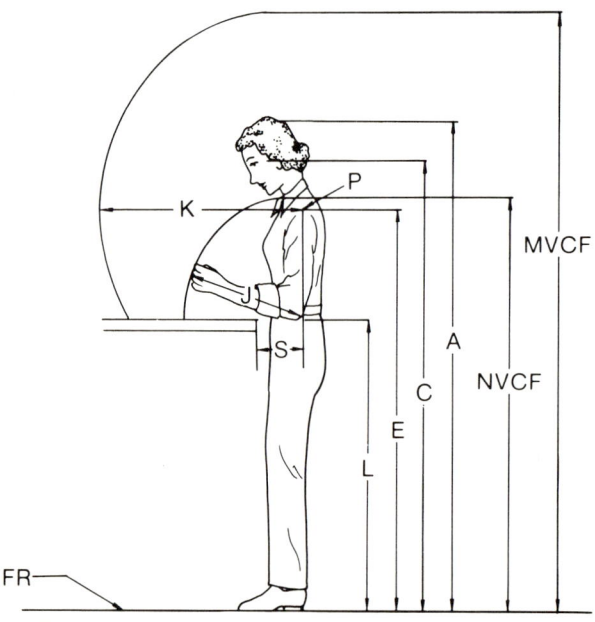

Figure 9.6 Normal and maximum working areas and clearances in the vertical plane for a standing (male or female) operator

Determination of workspace dimensions for the standing operator

The working area in the horizontal plane for a standing male or female operator is shown in Figure 9.4 (the same figure is used to represent seated and sit–stand male or female operator), whilst Figure 9.6 shows the working area in the vertical plane for a standing male or female operator. The normal and maximum working areas in both the horizontal and vertical planes were projected from the shoulder pivot point P. To establish the location of P in the horizontal plane, with respect to the edge of the workbench, it would be necessary to determine the length of S by using the body depth (item G) dimension. For designing industrial workplace layout, for example, for general male operators, the 95 th percentile value for item G would be 34.0 cm and therefore the length S would be one-half item G or 17.0 cm.

The vertical position of the shoulder pivot point P would be established from the floor or the vertical reference point FR. The distance from the floor to the shoulder pivot point P would be determined on the basis of 5 th percentile shoulder height (item E) to facilitate the reach of the smaller operator. Thus, for a standing male operator, the vertical distance from the floor to the shoulder pivot point P, would be equal to 138.0 cm. Other dimensions that should be considered to describe the workspace envelope would include the body height (item A), the eye level (item C) and the elbow height (item L). Since a platform would be provided to adjust the elbow height of the smaller operators and removed for the larger operators, the dimensions of the body height (item A) and the elbow height (item L) would be based on the 95 th percentile measurements. For the standing male operator, items A and L would be equal to 186.3 cm and 120.4 cm, respectively. The eye level (item C) would be based on the 5 th percentile measurement, so that the smaller operators can see their work properly. Thus, for the standing male operator, item C would be equal to 160.0 cm.

Once the shoulder pivot point and the clearance dimensions were established, it was possible to determine the normal and maximum working areas in the horizontal and vertical planes, following the same approach as was described earlier for the seated operator. Table 9.6 summarises the pertinent design dimensions for workplace layouts for the standing operator.

Again, using the same procedure outlined earlier for the seated operator, the normal and maximum horizontal clearance dimensions (NHCF, MHCF and NHCS) were determined. The normal vertical clearance (NVCF) dimension would be equal to the elbow height, standing (item L) plus the forearm length (item J). The maximum vertical clearance (MVCF) dimension would be equal to the shoulder height standing (item E) plus the arm reach (item K). To illustrate these calculations, the dimensions of a standing general male operator would be used. Items L, J, E and K would be equal to 120.4 cm, 37.1 cm, 138.0 cm and 68.3 cm, respectively. Thus NVCF would be equal to $(120.4 + 37.1) = 157.5$ cm and MVCF would be equal to $(138.0 + 68.3) = 206.3$ cm. Table 9.7 summarises the horizontal and vertical clearance dimensions for workplace layouts of the standing operator.

Table 9.6 Dimensions for workplace layouts for standing male and female operators

Item	Body feature	General male (cm)	General female (cm)	Combination of male and female (cm)	Individual male, percentiles (cm)			Individual female, percentiles (cm)		
					5th	50th	95th	5th	50th	95th
A	Total height (slump)	186.3	178.8	186.3	166.2	176.1	186.3	153.8	163.2	173.8
C	Eye height (slump)	160.0	143.6	143.6	160.0	164.9	174.8	143.6	153.5	163.4
E	Shoulder height	138.0	127.9	127.9	138.0	147.7	156.8	127.9	137.5	146.6
G	Body depth	34.0	27.6	34.0	26.7	30.2	34.0	21.8	24.6	27.6
H	Elbow-to-elbow	40.0	35.7	35.7	40.0	45.1	51.7	35.7	38.2	43.8
J	Forearm length	37.1	32.5	32.5	37.1	40.4	43.7	32.5	36.6	40.7
K	Arm reach	68.3	60.2	60.2	68.3	75.2	82.0	60.2	66.0	72.4
L	Elbow height	120.4	111.2	120.4	105.6	113.0	120.4	99.0	105.1	111.2

Note: (1) All dimensions based on US military population (2) Normal and maximum reach dimensions based on thumb and forefinger manipulation (items J and K) (3) Adjust items J and K values for: end-of-fingertip add 7.6 cm, push add 5.1 cm, flip add 6.4 cm and grip subtract 5.1 cm

Design for workplace layout for the sit–stand operator

A sit–stand workplace layout is generally more desirable than only a sit or only a stand workplace. Such a layout permits the operator to shift his or her posture at will and thus reduces the muscular fatigue which results from prolonged effort in one position. While designing industrial workplace layout for the sit–stand operator, the following design recommendations should be observed

(1) provide a raised seat, since the operator alternates between the sitting and standing positions;
(2) make sure that the seat is easily movable into and out of position;
(3) provide a footrest for the seated position to minimise muscle soreness and fatigue.

The sit–stand workplace layout is a compromise between seated and standing workplace layouts and, therefore, selected design parameters from each would be utilised to determine workspace dimensions for the sit–stand operator.

Determination of workspace dimensions for the sit–stand operator

The working area in the horizontal plane for the sit–stand male or female operator is shown in Figure 9.4 (the same figure is used to represent seated and standing male or female operators), whilst Figure 9.7 shows the working area in the vertical plane for a sit–stand male or female operator. To determine the location of the shoulder pivot point P, in the horizontal

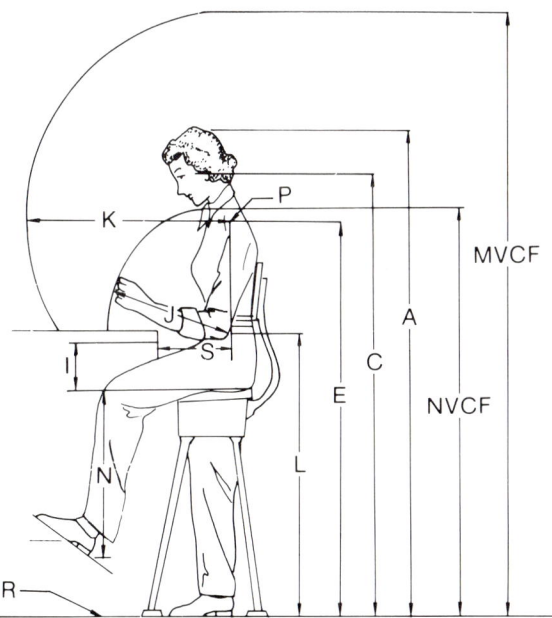

Figure 9.7 Normal and maximum working areas and clearances in the vertical plane for a sit-stand (male or female) operator

plane, with respect to the edge of the workbench, the same procedure as outline for the seated operator would be used.

The shoulder pivot point P in the vertical plane was located in the same manner as described for the standing operator. Other measurements which were used to describe the workspace envelope include the body height (item A), the eye level (item C), the elbow height (item L), the thigh clearance (item I) and the popliteal height (item N). In order for the larger operators to fit, the body height (item A), the thigh clearance (item I) and the popliteal height (item N) were based on the 95 th percentile measurements. For general male operators, the 95 th percentile values for items A, I, and N would be equal to 186.3 cm, 18.5 cm and 48.7 cm, respectively. In order for the smaller operators to see his or her work properly, the eye level (item C) would be based on the 5 th percentile measurement and for the general male operator, item C would be equal to 160.0 cm. Since a platform would be provided to adjust the elbow height of the smaller operators and removed for the larger operators, the dimensions of the elbow height would be based on the 95 th percentile measurement and for the general male operator, item L would be equal to 120.4 cm.

Once the clearance dimensions and the shoulder pivot point were established, it was feasible to determine the normal and maximum working areas in the horizontal and vertical planes, by following the same procedure, as was outlined earlier. Table 9.8 summarises the different design dimensions for workplace layouts for the sit–stand operator.

Again, the normal and maximum horizontal and vertical clearance dimensions (NHCF, MHCF, NHCS, NVCF and MVCF) were determined by using the same procedure, as outlined earlier. The horizontal and vertical clearance dimensions for sit–stand operator are summarised in Table 9.7. It should be noted that the horizontal and vertical clearance dimensions for workplace layouts for the standing and sit–stand operators were identical.

Table 9.7 *Normal and maximum horizontal and vertical clearance dimensions for workplace layouts for standing (also for sit–stand) male and female operators*

Population	Horizontal clearance (cm)			Vertical clearance (cm)	
	Normal, Farley (NHCF)	Normal, Squires (NHCS)	Maximum, Farley (MHCF)	Normal, Farley (NVCF)	Maximum, Farley (MVCF)
General male	54.1	65.9	85.3	157.5	206.3
General female	46.3	55.7	74.0	143.7	188.1
Combination of male and female	49.5	61.6	77.2	152.9	188.1
5 th percentile male	50.4	59.3	81.7	142.7	206.3
50 th percentile male	55.5	65.6	90.3	153.4	222.9
95 th percentile male	60.7	72.1	99.0	164.1	238.8
5 th percentile female	43.4	50.6	71.1	131.5	188.1
50 th percentile female	48.9	57.0	78.3	141.7	203.5
95 th percentile female	54.5	63.6	86.2	152.9	219.0

Note: (1) Reference points for horizontal and vertical clearances are operator back (Q) and floor (FR), respectively (2) Normal and maximum reach based on thumb and forefinger manipulation

Table 9.8 *Dimensions for workplace layouts for sit–stand male and female operators*

Item	Body feature	General male (cm)	General female (cm)	Combination of male and female (cm)	Individual male, percentiles (cm)			Individual female, percentiles (cm)		
					5th	50th	95th	5th	50th	95th
A	Total height (slump)	186.3	173.8	186.3	166.2	176.1	186.3	153.8	163.2	173.8
C	Eye height (slump)	160.0	143.6	143.6	160.0	164.9	174.8	143.6	153.5	163.4
E	Shoulder height	138.0	127.9	127.9	138.0	147.7	156.8	127.9	137.5	146.6
G	Body depth	34.0	27.6	34.0	26.7	30.2	34.0	21.8	24.6	27.6
H	Elbow-to-elbow	40.0	35.7	35.7	40.0	45.1	51.7	35.7	38.2	43.8
I	Thigh clearance	18.5	16.5	18.5	14.2	16.2	18.5	12.4	14.4	16.5
J	Forearm length	37.1	32.5	32.5	37.1	40.4	43.7	32.5	36.6	40.7
K	Arm length	68.3	60.2	60.2	68.3	75.2	82.0	60.2	66.0	72.4
L	Elbow height	120.4	111.2	120.4	105.6	113.0	120.4	99.0	105.1	111.2
N	Popliteal height (sitting)	48.7	43.6	48.7	42.4	45.7	48.7	37.3	40.6	43.6

Note: (1) All dimensions based on US military population (2) Normal and maximum reach dimensions based on thumb and forefinger manipulation (items J and K) (3) Adjust items J and K values for: end-of-fingertip add 7.6 cm. push add 5.1 cm. flip add 6.4 cm and grip subtract 5.1 cm

A comparative analysis between Farley's and Squires' concepts of the normal working area in the horizontal plane

A comparative analysis was made between Farley's and Squires' concepts for the determination of the normal working area in the horizontal plane, in terms of one-handed, two-handed (overlapping area in front of the operator) and total normal working areas and front and side ranges of the normal working area, for the general male, female and combination of both male and female operators for the 5 th, 50 th and 95 th percentiles. The details of the methodology employed in performing the analysis were stated elsewhere (Grady 1979). The main conclusions drawn from the analysis are stated below.

Squires' concept provided a substantial increase over Farley's concept regarding the determination of one-handed, two-handed and total normal working areas in the horizontal plane, for all types of worker population. The minimum increases in the one-handed, two-handed and total normal working areas were 348.5 cm^2, 298.7 cm^2 and 398.4 cm^2, respectively and the corresponding percentage increases were 36.1%, 117.4% and 23.8%, respectively. The maximum increases in the one-handed, two-handed and the total normal working areas were 876.3 cm^2, 558.9 cm^2 and 1193.8 cm^2, respectively and the corresponding percentage increases were 56.5%, 179.4% and 42.7%, respectively. The minimum and maximum increases were noted for the 5 th percentile female and 95 th percentile male, respectively.

The front range of the normal working area as determined by Squires' concept provided a considerable increase over Farley's concept, for all types of worker population. The minimum and maximum increases in the normal front range were 7.2 cm for the 5 th percentile female and 12.1 cm for the combination of male and female, respectively and the corresponding percentage increases were 33.3% and 78.1%, respectively.

However, for the side range of the normal working area, Squires' concept resulted in a slight decrease in the normal side range, in all but one instance, which involved the combination of male and female operators. The minimum and maximum decreases in the normal side range were 0.6 cm for the general male and 14.6 cm for the 95 th percentile female, respectively and the corresponding percentage decreases were 0.6% and 12.1%, respectively.

The movement of the arm is dynamic when the hand sweeps an arc in the normal working area in the horizontal plane; this is the concept proposed by Squires. Therefore, Squires' concept is more realistic than Farley's concept, which assumes that the arm remains in a static position during the sweep of the forearm. Squires' concept should be adopted, instead of the most frequently used Farley's concept, because of the substantial gain in the one-handed, two-handed and the total normal working areas and the front range of the normal working area. The slight loss in the side range of the normal working area, as a result of the adaptation of Squires' concept, would be offset by the overall gain as stated above. Furthermore, Squires' concept is more logical than Farley's concept.

Summary and conclusions

The manner in which the physiological, environmental and dimensional factors affect the design of industrial workplace layout was explored in some detail. It was pointed out that a comprehensive approach to the design is essential to appreciate the impact or contributions of several discipline areas such as, industrial engineering, human factors engineering or ergonomics, industrial hygiene and safety engineering, behavioural science and industrial psychology, Each discipline area looking at the problem on the basis of its own orientation and interest. This chapter basically dealt with the dimensional factors affecting the design and consequently the emphasis was on the application of engineering anthropology to design industrial workplace layout. A systematic review of literature was made to trace the development of industrial workplace layout design with particular reference to the use of engineering anthropology to develop such a design.

The present research was undertaken to determine industrial workplace layout design parameters or dimensions, through the application of the existing anthropometric data, and present them in a usable form, which could be employed readily by a designer. Since the existing anthropometric data were developed on the basis of the measurements from the nude subjects, the data were duly adjusted to account for the clothing and shoe allowances. Also, the data were adjusted to account for the slump posture involved in the normal standing and sitting positions. The normal and maximum reach dimensions were based on the most commonly used industrial operations, which require a grasping movement. All the same, to adjust the reach dimensions for other industrial operations, appropriate allowances were provided. The concepts developed by Farley and Squires were employed to determine the workspace envelope for the individual operator. The normal and maximum working areas and other pertinent design dimensions were established mathematically. For determining the limits of reach and clearance requirements, the dimensions of smaller (5 th percentile) and larger (95 th percentile) operators were used, respectively.

For the purpose of performing industrial tasks in sitting, standing and combination of both sitting and standing positions, workplace layout design dimensions were determined, for the general male, female and combination of both male and female operators and the individual male and female operators for the 5 th, 50 th and 95 th percentiles. In order to facilitate the design of the industrial workplace layout, the normal and maximum clearance dimensions, as well as, the reference points for the horizontal and vertical clearances were established.

A comparative analysis between Farley's and Squires' concepts for the determination of the normal working area in the horizontal plane, showed that by adopting Squires' concept, a substantial gain over Farley's concept could be achieved, in terms of the one-handed, two-handed and the total normal working areas and the front range of the normal working area. The relatively slight loss in the side range of the normal working area, as a consequence of the adaptation of Squires' concept, would be offset by the overall gain, as mentioned above. Furthermore, Squires' concept is more realistic than Farley's concept, since the former recognises that the movement of the arm is dynamic, when the hand sweeps an arc in the normal working area in the horizontal plane, and the latter assumes that the arm is static, during the sweep of the forearm. Hence Squires' concept is recommended in preference to the most frequently used Farley's concept.

References

ASA, M. (1942). *A study of Workplace Layout*, M. Sc. Thesis, State University of Iowa.

BARNES, R. M. (1940). *Motion and Time Study*, 2nd Edition, John Wiley and Sons, New York.

BARNES, R. M. (1958). *Motion and Time Study*, 4th Edition, John Wiley and Sons, New York.

CHAFFEE, J. W. & EMANUEL, A. F. (1964). 'Maximum reach on instrument racks from the seated position', *Boeing Company Report*, D2–90549, 1–46.

FARLEY, R. R. (1955). 'Some principles of methods and motion study as used in development work', *General Motors Engineering J.*, **2**, No. 6, 20–25.

FAULKNER, T. W. &DAY, R. A. (1970). 'The maximum functional reach for the female operator', *Am. Inst. Industrial Engrs Trans.*, **2**, No. 2, 126–131.

GRADY, R. M. (1979). 'Design of industrial workplace layout through the application of engineering anthropology', *Master of Engineering Report*, Texas A & M University.

HERTZBERG, H. T. E. (1972). 'Engineering anthroplogy', (in *Human Engineering Guide to Equipment Design*, Van Cott, H. P. & Kinkade, R. G. (eds), *Revised Edition*, McGraw-Hill Book Company, New York.

KENNEDY, K. W. (1964). Reach Capability of the USAF Population, Aerospace Medical Research Laboratory, TDR–64–59, (AD 608269).

KHALIL, T. M. (1972). 'Design tools and machines to fit the man', *Industrial Engineering*, **4**, No. 1, 32–35.

KONZ, S. (1967). 'Design of work stations', *J. Industrial Eng.*, **18**, No. 7, 413–423.

KONZ, S. (1979). *Work Design*, Grid Publishing, Columbus, Ohio.

KONZ, S. & GOEL, S. C. (1969). 'The shape of the normal working area in the horizontal plane', *Am. Inst. Industrial Eng. Trans.*, **1**, No. 1, 70–73.

MAYNARD, H. B. (1934). 'Workplace layouts that save time, effort and money', *Iron Age*, **134**, No. 23, 28–30; 92.

ROTH, J. T. *et al.* (1977). *Seating, Console and Workplace Design: Seated Operator Reach Profiles*, Proc. of the Human Factors Society, 21st Annual Meeting, 83–87.

SQUIRES, P. C. (1956). *The Shape of the Normal Working Area*, US Navy Department, Bureau of Medicine and Surgery, Medical Research Laboratories, New London, Connecticut, Report No. 275.

TICHAUER, E. R. (1975). *Occupational Biomechanis: the Anatomical Basis of Workplace Design*, Institute of Rehabilitation Medicine, New York University Medical Centre, Rehabilitation Monograph No. 51.

Van COTT, H. P. & KINKADE, R. G. (1972). *Human Engineering Guide to Equipment Design, Revised Edition*, McGraw-Hill Book Company, New York.

WOODSON, W. E. & CONOVER, D. W. (1964). *Human Engineering Guide for Equipment Designers*, 2nd Edition, University of California Press, Berkeley and Los Angeles.

Chapter 10

Check diagrams to solve ergonomic problems

K. Noro

Design of economy and efficiency systems dealing with human elements

A clear recognition of the objectives of man–machine systems is important. For example, design emphasis greatly varies depending on whether an automatic machine serves a public function or private management function. In the former case, social norms, such as respect of man's life and dignity and precedence of man over machine, are all important. In other words, systems which have respect for man's life and dignity and precedence of man over machine as absolute requirements to be met should be considered as objects of public service.

In the latter case, the issue is more complicated. International competition in trade and industry calls for economy-based systems of higher efficiency and imposes severer working conditions and burdens on man. In other words, design adapted to man is essential. In addition, industrial production has now moved away from primitive processes which depend on man's muscular strength, and has developed through processes which utilise machines to automatic fully processes which need no direct human intervention. Hayashi and Noro (1971) pointed out that human factors should be considered even in unmanned systems. The man–machine relationship varies with each of the three industrial methods of production.

This chapter describes a check diagram to design the allocation of man and machine functions in a highly advanced industry under severe limitations. The check diagram utilises a wealth of ergonomic knowledge and theory accumulated in the pursuit of economy and efficiency.

Industrial automation and ergonomic research in Japan

In the 1960s Japan achieved rapid economic growth and realised a high degree of prosperity. Such economic development was unquestionably stimulated by advanced mechanisation in various fields of manufacture. Although many reasons may be cited for Japan's industrial development, one of the most important is the improvement in productivity brought about by automation.

The improvement in labour productivity in the Japanese automobile industry in the last half of the 1960s is striking as shown in Figure 10.1. The automation techniques which have led to such a marked rise in productivity are as follows. Automation of machining was started with the introduction

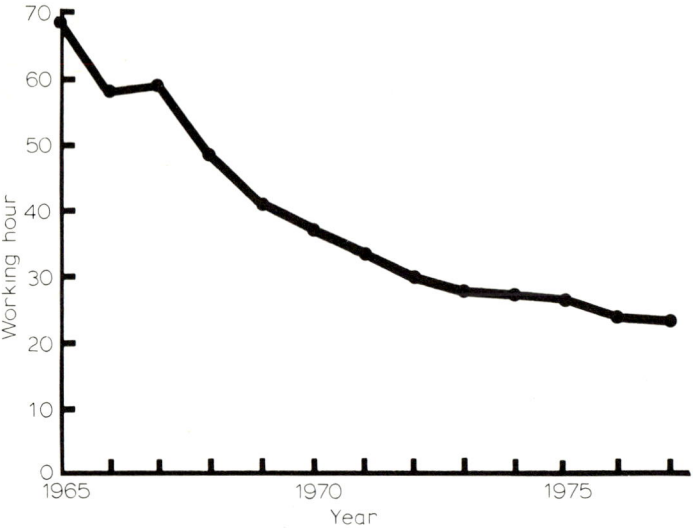

Figure 10.1 Working hours directly required for production of one Japanese subcompact car (from The Ministry of Labour, 1979)

of transfer machines in 1956. Press forming of sheet metals was automated in the last half of the 1960s; casting, forging and body welding about 1965; and engine assembling around 1970. Oshima *et al.* (1980) described the role ergonomics has played in this high degree of industrialisation in Japan. This chapter gives a more specific explanation of what has been described in their paper.

Man and machine function allocation in plant labour saving and automation plans

The best method to carry out labour saving and automation is to draw up a plan on the basis of accurate judgement of the situation regarding the plant in consideration. Determination of how to allocate functions to man and machine under given constraints is necessary for labour saving and automation. The basic method to allocate functions between men and machines is described by Meister (1971). The concrete flow by system scale is illustrated by Noro (1977). This section discusses check diagrams for large manufacturing companies. The following five steps are used to determine this functional allocation. Figures 10.2 to 10.6 approximately correspond to these steps. Each diagram consists of blocks for check (screened blocks) and blocks showing work-improving measures. The plan manager clarifies in what check block of the diagram his plant or process is located. Once this is done, he can easily judge to what degree the plant is mechanised or automated, what is the next target for mechanisation, and what are the ergonomic problems to be solved.

Step 1: Promotion of standardisation

Work which depends on man's muscular strength and simple tools is referred to as *primitive work*. This type of work often calls for high muscular power and causes muscular and low back pain. Human motions have high degrees of freedom. As work standardisation is closely related to labour saving, it is necessary to investigate to what degree the work is standardised. Labour saving refers to decreasing or replacing human labour by machinery through operation rationalisation. The higher the work standardisation, the more easily the labour saving is realised and the more readily the effect of labour saving is obtained. For example, welding robots which are used in very large numbers in Japan's automobile industry completely imitate standardised human motions. Figure 10.2 shows the flow from examination of the degree of work standardisation to replacement of some human operations by machinery. A man–machine comparison table comes in handy for performing the last step in the diagram. An example is the tentative lists of statements of Woodson and Conover (1964) which compare man and machine.

Step 2: Reduction in muscular labour and mechanisation

Mechanisation refers to substitution of units and systems for human labour. In the processes using machinery to reduce man's muscular labour, man performs light muscular work. Operations easy to achieve technically are labour-saved or mechanised, whilst operations difficult to perform are left to man. Most of the remaining operations involve light muscular labour. Under these circumstances, the worker suffers not only from pain when he does not use his muscles in a balanced manner, but also frequently complains of monotony. When the above two problems are solved, the operation is checked to see if it is suitable to be done by one worker. This check calls for subjective evaluation as well as objective measurement. Grandjean (1980) stresses the importance of back-up by subjective feelings and briefly explains this as it relates to fatigue.

The operation which has passed the check is checked further to see if it does not lower the efficiency of the entire system or line. When it also passes this check, the operation represents an appropriate working method at this level. Appropriate work is defined here as intellectual labour which involves some light muscular motions and which is based on man's pace. The above process is illustrated in Figure 10.3. This diagram shows the flow following the arrow of Figure 10.2.

Even if an operation is originally recognised to be an appropriate one, its efficiency becomes a problem as economic or technical conditions change. For this reason, the procedure goes to the next step. In the next and succeeding steps, one finds it difficult to maintain one's pace. It should be recognised, therefore, that ergonomic measures also change greatly. Those measures which are focused on human factors alone become practically meaningless in such a case.

Considering the rapidity with which new techniques for mechanisation and automation described in the next step are introduced, the following must be performed

132

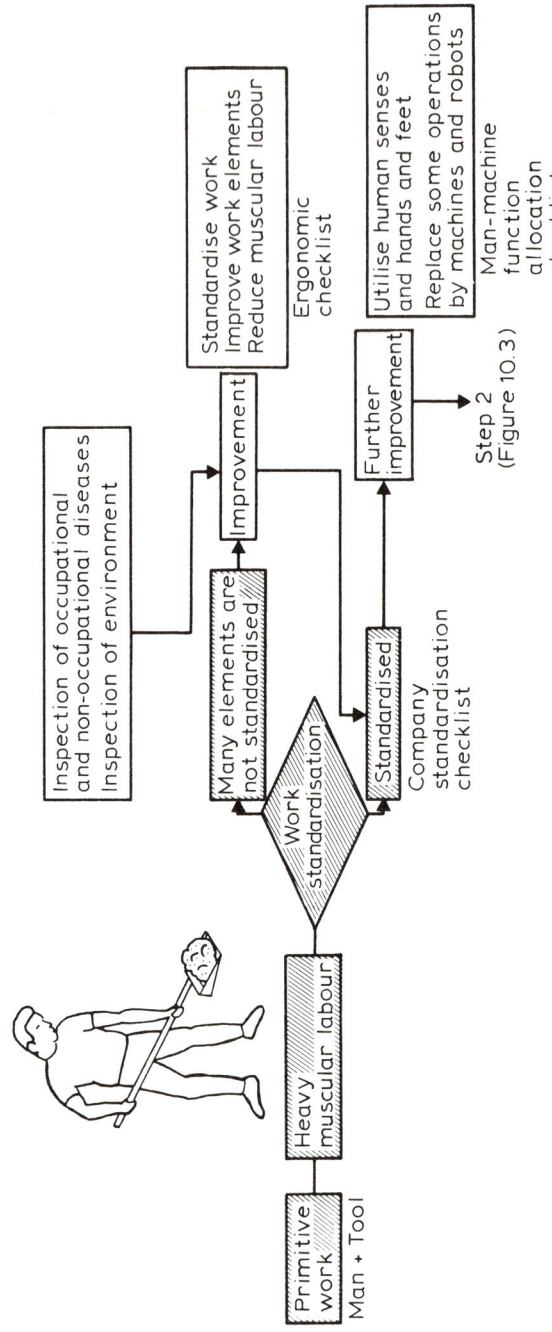

Figure 10.2 Check diagram for primitive work or heavy muscular labour. Work-improving measures shown after further improvement are required to go to the next step. The block of inspection of occupational and non-occupational diseases and inspection of environment is for occupational hygienists

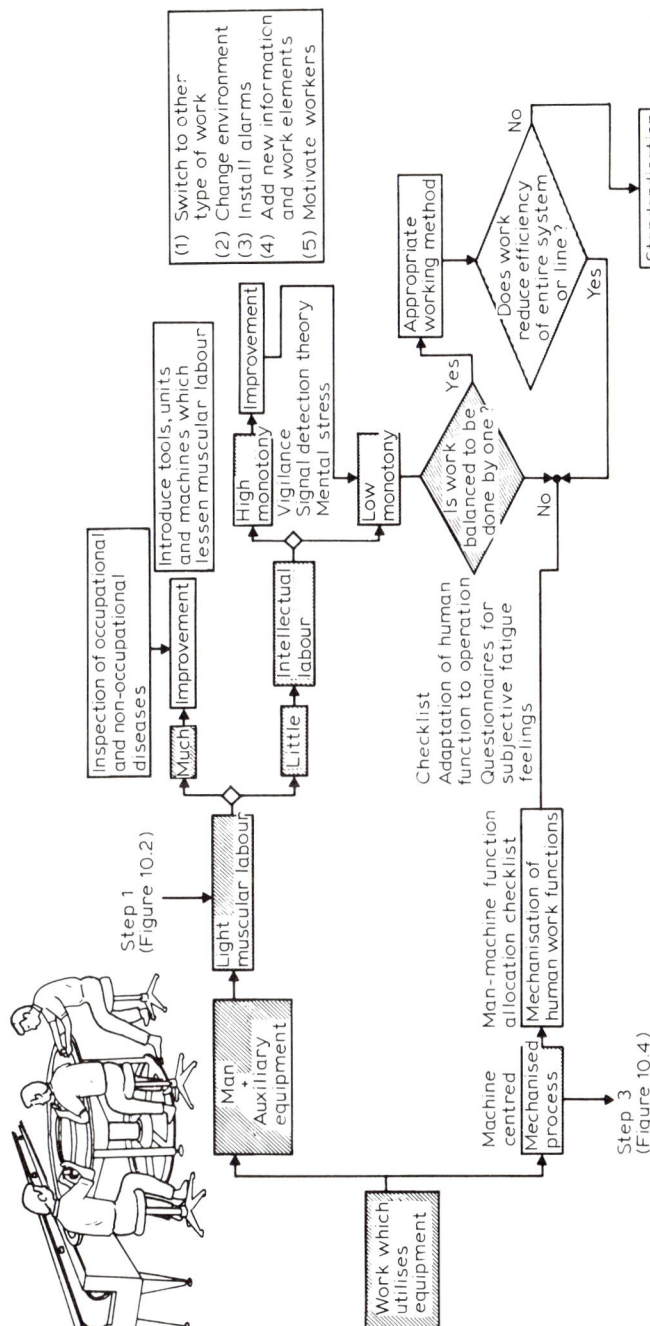

Figure 10.3 Check diagram for going from light muscular labour to machine-centred process. The block of inspection of occupational and non-occupational diseases and inspection of environment is for occupational hygienists

(1) Predict the effect on human factors of the new techniques to be introduced;
(2) Conduct engineering design on the basis of the predicted results.

Ergonomics which is based on this way of thinking may be called *preventive* or *future ergonomics*. Hayashi and Noro (1973) express and review the ergonomic considerations given to Japan's Shinkansen development in more concrete flow, based on the flow of structured rationalisation of creative action by Jantsch (1972).

Step 3: Improvement in human work in automatic processes

Automation refers to the development and use of a system in which a plant is programmed for machinery to automatically accomplish a given purpose without human operation. In such a system, man performs the assigned task in a place physically isolated from the production process; for instance, a central control room. This automation turns the machine industry into a kind of process industry.

Figure 10.4 shows that an automatic process branches out into a control method (centralised or individual), management method (centralised or intensive) and display method (instrument or CRT), and finally reaches an interactive level with a CRT console.

At this level, muscular motions are few, and information processing is a major element of work. This work is characteristic in that it strains the sense of sight and that it is repeated for a considerable length of time and calls for mental alertness. Grandjean and Vigliani (1981) report many ergonomic studies on this type of operation. Frequent complaints are eye strain and mental stress. To alleviate these complaints, one must improve units, change to CRT display and/or reduce size of panels or consoles, redesign operations, reduce the visual angle, summarise information and rationalise work areas. Further improvement calls for change in the awareness of the company's executives, workers and ergonomists.

In society where automation is pushed to a high degree, the burden of labour has sharply decreased. For example, today's working environment rarely exposes workers to 85 dB noise. However, young workers will dance to 95 dB music in discotheques in their free time. In the near future, it will become meaningless to discuss workers' environment and behaviour only during working hours. Chapanis (1979) points out the increasing importance of ergonomics in the future and emphasises the need for the participation of ergonomists in social planning and issues.

Step 4: Improvement in inspection method

There are two types of inspection conducted by man. One is inspection which cannot be essentially performed by other than man, e.g. taste tasting. The other is inspection which is concerned with physical characteristics of objects. This type may be conducted by either man or machine, but can be more easily performed by man using his senses. In this case,

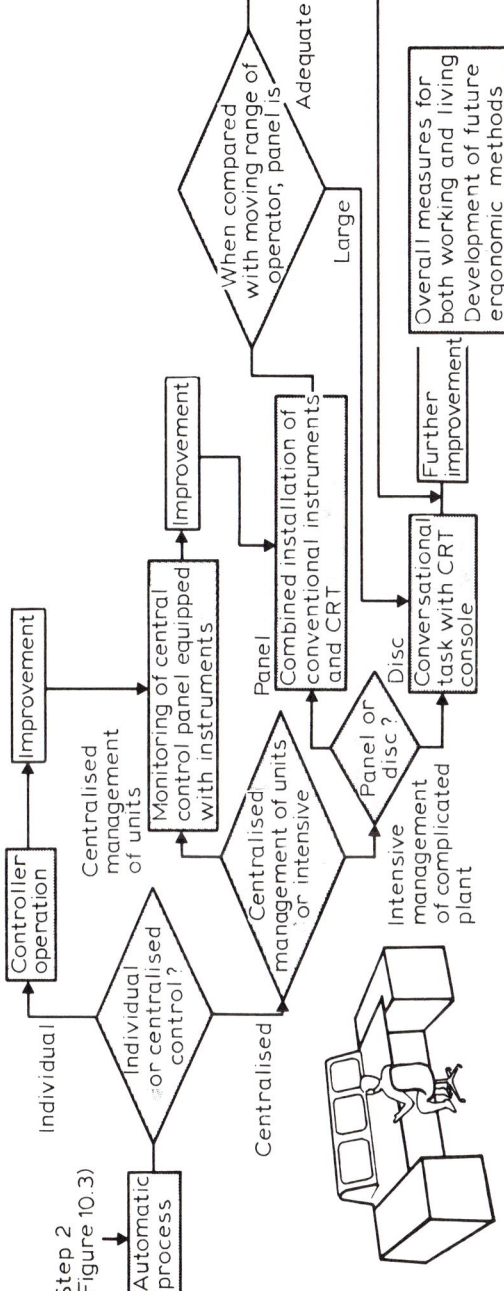

Figure 10.4 Check diagram for automatic process. The block of inspection of occupational and non-occupational diseases and inspection of environment is omitted. Refer to the corresponding blocks in Figure 10.3

136

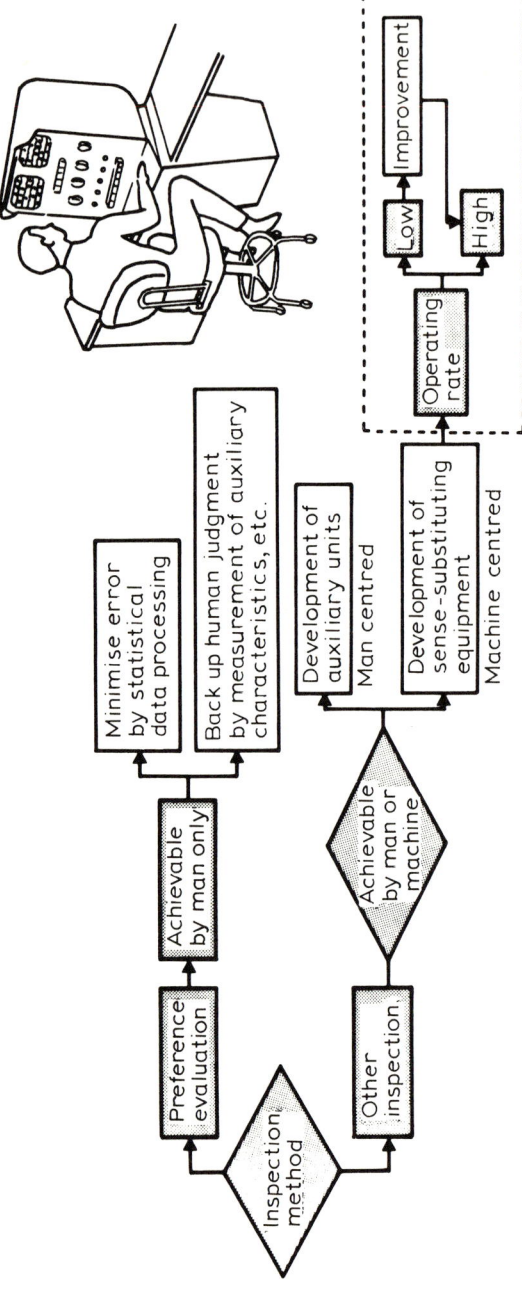

Figure 10.5 Check diagram for inspection process. Area enclosed by dotted lines is the option added by the machine manufacturing company

mechanisation is feasible. The trade-off between man and machine is determined by

(1) technical feasibility and investment limit;
(2) human physiological surplus;
(3) required inspection accuracy.

Figure 10.5 is a check diagram which shows measures for improvement by type of inspection. Good suggestions for improvement are obtainable from the Japanese Industrial Standard JIS Z 9080 on sensory evaluation and from Noro (1978). When required, this step may be used independently of steps 1 to 3.

Step 5: Prevention of human and system errors

A human error is an error for which man alone is responsible, whereas a system error is an error for which both man and machine are responsible. Human inattention and machine misoperation look like childish mistakes to many people but are often peculiar to highly labour saving or automatic systems. Valve misoperation, for example, is very commonplace, but has resulted in many industrial accidents, such as the accident at Three Mile Island in the United States. Figure 10.6 shows a check diagram for the prevention of these human and system errors. When required, this step may be used independently of steps 1 to 3.

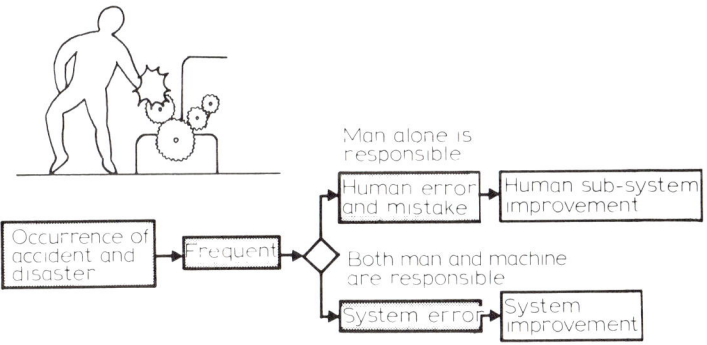

Figure 10.6 Check diagram for safety

Applications in machine industry

The proposed check diagrams help the plant manager to judge easily to what degree the plant is mechanised or automated, what is the next target for mechanisation or automation, and what are the ergonomic problems to be solved. Applications of the check diagrams in a machine manufacturing company are descibed below.

At the machine manufacturing company, its plants were investigated for possible mechanisation. Prior to this inspection, weights for evaluation were established for major items in the diagrams, except Figures 10.4 and 10.6 (Table 10.1).

Table 10.1 *Weights for searching for problems in a machine manufacturing company*

Work level	Weight	Corresponding figure
Heavy muscular labour, not standardised	9	10.2
Heavy muscular labour, standardised	8	10.2
Light muscular labour in many cases	7	10.3
Intellectual labour, high in monotony	6	10.3
Intellectual labour, low in monotony	5	10.3
Mechanised process	4	10.3
Inspection by man	3	10.5
Inspection by machine, low in operating rate	2	10.5
Inspection by machine, high in operating rate	1	10.5

Figure 10.4 was excluded because the company did not yet aim at automation and Figure 10.6 was excluded because the company had no safety problems. The company attached importance to the operating rate of inspection machinery and added the check of this operating rate to Figure 10.5 and Table 10.1.

The evaluation value of individual operations is determined by

Evaluation value of individual operation =
Number of workers × Weight based on work level as shown in Table 10.1

At each plant, eight staff members in the production engineering section patrolled all the processes, discussed the findings, and determined weights for each process. Labour saving and mechanisation evaluation values for all the processes at all the plants were calculated from the weights by process and the number of workers by process, as shown in Table 10.2.

Figure 10.7 shows actual and target average evaluation values by process. The target values were established as the company's policy for mechanisation. That is, the company decided to mechanise all the plants and processes. Referring to the differences between the actual and target values, the company made assembling, finishing and inspection its central targets of mechanisation.

Finishing and inspection were selected because the difference between the actual and target values was large. As far as assembling is concerned, the different between the actual and target values is not large, but many workers are engaged in this process, and there are many problems involved, such as working postures. Assembling was selected because technical levels must be raised to develop further mechanisation.

Table 10.2 Work evaluation by process and plant

Plant		Acceptance and shipment	Machining	Press forming	Forging	Welding	Finishing	Heat treatment	Cleaning	Assembling	Inspection	Total
A	Number of steps	7	5		9		7	5		6	9	—
	Number of workers	78	142		294		181	114		97	45	951
	Evaluation value	546	710		1698		1267	570		582	405	5778
B	Number of steps	6	5	7		6		6		5	9	—
	Number of workers	87	39	6		17		11		357	58	575
	Evaluation value	522	195	42		102		66		1785	406	3118
C	Number of steps	8	5					8	9	7	7	—
	Number of workers	50	223					57	2	69	51	452
	Evaluation value	400	1115					399	14	483	357	2768
D	Number of steps	8	6					6		7	8	—
	Number of workers	42	60					29		175	25	331
	Evaluation value	336	360					174		1225	200	2295
E	Number of steps	8	4						8	6	6	—
	Number of workers	120	363						21	374	124	1002
	Evaluations value	812	1452						151	2244	744	5413
F	Number of steps	8		6		6	9	6		7	9	—
	Number of workers	73		290		48	51	44		20	73	618
	Evaluation value	584		1740		288	357	264		140	657	4144
Total	Number of workers	450	846	296	294	65	232	255	23	1092	376	3929
	Evaluation value	3200	3946	1782	1698	390	1624	1473	175	6459	2767	23532
	Average	7.1	4.7	6.0	5.8	6.0	7.0	5.8	7.5	5.9	7.4	—

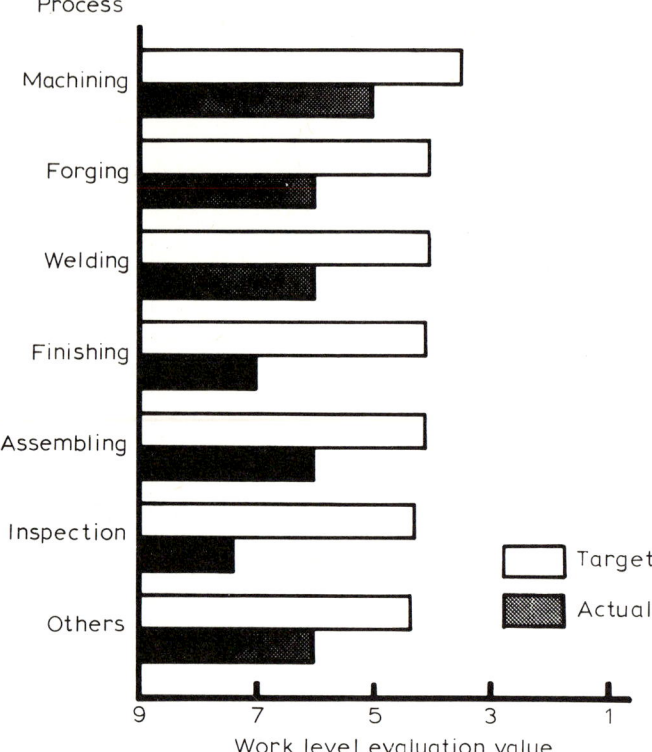

Figure 10.7 Actual and target average evaluation values by process

Conclusion

This approach is not centred on hardware and investment, as in conventional labour saving and automation plans, and starts with the understanding of human activities. For this reason, it is easily understood by the workers concerned. The proposed check diagrams provide ergonomists with adequate and concise information to understand problems in a wide perspective from past to future. These check diagrams also suggest one direction of action for the next generation of ergonomists.

References

CHAPANIS, A. (1979). 'Quo Vadis, Ergnomia', *Ergonomics*, **22**, No. 6, 595–605.
GRANDJEAN, E. (1980). *Fitting the Task to the Man*, Taylor & Francis, London.
GRANDJEAN, E. & VIGLIANI, E. (eds) (1981). *Ergnomic Aspects of Visual Display Terminals*, Taylor & Francis, London.
HAYASHI, Y. & NORO, K. (1971). *Unmanned Systems*, [*Mujinka shisutemu*], The nikkan kogyo shimbun, Tokyo.

HAYASHI, Y. & NORO, K. (1973). 'System Study of Shinkansen Project', [Shinkansen purojekuto no shisutemu ron teki kousatsu], (in *Japanese ways of big project management* [*Nohon teki biggu purojekuto*], Oshima, K. (ed)) Japan Society for the Promotion of Machine Industry, Tokyo.

JANTSCH, E. (1972). *Technological Planning and Social Futures*, Cassell, London.

MEISTER, D. (1971). *Human Factors: Theory and Practice*, Wiley-Interscience, New York.

MINISTRY OF INTERNATIONAL TRADE AND INDUSTRY. (1979). *General Rule for Sensory Tests, JIS Z 9080*. Auther, Tokyo.

NORO, K. (1977). 'Factory improvement by low-cost automation; [Toshi ni tayoranai shoryoku ka niyoru kojo kaizen no susume kata], *Labour saving and automation*, March, Tokyo, 52–55.

NORO, K. (1978). *Introduction to Sensory Evaluation for Production and Quality Engineers*, [*Kojo gijutsusha no tame no kanno kensa nyumon*], Japanese Standards Association, Tokyo.

OSHIMA, M. *et al.* (1980). 'Human factors which have helped Japanese industrialization', *Human Factors*, **22** No. 1, 3–13.

WOODSON, W. E. & CONOVER, D. W. (1964). *Human Engineering Guide for Equipment Designers*, University of California Press, Berkeley, 1–23.

Chapter 11

Criteria for the evaluation of shift systems

J. Rutenfranz & P. Knauth

Introduction

The technological, economic and social reasons for which shift work exists mean that it will not be possible to eliminate it. However, one can ameliorate the discomfort of shift work by selecting suitable personnel and one can also influence the organisation of shift schedule. Over the last few years more than 500 different shift systems have come to our notice; it is *a priori* improbable that all are equally good. One cannot, therefore, leave the construction of shift schedules to the plant alone (Rutenfranz *et al.* 1980).

The general theoretical background for the evaluation of shift systems is given in Figure 11.1. In terms of the stress–strain concept of modern occupational medicine (Rutenfranz 1976; 1981), shiftwork problems can be described in the following manner (Colquhoun and Rutenfranz 1980).

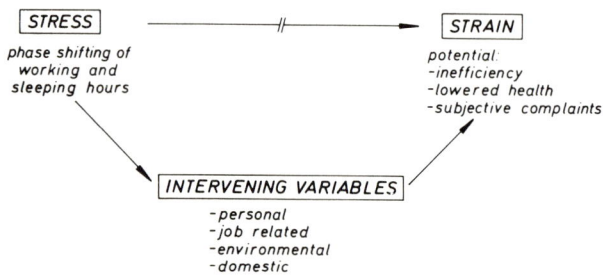

Figure 11.1 Model of relations between stress, intervening variables and strain in connection with shiftwork (after Rutenfranz 1976; 1981)

(i) The objective stress of shiftwork

This means the exposure of everybody working in shifts to the phase shifting of working and sleeping hours in relation to the normal phases of the circadian rhythms of physiological functions or performance functions.

142

A special aspect of this problem is the time course of the adaptive processes in physiological functions after a shift in the working hours, i.e. their re-entrainment.

(ii) The subjective strain caused by this stress

This strain may express itself in complaints, lowering of well-being and possible negative health effects. At the present time many governments are mainly interested in the health effects of shift work. This can be seen from the discussions about shift work as possible cause of disease, especially gastro-intestinal disease, although there is very little evidence of this. Nevertheless, shiftwork *does* produce many non-clinical complaints because of disturbed sleep, changes in eating habits and disruptions of family and social life. However, the importance of these disorders for a particular person depends on

(iii) Intervening variables

Housing standards, (especially sleeping conditions)
The family situation (age of children; acceptance of shiftwork by the family as a whole)
Personality
Differences in physiological adaptability.

These intervening factors determine if a particular person is able to cope with shift work, or if the disturbances of well-being will be augmented to such a degree that actual diseases will occur (Harrington 1978).

To cope with these problems it is necessary to develop research-based principles for selection of shift workers, compensation for shiftwork and construction of shift work schedules. This paper deals only with the criteria for the construction of shift work schedules.

Different types of shift work

Relative to the various reasons for shift work a large number of different shift systems can be categorised according to the number of teams involved, the marginal conditions and with or without weekend work. A further category to be considered is the regularity or irregularity of the system (Rutenfranz *et al.* 1976).

A large number of different shift systems exists, but it is possible to categorise the majority of them under one of the following headings.

(1) Systems without night work

Two-team ('double-days')
   (a) non-overlapping (e.g., 0600–1400, 1400–2200)
   (b) overlapping (e.g., 0600–1400, 1330–2130)

(2) Systems with night work

Two-team (up to 12 h shifts) ('days and nights')
Three-team (8 h shifts)
One-team (night work only) ('permanent night shift'): often combined
with type (1) to provide complete coverage of the 24 h period.

*(3) Systems with night work and including weekend work ('continuous shift
work')*

Regular
   (a) four-team (12 h shifts)
   (b) four team (8 h shifts)
Irregular (varying number of teams and cycle lengths)

The complexity of the arrangements is greatest with the systems of type (3)
(continuous shift work).

Physiological and psychosocial criteria for schedule construction

It is impossible to construct one single shift schedule which is optimal for
all shift workers and for all working and living conditions. As workers seem
generally to vote for the shift system they have been working on (Wyatt
and Marriott 1953; Ulich 1957) recommendations for optimal shift systems
can rarely be obtained from questioning shift workers.

Therefore it was of importance for ergonomics research to develop
objective criteria for optimising shift systems (Colquhoun *et al.* 1975;
Rutenfranz and Colquhoun 1978). These criteria – mostly physiological or
psychosocial – contain measures to follow the re-entrainment of circadian
rhythms, to avoid sleep reductions, to maintain sufficient leisure time
between the individual shifts as well as measures for decreasing the social
isolation of shift workers by making regular contacts with the 'normal'
population possible.

Based on present knowledge, mostly from results of experimental
studies of shift work or on field studies, the following criteria can be set for
schedule evaluation and construction (Rutenfranz *et al.* 1980; Rutenfranz
and Knauth 1981).

(a) Single night shifts are better than consecutive night shifts

Because a single night shift does not significantly disturb circadian rhythms
and because more than seven consecutive night shifts are required for
re-entrainment of the rhythms (Colquhoun *et al.* 1968, 1969; Knauth and
Ilmarinen 1975; Pátkai *et al.* 1975). It could be argued that a sequence of
consecutive night shifts longer than seven days would therefore be
acceptable. However, for psychosocial reasons most workers need either
to change their shift or to have some rest days after no more than one
week, so re-entrainment is not normally possible in practice.

(b) At least 24 h of free time should be allowed after each night shift

Sleep disturbances and reduction of sleeping time are the most common complaints of shift workers, particularly night workers. The resultant accumulation of sleep deficit over several days may be a risk factor. Thus, for preventing the harmful effects of sleep deprivation, a substantial recovery period is necessary after each nigh shift (Graf 1955; Knauth and Rutenfranz 1972a, 1972b; Knauth *et al.* 1975; Rutenfranz 1973; Rutenfranz *et al.* 1977). A similar problem can arise with the morning shift when the starting time is so early that the worker gets an insufficient amount of sleep the night before; in this case a 24 h break after each such shift should also be allowed. (Alternatively, of course, it may be possible to delay the starting time of the shift by reorganisation of the system (McEwan Young 1980).)

(c) The length of the shift should be related to the type of work

This applies particularly to the energy expenditure required by it. If the work is light the length of the shift may (with caution) be extended to 12 h (Nachreiner *et al.* 1975), but it should not normally exceed 8 h (or even 6 h for certain types of work, e.g. work involving particularly heavy physical energy expenditure or a considerable mental load).

(d) The cycle of a shift system should not be too long

(Four weeks, for example, is better than 40 weeks). It is also better to have a regular system of rotation than an irregular one. Short cycles and regular systems make it easier for the worker and his family to plan their social life.

(e) In the case of continuous shift work

It is important to arrange as many free weekends as possible for the worker in order that he can participate at these times in the normal social life of his friends who do not do shift work.

Choice of ergonomically appropriate shift systems

For the choice of ergonomically appropriate shift systems the following main constitutions of a shift system have to be considered (Knauth *et al.* 1979).

(1) Longest duration of the average daily working time

The many theoretically possible shift systems can be systematised according to the proportion of free days and working days. This ratio will of course determine the daily working hours; therefore the shift system with the same relation between the number of working days and the number of free days has the same average daily working times. The agreements with the trade unions about the weekly working times present a further problem. The week having 168 hours, and this being divisible by 42 h, all

42 h shift plans for continuous work are easier to organise than 40 h shift plans. When changing from the 42 h to the 40 h week, therefore, it often seems appropriate to keep the established 42 h arrangement and to compensate the extra work of 2 h per week by free shifts (Nachreiner *et al.* 1975).

Therefore the average weekly working times in Figure 11.2 were worked out on the basis of the 42 h week. In the figure the highest limit of 8.0 was stated. Because of the special case of the 12 h shifts mentioned previously the first line in Figure 11.2 was not ruled out.

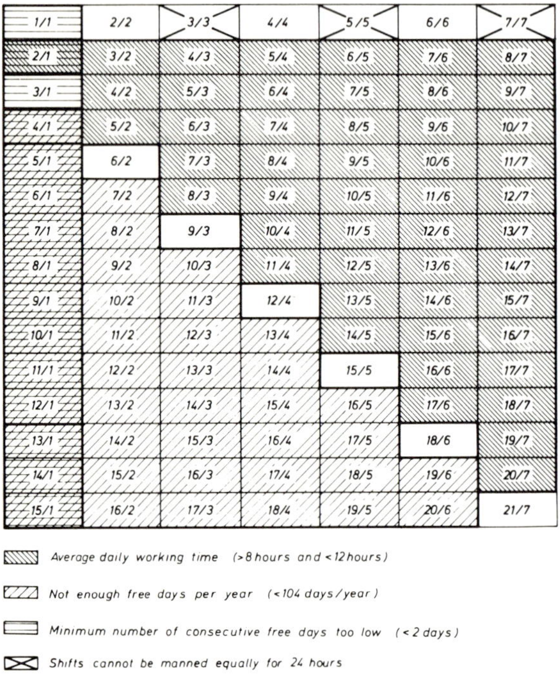

1/1	2/2	3/3	4/4	5/5	6/6	7/7
2/1	3/2	4/3	5/4	6/5	7/6	8/7
3/1	4/2	5/3	6/4	7/5	8/6	9/7
4/1	5/2	6/3	7/4	8/5	9/6	10/7
5/1	6/2	7/3	8/4	9/5	10/6	11/7
6/1	7/2	8/3	9/4	10/5	11/6	12/7
7/1	8/2	9/3	10/4	11/5	12/6	13/7
8/1	9/2	10/3	11/4	12/5	13/6	14/7
9/1	10/2	11/3	12/4	13/5	14/6	15/7
10/1	11/2	12/3	13/4	14/5	15/6	16/7
11/1	12/2	13/3	14/4	15/5	16/6	17/7
12/1	13/2	14/3	15/4	16/5	17/6	18/7
13/1	14/2	15/3	16/4	17/5	18/6	19/7
14/1	15/2	16/3	17/4	18/5	19/6	20/7
15/1	16/2	17/3	18/4	19/5	20/6	21/7

Average daily working time   (>8 hours and <12 hours)

Not enough free days per year   (<104 days/year)

Minimum number of consecutive free days too low   (<2 days)

Shifts cannot be manned equally for 24 hours

Figure 11.2 Selection of shift systems when using 42 h shift plans to an average weekly working time of 40 h (after Knauth *et al.* 1979; Rutenfranz and Knauth 1981)

(2) Minimum number of free days per calender year and minimum number of consecutive free days per shift plan

The number of appropriate shift systems can further be limited by the minimum number of free days per calender year. In Figure 11.2 holidays and bank holidays were not considered, as they are the same for all shift systems. This minimum number of free days per calender year should be 104 days, comparable with the weekends of a year. The possibility of working 42 h per week, even when 40 h were negotiated, and to compensate the extra work by free shifts has already been mentioned above. In this case the number of free days per calender year increases. When 42 h shift plans are applied, the extra work of 104 h per year must be compensated by additional 13 free days (104 h : 8.0 h daily working time = 13.0 days). In

Figure 11.2 the total for the 6/2 system is worked out as 91.3 + 13.0 = 104.3 free days per year. For example of the 2/2 shift systems the corresponding calculation (182.5 + 104/12 = 191.2) totals about 191 free days per year.

Starting from the now widespread 5 day week with two following free days in normal day work, at least two consecutive free days per shift rota should also be demanded for shift workers. Because of this further limitation all shift systems in the first column of Figure 11.2 were excluded, but almost all of them had already been excluded by other limiting conditions.

These systematic considerations were at first simplified by assuming that all free days within the calender year could be valued as equal. When considering an actual shift plan, however, two additional questions must be taken into consideration. Firstly, how many free days per calender year fall on the various days of the week, and secondly, which shifts are before and after the free days, i.e. how long is the time free of work between two shifts in reality.

(3) Compilation of recommendable shift systems

If all the limits mentioned so far are marked in Figure 11.2, the number of appropriate shift systems is reduced considerably, if a 42 h shift plan is adhered to, despite a 40 h week. As can be seen from Figure 11.2, only a few shift systems remain. But of these the systems 3/3, 5/5, 7/7, etc. are questionable, as they do not allow even shift manning.

If the shift crews are to have the same strength over 24 h, only the following recommendable shift systems remain

  (a) with eight hours of shift work
       6/2, 9/3, 12/4, 15/5, 18/6, 21/7, etc.,
       or generally: 3n/n with n > 1
  (b) with twelve hours of shift work
       2/2, 4/4, 6/6, etc.,
       or generally: 2n/n

All shift systems chosen so far leave room for numerous shift plans, which again may be favourable or unfavourable from the work physiological point of view.

Shift plan examples

Unfavourable shift plan examples

For the previously chosen shift systems some shift plan examples not to be recommended are given in Figure 11.3. Among other things shift plans are to be considered as negative if

  no consecutive leisure times occur
  consecutive working periods are too long
  many night shifts follow one another
  the distribution of leisure time is inconvenient.

Shift System (working days/free days)	Shift Rota (8-hour-systems) (M,A,N = morning, afternoon or night shift, - = off)	Remarks (see footnote)
21/7	MMMMMMM--AAAAAAA--NNNNNNN--- MAN-MMM-AAA-NNN-MMA-MAA-NNN-	1) 2)
6/2	MMA-ANN- MMAAN-N-	2) 2)
9/3	MMMAAANNN--- MMM-AAA-NNN-	3),4) 2)
12/4	MMA-MAA-MA-NNNN- MMMMAAAANNNN----	1),2) 1),3),4)
15/5	MMAAA---MMMAA-NNNNN- MAN-MAA-MMA-MNN-ANN-	1) 2)
18/6	MMMAAA--MMMAAA--NNNNNN-- MMMAAANNNN-MMMAAANN-----	1) 1),3),4)
Shift System (working days/free days)	Shift Rota (12-hour-system) (D̄,N̄ = day or night shift, - = off)	Remarks (see footnote)
2/2	D̄-N̄-	2)
4/4	D̄D̄ N̄N̄----	4)
6/6	D̄N̄N̄N̄-D̄D̄-----	4)

Remarks: 1) too many consecutive night shifts
2) no consecutive free shift
3) consecutive working period too long
4) disadvantageous distribution of free time

Figure 11.3 Examples of disadvantageous shift plans (after Knauth *et al.* 1979)

Shift System (working days/free days)	No.	Shift Rota (8-hour-systems) (M,A,N = morning, afternoon or night shift, - = off)	Duration of Cycle (weeks)	Number of Free Weekends (Sat + Sun) per Cycle
21/7	1	N-MAN---MAN-MMMAN-MAAAN-MANN	4	1
	2	MAN-M--AN-MAAAN-MANNN-MAN-MM	4	1
	3	MMAANNN--MMAAANN--MMMAANN---	4	1
6/2	4	MMAANN--	8	1
9/3	5	MMAANN--MAN-	12	1
12/4	6	MAAANN--MMMANN--	16	2
15/5	7	MMANN--MMANN--MAAAN-	20	2
18/6	8	MMAANN--MMMANN--MAAANN--	24	3
Shift System (working days/free days)	No.	Shift Rota (12-hour-systems) (D̄,N̄ = day or night shift, - = off)	Duration of Cycle (weeks)	Number of Free Weekends (Sat + Sun) per Cycle
2/2	9	D̄N̄--	4	1
4/4	10	D̄D̄--N̄N̄--	8	2
6/6	11	D̄N̄--D̄D̄--N̄N̄--	12	3

Footnote for No. 1) Suggestion according to GRAF (1955), see Tab. 5
2) Suggestion according to GRAF (1955)
3) 2-2-3-system ("continental rota")
4) 2-2-2-system ("metropolitan rota")

Figure 11.4 Examples of recommended shift plans (after Knauth *et al.* 1979)

Recommendable shift plan examples

The shift plan examples in Figure 11.4 are to be considered as good or acceptable compromises, as they can never respond to all demands at the same time.

From the last two columns of Figure 11.4 it can be seen that the shift plan examples for the 21/7 and 2/2 systems are especially convenient, as they have a cycle duration of four weeks as well as a free weekend (Saturday plus Sunday) every four weeks, whereas in other systems (not shown in Figure 11.4) cycle durations of up to 168 or 84 days occur.

Analysis of the free shifts of one shift plan example (Graf 1955)

In Figure 11.5 the types of weekends, their number per year as well as the distribution of the free shifts on the days of the week are demonstrated for one shift plan example. However the duration of free time on a work-free day is not always 24 h, as it depends on the end of the previous and the beginning of the following shift.

Mon	Tue	Wed	Thur	Fri	Sat	Sun
N	-	M	A	N	-	-
-	M	A	N	-	M	M
M	A	N	-	M	A	A
A	N	-	M	A	N	N

Types of Weekends and Number/Year

Saturday	Sunday	Monday	Number/Year
-	-	-	13
M	M	M	13
A	A	A	13
N	N	N	13

$$\Sigma = 52$$

Number of Free Weekdays/Year

Weekdays (6-6 o'clock)	Mon	Tue	Wed	Thur	Fri	Sat	Sun	Sat+Sun	Sat+Sun+Mon
n	13	13	13	13	13	13	13	-	13

M = morning shift   A = afternoon shift   N = night shift   - = off

Figure 11.5 Recommended shift plan for a (rapidly) rotating 21/7 shift system with a list of the free shifts per year for all days of the week (after Graf 1955)

For the shift plan in Figure 11.5 it is to be assumed that the early shift lasts from 6.00 h till 14.00 h, the late shift from 14.00 h till 22.00 h and the night shift from 22.00 h till 6.00 h. The first Saturday in this shift plan cannot be rated as a completely free day, as the free time lasts only 18 h and not 24 h. However, the deficit of 6 h can be compensated on the following days: the continuous free time from the end of the night shift on Saturday till the beginning of the early shift on Tuesday totals 72 h, i.e. three times 24 h.

The work-free days from Tuesday to Friday are all between a night shift (end 6.00 h) and a morning shift (begin 6.00 h) and therefore have a length of 24 h. The continuous free times are longer if a work-free day is not followed by an early but by a late or even a night shift.

Larger blocks of free time generally have a higher disposal value than short free time units. Therefore exact analyses of free time can sometimes facilitate the final decision.

Discussion

Next to the selection and medical supervision of shift workers the organisation of shift plans offers an important opportunity for minimising the stress of shift work (Knauth *et al.* 1979). During our surveys in various economic sectors we found that only occasionally objective physiological criteria were used for the choice of shift plans. Therefore the present paper is intended to cause shift plans which are in use to be reconsidered and to give indications for appropriate shift plan selection.

In addition to the demonstrated limitations the selection of a shift plan for a given job can be narrowed by other limiting conditions. The highest number of possible shift crews, for instance, can decrease the number of shift systems in question.

Furthermore the limits stated in this paper, e.g. those of the daily working time, must be checked in the individual case. If a working time of 40 h per week has been agreed with the trade unions, not all recommendations given at the beginning can be realised fully and at the same time. Even the recommendable shift plans can therefore only be considered as compromises.

References

COLQUHOUN, W. P. & RUTENFRANZ, J. (eds). (1980). *Studies of Shiftwork*, Taylor & Francis Ltd, London.

COLQUHOUN, W. P. *et al.* (1968). 'Experimental studies of shiftwork. II Stabilized 8-hour shift systems', *Ergonomics*, **11**, 527–546.

COLQUHOUN, W. P. *et al.* (1969). 'Experimental studies of shiftwork. III Stabilized 12-hour shift systems', *Ergonomics*, **12**, 865–882.

COLQUHOUN, P. *et al.* (eds). (1975). 'Experimental studies of shiftwork', [Forschungsberichte des Landes Nordrhein–Westfalen], No. 2513, Westdeutscher Verlag, Opladen.

GRAF, O. (1955). 'Vorschläge einer Neuregelung', (in *Gutachten über die kontinuierliche Arbeitszeit in SM–Werken der Hüttenwerk Oberhausen* A. G. Blume, E. *et al.*), Gutachten im Auftrage des Arbeits– und Sozialministeriums des Landes Nordrhein–Westfalen. (Unveröffentlicht.)

Harrington, J. M. (1978). *Shift Work and Health. A Critical Review of the Literature*, HMSO, London.

KNAUTH, P. & ILMARINEN, J. (1975). 'Continuous measurement of body temperature during a three-week experiment with inverted working and sleeping hours', (in *Experimental Studies of Shiftwork*, Colquhoun, P. *et al.* (eds)), 66–73, Westdeutscher Verlag, Opladen.

KNAUTH, P. & RUTENFRANZ, J. (1972a). 'Untersuchungen zum Problem des Schlafverhaltens bei experimenteller Schichtarbeit', *Internationales Archiv für Arbeitsmedizin*, **30**, 1–22.

KNAUTH, P. & RUTENFRANZ, J. (1972b). 'Untersuchungen über die Beziehungen zwischen Schichtform und Tagesaufteilung', *Internationales Archiv für Arbeitsmedizin*, **30**, 173–191.

KNAUTH, P. *et al.* (1975). 'Analyse der Verteilung verschiedener Tageselemente bei kontinuierlicher Arbeitsweise mit Hilfe von "time-budget-studies"', (in *Schichtarbeit bei kontinuierlicher Produktion*, Nachreiner, F. *et al.*), 17–82, Wirtschaftsverlag Nordwest, Wilhelmshaven.

KNAUTH, P. *et al.* (1979). 'Systematic selection of shift plans for continuous production with the aid of work-physiological criteria', *Applied Ergonomics*, **10**, 9–15.

McEWAN YOUNG, W. (1980). 'Shift work and flexible schedules: are they compatible?', *International Labour Review*, **119**, 1–17.

NACHREINER, F. *et al.* (1975). *Schichtarbeit bei kontinuierlicher Produktion*, Wirtschaftsverlag Nordwest, Wilhelmshaven.

PÁTKAI, P. *et al.* (1975). 'The diurnal pattern of some physiological and psychological functions in permanent night workers and in men working on a two-shift (day and night) system', (in *Experimental Studies of Shiftwork*, Colquhoun, P. *et al.* (eds)), 131–141, Westdeutscher Verlag, Opladen.

RUTENFRANZ, J. (1973). 'Probleme der Schichtarbeit', (in *Ploegenarbeid*, Zielhuis, R. L. & Huisdrukker, J. (eds)), 3–25, University of Amsterdam.

RUTENFRANZ, J. (1976). 'Arbeitsmedizinische Erwartungen an die Ergonomie', (in *Ergonomische Aspekte der Arbeitsmedizin*, Brenner, W. *et al.* (eds)), 31–37, A W Gentner Verlag, Stuttgart.

RUTENFRANZ, J. (1981). 'Arbeitsmedizinische Aspekte des Stressproblems', (in *Stress, Theorien, Untersuchungen, Massnahmen*, Nitsch, J. R. (ed.)), 379–390, Verlag Hans Huber, Bern-Stuttgart-Wien.

RUTENFRANZ, J. & COLQUHOUN, W. P. (eds). (1978). 'Shiftwork: theoretical issues and practical problems', *Ergonomics*, **21**, 737–874.

RUTENFRANZ, J. & KNAUTH P. (1981). 'Arbeitsmedizinische Gesichtspunkte für die Organisation von Schichtarbeit', *Zeitschrift für Betriebswirtschaft*, **51**, 66–74.

RUTENFRANZ, J. *et al.* (1976). 'Hours of work and shiftwork', *Ergonomics*, **19**, 331–340.

RUTENFRANZ, J. *et al.* (1977). 'Biomedical and psychosocial aspects of shiftwork. A review', *Scandinavian J. Work, Environment and Health*, **3**, 165–182.

RUTENFRANZ, J. *et al.* (1980). 'Shift work research issues', (in *The Twenty-Four Hour Workday*, Johnson, L. C. *et al.* (eds)), Proceedings of a symposium on 'Variations in work–sleep schedules', 221–259, US Department of Health and Human Services, Public Health Service, NIOSH, Division of Technical Services, Cincinnati, Ohio.

ULICH, E. (1957). 'Zur Frage der Belastung des arbeitenden Menschen durch Nacht- und Schichtarbeit', *Psychologische Rundschau*, **8**, 42–61.

WYATT, S. & MARRIOTT, R. (1953). 'Night work and shift changes', *Br. J. Industrial Med.*, **10**, 164–172.

Chapter 12

Design of a pre-employment screening program

M. A. Ayoub

Introduction

Industry has three basic options for meeting the challenges presented by jobs with high physical demands – to train the workers in techniques for reducing job hazards; to reduce the physical requirements of the job by redesign, and to select only those individuals whose work capacities meet or exceed the high demands. A fourth option exists and is often defaulted to – industry may choose simply to ignore the problem, a choice that may prove to be costly in the long run.

Training

Training strives to minimise the risk inherent in performing one's job. For example, by teaching the worker the 'safe lifting' method (Ayoub *et al.* 1970; Handley 1977), hazards typical of handling jobs can be controlled, if not eliminated. The safe lifting method calls for the worker to maintain a straight back (to assure that the applied pressure on each spinal disc will be

---

In the course of prescribing safe lifting as a method for back injury control, the following assumptions are made.

(1) The worker will always be in a position to maintain straight back/bent knees.
(2) The object to be handled is located in a place free from obstacles or barriers.
(3) The shape of the object/container is always considered to be that of a box, and (in many instances) equipped with handles or equivalent.
(4) The container can be handled without the use of special coupling devices.
(5) To keep the lever arm to a minimum, it is almost mandatory to be able to place the container between the knees when using straight back/bent knees method.
(6) The load is free (separate and unattached) to be manipulated by the worker.
(7) The pace (speed) of lifting is of such magnitude as to render the dynamic components of forces and torques acting on the body as inconsequential.
(8) The safe lifting method presupposes that the worker will always be in a position to fully appreciate the magnitude of the load and the difficulty which may be involved in handling it.

Unfortunately, validity of the above assumptions is questionable, and in many instances, may lead to disastrous results. Ayoub (1979) offers many examples showing the impracticality, and at times, the absurdity of the above assumptions.

Figure 12.1 Limitations of the safe lifting method

evenly distributed) and to keep the load as close as possible to the body (to keep the lever arm to a minimum). In addition, when correctly applied, the method promotes stability through location of the feet and mode of holding the object.

In industry, the safe lifting method provides an attractive solution to the old problem of back injury and trauma. The method does not require prior assessment of the job, the workplace, or the worker. All that is needed is to train the worker in how to use the method. Unfortunately, implementation of the method suffers from many shortcomings, *for its underlying prerequisites are questionable* (Figure 12.1).

Consider the following case. A railroad maintenance man was asked by his supervisor to uncouple two flatbed rail cars. The cars are typically used to carry boxed containers. During loading of these containers, the flatbed cars are joined together by bridge plates (Figure 12.2). These plates provide tracks upon which the boxed containers can be moved from one car to the next. Each flatbed car comes equipped with two plates, both of which are hinged on to the car at one end. To couple two cars, the plates are lowered to a horizontal position so that their free ends rest on the edge of the adjacent car. To uncouple the cars, a person is required to stand on the edge of one car and lift off the plate by grasping both of its sides, and then swing it to an upright position, making a 90° angle with the surface of the car. Before releasing the plate, the employee should secure it in its final position by pushing a pin (located on the side of plate) into two rings on the car side.

Each bridge plate measures two feet wide and four feet long. Each is a flat slab reinforced with a number of longitudinal and cross bars. When the plate is horizontal (joining the two cars), the portion appearing above the surface (i.e., the portion visible to the worker) is approximately two inches thick. The plate is equipped with no handles or any special features to facilitate the lifting task. The worker had no experience in handling such plates. However, he had watched other workers handling such plates on many occasions.

In the course of moving the plate, and at a point approximately one-third of the distance between the two cars, the worker felt a burning sensation in his back. However, he did not stop (the plate was already up) and decided to continue with the task. Upon concluding, he stepped off the car in severe pain. It was severe enough to have him sent to the emergency room of a nearby hospital. The end result of his visit was the loss of a disc (L_5/L_{5_1}) as well as his job with the railroad company. The worker sued the company on the grounds that the accident happened because of negligence. (The court proceedings took seven years, and eventually the judgement was in his favour.)

The company's defence rested with the fact that the worker did not follow the prescribed lifting method in which he was thoroughly trained. In support of this contention, the company cited the following excerpts from its safety manual.

(42) Lifting beyond safe capability is prohibited. Obtain help for heavy or cumbersome objects. Avoid jerking or awkward positions.

154

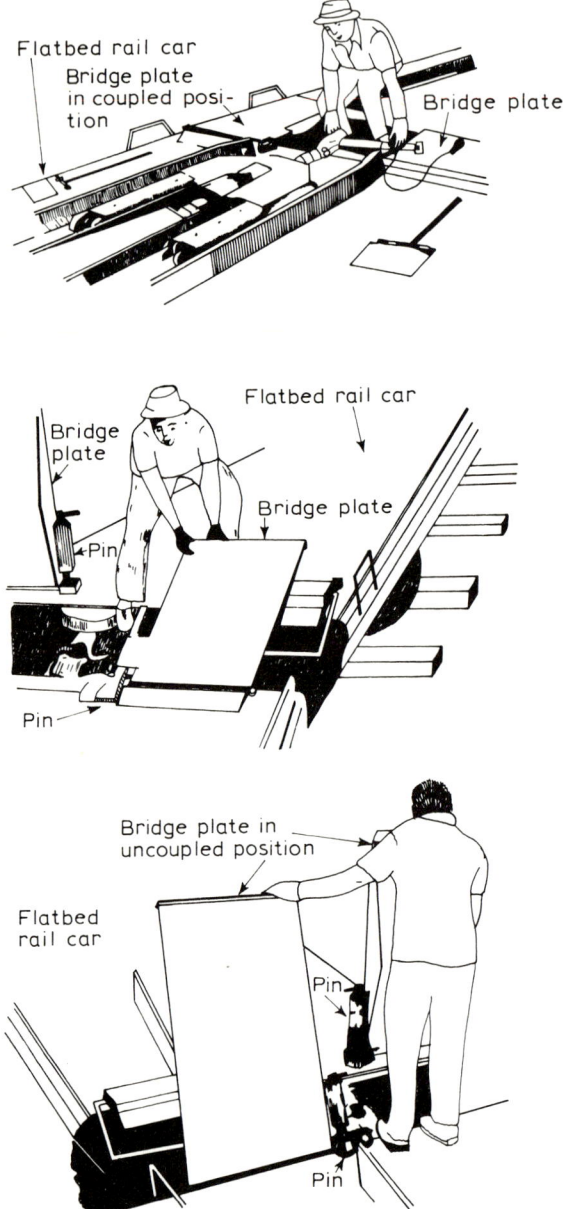

Figure 12.2 Two views of the bridge plate

(43) When lifting, employees must
   (a) have secure footing, feet slightly spread, body balanced
   (b) bend the knees, and keep back erect
   (c) take firm grasp. Preferably wear gloves. Avoid sharp corners, edges, splinters, nails, metal bands, etc
   (d) straighten the legs slowly. Keep back erect, and load near body
   (e) avoid pinch points
   (f) when assisted, move in unison by prearranged signals or commands.

The lifting task described above is, however, *atypical* for the following reasons.

(1) Safe lifting method was not applicable to the particular task at hand. The striking contrast between this task and other general lifting tasks (where the method can be used) is the fact that the worker is not free to move the load (plate) close to his body for the plate is fixed in place (hinged on one side). Instead, the plate moves away from the back. In addition, it would be difficult for the worker to maintain a straight back during the motion. Furthermore, the maximum torque does not occur at the start of the lifting action; instead it occurs at about one-quarter of the motion distance. Finally, because of the width of the plate (two feet) the worker is not able to assume the initial configuration recommended for the safe handling of the load. (Note – the worker cannot change the position of his feet since any change would send him into the gap between the two cars.)

(2) Moving the plate is a task that combines two activities: lifting and pushing. At the start of the motion, lifting is predominant; at the end of the motion, the task is reduced simply to pushing the plate in place.

(3) The lifting force (static) is maximum at the start of the motion and decreases linearly to reach zero at the end of the motion. The computation of the static torque (due to the weight of the plate) is based on the free body diagram given in Figure 12.3. From Figure 12.3, the maximum torque is reached at a distance of about one foot from the start of the lift, and this torque is equivalent to that generated by holding statically 150 pounds flat against the abdomen.

In summary, failure of the safe lifting method to provide an adequate answer to the back problem led to the development of other control approaches which attempt to consider worker characteristics (limitations) as well as job demands. Two such methods are the strength assessment method and the acceptable work load method. Both these methods are basically oriented toward minimising, if not eliminating, back injury through job selection and placement. Furthermore, the essence of these two methods is that of controlling lifting hazards through limiting (reducing) the maximum weight handled.

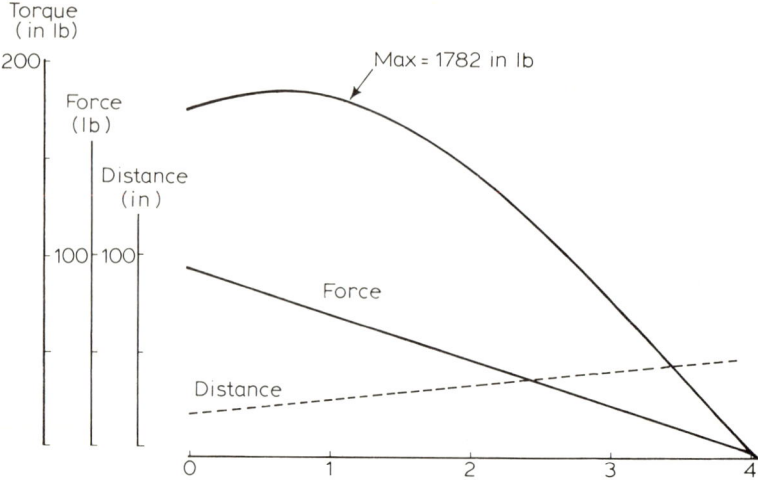

Figure 12.3 Lifting force and torque exerted in the course of handling the plate

Before proceeding, one point should be clear. We are not advocating that training in safe handling should be abandoned. Safe handling, when applied correctly, is a valid approach that should be used to complement and supplement other hazard control methods, such as pre-employment screening.

Job design

The thrust behind job redesign is to change jobs in such a way that the demands can easily be met by a majority of the population (Snook 1978). Since almost anyone could meet the new requirements, pre-employment selection procedures would not be needed. One such approach in redesigning jobs is to determine the acceptable work load. This method attempts to establish the task content that would be acceptable to industrial workers at large. The approach is based on psychophysical methods of behavioural research (Snook 1978). The application of the method is straightforward. Firstly, a group of workers representative of the industrial population is selected; secondly, the task and workplace variables are defined and their levels clearly determined; and thirdly, each worker is asked to perform the task starting at a level (specific combination of task variables) chosen by the investigator. The worker is then asked to adjust the level of task variables upwards or downwards until a preferred task design is reached. The design arrived at via this procedure will, at least theoretically, be acceptable to the worker if he is asked to perform the task continuously. Practically all the psychophysical studies of lifting take place in the laboratory under too-idealised conditions. They seldom last for more than an hour, and the lifting task is the sterile one which assumes that the container is in box form. The results of these studies are usually presented in chart or tabular forms (Table 12.1). In some studies, regression functions are used to relate the population definition of an acceptable task

Table 12.1 *Psychophysical results from low lifting tasks performed at Liberty Mutual* (Snook 1978)

Sex	Task frequency	Mean weight (kg)	SD	Source
M	14 s	20.4	4.7	Snook *et al.* (1970)
M	16 s	21.1	5.4	Snook *et al.* (1970)
M	60 s	24.4	5.9	Snook *et al.* (1970)
M	15 min	29.9	5.0	Snook & Irvine (1967)
M	8 h	39.2	10.7	Snook *et al.* (1976)
F	14 s	15.3	3.1	Snook & Ciriello (1974a)
F	16 s	15.4	2.6	Snook & Ciriello (1974a)
F	60 s	16.9	3.1	Snook & Ciriello (1974a)
Γ	8 h	20.7	9.6	Snook *et al.* (1976)

to the physical and physiological characteristics of the population (subjects). Mathematically, this can be stated as follows

$$Y_j = f(X_i) \qquad i = 1, \ldots ,n$$

where Y_j = the jth task variable, e.g., weight to be handled, X_i = the *i*th characteristics of the worker, e.g., back strength and n = number of characteristics deemed to be significant.

Ayoub *et al.* (1978) offer an example of such functions. To use these functions, one needs to measure the personal characteristics of the task population; from these characteristics, the permissible task parameters that can be handled by a majority (or perhaps by the entire population) will be determined by direct substitution in the functions. The opposite of this can also be done; i.e., for a given task design, one can determine the characteristics of the population that would be suitable for the task at hand. In other words, it can be used as a screening tool for eliminating individuals who would be working at high risk.

Care should be exercised when using a predictive function that involves terms referring to muscular strength. To assure compatibility and hence validity, strength values substituted in these functions should be obtained with body postures identical to those utilised in the course of their development. With the obvious differences among investigators in defining strength postures (e.g., back and leg strengths), it would be difficult to cross-validate many of the available predictive functions.

Jobs designed or populations screened using the psychophysical functions (developed for lifting tasks) may not prevent back trauma or disease, simply because *they were not developed or intended to guard against such things*. Rather, they should be viewed only as a means for determining the preference of a group of workers for certain task parameteres, and certainly should not be viewed as diagnostic tools. As is typical with the results of many laboratory studies, data generated using the psychophysical method reflect the characteristics of a too-idealised lifting task – the lifting container is a standard box equipped with two handles and lifting takes place in the sagittal plane in one of three motion ranges (floor to knuckle height, knuckle height to shoulder height, shoulder height to arm reach).

These characteristics are not representative of many industrial tasks. For this reason, direct application of psychophysical data in industry would be inappropriate, if not meaningless. If the lifting task can be described in terms of the standard task (e.g., the one repeatedly described by Snook *et al.* 1978) then some use of the available data can be realised. To accomplish this, one needs to satisfy the following.

> (1) For a given container (size and weight), the biomechanical equivalent should be determined (Tichauer 1978). This equivalent is the weight that would be carried in the standard box in order to produce the same spinal stress (torque) as that to be expected from handling the container.
> (2) The lifting task is restricted to the sagittal plane.
> (3) The lifting motion is mapped into one of the standard lifting ranges.

Again, all of these prerequisites significantly reduce the utility of the available data to industry at large.

Aside from the difficulties inherent in determining job demands acceptable for a majority of workers, a number of persons (extreme cases) will still not be capable of meeting even the new reduced demands. Some sort of screening would therefore be needed. More important, however, economic and technological considerations make job redesign untenable as a solution for industry, especially in the case of jobs with excessive physical demands.

Pre-employment screening

Pre-employment screening is the best means presently available for controlling the liabilities associated with physically strenuous work in industry. This is not to say that training and job redesign do not have their place. They should be used cautiously, however, and in most cases, only in conjunction with an effective selection and placement procedure.

Pre-employment screening programs in the past have taken on a number of different perspectives. Back x-rays, strength testing, medical examinations, psychological tests, and job simulators have formed the focus of various selection procedures. Each of these is briefly reviewed below.

Back x-rays

The use of back x-rays as a pre-employment screening device is predicated on the intuitive appeal that abnormalities of the lumbar spine will cause increased susceptibility to back injury and pain. In fact, as early as 1923, Straub (1923) asserted that congenital defects demonstrable by x-ray structurally weakened the back, making it prone to injury and prolonged recovery. From that time until the present, back injury and the x-ray have been the subject of intense debate. The state of the art in this area can perhaps best be expressed by a statement made at a conference about the use of back x-rays in pre-employment examinations held by the American College of Radiology in 1973. They summarised their meeting by stating that there were 56 participants but 'not quite 56 different opinions'

(Present 1974). In a comprehensive review of pre-employment back x-rays, Montgomery (1976) concludes that developmental abnormalities do not necessarily predispose the individual to low back injury. It thus appears that while pre-employment x-ray examinations may be of value in assessing patients' current status, they offer little assistance in predicting any future trauma or disability resulting from on-the-job stress (Present 1974).

Strength testing

Chaffin *et al.* (1978) maintain that muscular strength demand is the limiting criterion (or perhaps a sensitive criterion) in safe handling of materials. Specifically, they postulate that jobs which demand high percentages of workers' strength capability may be classified as hazardous as well as injurious to workers' health.

Before we pursue the point further, it is important that the concept of 'strength' be defined and delineated. Strength is a term which encompasses many definitions and interpretations in the literature. For the sake of brevity, we should accept the fact that strength is not a basic physical quantity as mass, force, etc. rather it is an output which depends on force exerted by a muscle or muscle group assuming a certain posture. There-fore, when we speak of strength we speak of the force output that can be produced with a given body posture. In the literature, this force is traditionally referred to as 'strength'. Strength values given without referencing the body posture used are meaningless to the extent that comparison among different individuals is fruitless. This is one of the primary reasons behind the great emphasis and attention given to the definition of postures used in strength testing of various muscle groups.

Throughout this paper, we will use the term 'strength' to refer to a maximum force output produced by the body assuming a given and fixed (static) posture. This is at variance with the definition given by Kroemer (1970) which is as follows.

> *Static strength is the maximal force muscles can exert isometrically in a single voluntary effort.*

With this definition, and from the text provided, Kroemer implies that the force (magnitude and direction) would describe the body posture em-ployed. This is simply not possible, for the posture assumed during exertion cannot be deduced from the direction of the force (output).

Chaffin *et al.* (1977a) assess the stress (physical associated with lifting tasks or, for that matter, manual handling in general) as a function of the weight handled and the corresponding strength that can be maintained by an employee or group of employees. Specifically, a strength ratio is defined as

$$\text{Lift strength ratio (LSR)} = \frac{\text{Weight}}{\text{Position strength}}$$

The weight refers to the object or tool handled on the job; it represents the job demand. On the other hand, position strength refers to the maximum voluntary strength (static) that can be measured at a point in the workplace envelope at which the weight is maintained. In this sense, position strength reflects the muscle groups utilised and body posture assumed in the course of handling the weight. In general, position strength can be determined experimentally or predicted through empirical relationships and biomechanical modelling.

Experimental strength determination requires a subject to exert a maximum force on a handle connected by a chain to a force transducer (a load cell) whose output is displayed on an appropriate meter. (Note – simpler analogue systems as well as more sophisticated systems do exist.) The position of the hands, and consequently the body posture assumed, are identical to those of the job. Instrumentation for strength measurements is quite straightforward and indeed can be assembled using 'off-the-shelf' components. However, the procedure to be followed during the test has to be carried out with great care (Kroemer 1970).

Prediction of position strength can be accomplished by using one of three approaches (Chaffin *et al.* 1977b).

(1) Strength for any job position can be predicted from profiles generated in previous studies. Figure 12.4 is an example of such profiles. (Note – Laubach (1978) provides a comprehensive summary of published strength data for men and women assuming different body postures.)

(2) If accuracy is desired and resources permit, a computerised simulation model can be utilised to predict strength for a given job position. To make such prediction, the model generated several feasible body postures that will place the hands at the desired point and will not cause torques at articulation joints to exceed their

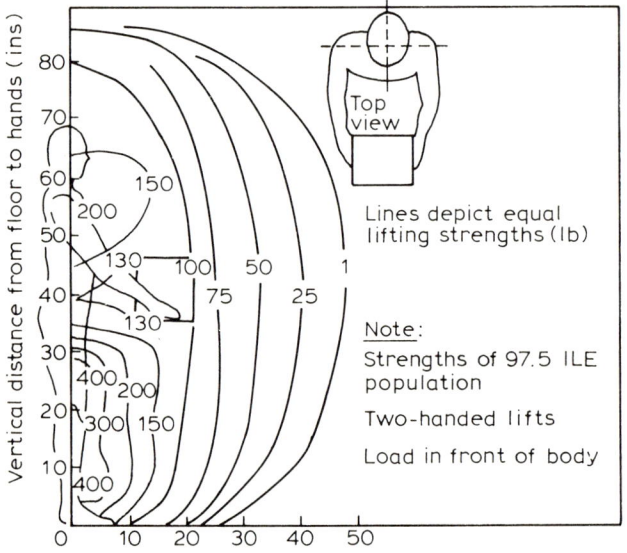

Figure 12.4 Predicted strength profile of a large, strong male

respective limits, define angles that cannot be assumed by the
body segments or force the body to go out of balance. The feasible
posture that produces maximum strength will be selected and its
strength value will be taken as the position strength for a given
task.

(3) A compromise between graphical profiles and modelling is
strength determination using empirical functions. An example of
these functions is

Position strength = 44.177 + 0.102 (arm strength)
+ 0.0023 (back strength × arm strength)
+ 2.2245 (worker height) + 0.6533 (worker
age).

In lieu of the above and similar functions, Chaffin *et al.* (1978) have
proposed another set of predictive functions that divide the workplace into
three zones. Strength in each zone is a function of a particular muscle
group, and can be determined by using standardised isometric strength
tests. Three basic values are determined for the three zones – arm, back,
and leg strengths. These values are modified (discounted) for loads that are
located at a position horizontally displaced from the standard test position.
Two empirical expressions are provided to compute modified strength
values (Figure 12.5).

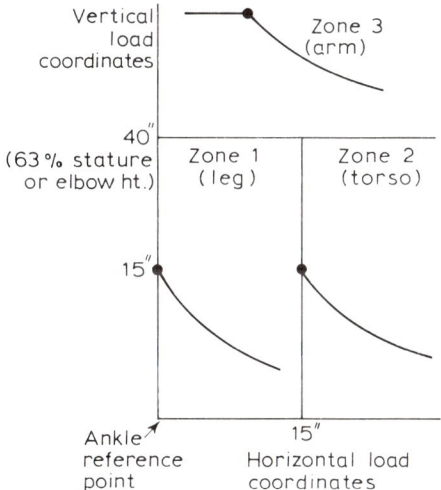

Figure 12.5 Three zone strength prediction model

In addition to LSR, Chaffin *et al.* (1977a) have proposed and discussed a
number of strength ratios which can be classified into two groups: (a) ratios
for rating strength demands and (b) ratios to assess the degree of matching
between employees' capability (physical) and the job demands. Table 12.2
summarises all the suggested strength ratios.

Following detailed analysis of approximately 900 jobs spanning six
plants, Chaffin *et al.* (1977a) arrived at the obvious conclusion that the
lower the LSR value, the less risky the job. They imply that a value of less
than 0.5 is an ideal target for many lifting jobs (in one paper a value of 0.2

Table 12.2 *Strength ratios* (Chaffin *et al.* 1977a)

(A) RATING JOBS

   (1) Lift strength rating (LSR)

$$\text{LSR} = \frac{\text{Object weight on job}}{\text{Predicted strength in job position}}$$

   (2) Job strength rating (JSR)

$$\text{JSR} = \frac{\text{Object weight on job}}{\text{Average strength of employees on job}}$$

   (3) Predicted mean job strength rating (Pred. MJSR)

$$\text{Pred. MJSR} = \frac{\text{Object weight on job}}{\text{Average predicted strength of employees on job}}$$

(B) EMPLOYEE MATCHING

   (4) Employee strength rating (ESR)

$$\text{ESR} = \frac{\text{Object weight on job}}{\text{Employee strength demonstrated in job position}}$$

   (5) Some variations of ESR

$$\text{FREQ} \times \text{ESR} = \frac{\text{Object weight} \times \text{Frequency of handling per week}}{\text{Employee strength demonstrated in job position}}$$

$$\text{HOR} \times \text{FREQ} \times \text{ESR} = \frac{\text{Horizontal distance} \times \text{Frequency} \times \text{Weight}}{\text{Employee strength}}$$

---

was recommended (Herrin and Chaffin 1978)). The value of 0.5 simply means that no person should be asked to handle more than 50% of his/her measured static strength.

In general, a value of 0.5 for LSR would imply a maximum load of approximately 60 pounds for a strong male, a figure that is much lower than that recommended by the International Labor Office (ILO 1964; 1967). Strength testing approaches to pre-employment screening suffer from a number of shortcomings. One of these rests with the fact that the approach does not allow for the repetitive nature of most industrial tasks. Strength is seen as the sole limiting factor in the individual's ability to perform physical work. The importance of cardiac and pulmonary functions is, thus, ignored. Other shortcomings of this approach, such as its blindness to additional stressors (e.g., heat) are summarised by Ayoub (1979).

Medical examinations

Medical examinations are part of the hiring process in most companies today. Lincoln (1968) cites a number of reasons usually given as justification for pre-employment physicals

   (1) obtain healthy, physically efficient workers
   (2) help control health and life insurance costs
   (3) protect retirement benefits

(4) limit future liability under Workmens' Compensation laws
(5) limit administrative load resulting from poor selection and placement
(6) record baseline data
(7) protect the individual and public from unsafe acts resulting from detectable physical or emotional factors.

The pre-employment medical evaluation is then done to assure that the job description matches the physical and mental capabilities of the applicant for reasons of health and safety. A number of factors, however, often prevent this goal from being met. For one, just how is the examiner supposed to determine the 'match between job demands and worker capability?' As it turns out in practice, the physician may have only a vague notion of what a job requires and accordingly would have not means of assessing the applicant's ability to meet job demands. By default, the screening can reject only those individuals with gross abnormalities. While the effectiveness of such a procedure is questionable for even light duty jobs, it is certainly inadequate for highly strenuous work. The pre-employment physical, therefore, is a necessary but not sufficient screening procedure for highly physical work.

Psychological tests

The use of psychological tests in pre-employment screening has been a common practice over the years. The idea behind the use of these tools is that certain behavioural attributes can be used as predictors of job performance. By measuring these attributes in applicants, a more favourable workforce can be chosen. Personal maturity, motivation and aptitudes for certain activities are commonly included in these tests. It should be added that EEOC guidelines require that the predictiveness of these tests must be validated if they are to be used in screening. Inclusion of test items must, therefore, be based on extensive research and not just on the employer's intuition. There is little doubt that behavioural tests are important tools for selection in many sedentary type jobs. Their value in screening for physical work, however, is to be questioned. While it is important that workers be 'motivated' in order to perform well in strenuous jobs, no amount of motivation can overcome a lack of physical capacity to work. No matter how hard an individual wants to lift a 100 kg block, he simply cannot if his strength capacity falls short.

Job simulators

As the name implies, job simulators attempt to simulate actual work. For example, if a job requires the torquing of a wheel to open or close a control valve, the simulator would contain a similar wheel with comparable resistance. The test for an applicant would be simply to have him attempt to open and close the valve. Evaluation could be either by objective (e.g. measuring the applied torque) or subjective means (e.g. rating the applicant's performance by direct observation).

Job simulators, thus, come closest of the approaches reviewed, to evaluating actual ability to perform the work in question. Several considerations, however, limit their usefulness in the industrial setting. Economic considerations are an obvious impediment in this concern. The simulators required to evaluate applicants for many (perhaps most) jobs are expensive. Take this in conjunction with the fact that a separate simulator is needed for each job. Since screening often is performed for more than one job opening, it should not be difficult to envision many hours of testing for each applicant – a prospect that may send shock waves through many already overloaded medical departments.

Another shortcoming of job simulators is the question of safety. If selection is to be useful, applicants must be rejected on the basis of their inability to do work. A situation develops with an individual lacking the physical capacity to perform a strenuous task, but motivated to do so by the promise of employment. With the large forces required and the dynamics of the testing situation, the potential for injury cannot be overlooked. Job simulators, in addition, tell us little about the work capacity of the applicant. Consider the case of a simple simulator consisting of a box weighted to 25 kg. The applicant's task is to lift the box and place it on a shelf three feet high. Individuals not able to perform this lift would obviously be rejected for employment. However, what about those who can do the lift? Is 25 kg their capacity or could they really lift 50 kg? This is important information as it would certainly be desirable to hire an individual with a certain 'reserve' if he is to perform this task on a continual basis. It follows that the usefulness of job simulators as a means for pre-employment screening is rather limited if not outright questionable for many industrial settings.

From this brief review, it should be apparent that a need does exist for developing a pre-employment screening program suited for physically demanding jobs. The design of such a program is given in the following section.

Design for pre-employment screening program

A screening program should be predicated on the principle that it will separate the fit from the unfit; the normal from the unhealthy. The results of the screening program should assure that job demands would not tax the individual's work capacity beyond safe limits. To accomplish this, we have to define jobs and individuals using common scales and determinants. In other words, it is no longer satisfactory to describe jobs in accordance with the standard practice virtually common to all personnel manuals, e.g., describing jobs in terms of output requirements such as production standards. Similarly, describing the abilities of potential employees in terms of their personal characteristics (sex, age, education, etc.) is not adequate insofar as job placement is concerned. A solution to this dilemma would be to describe jobs and potential employees as a function of their demands and their capacities, respectively.

The capacity to do work or exercise depends on the functional performance of the body respiratory, cardiovascular and muscular systems. In general, work capacity of an individual is the integrative description of all these physiological systems, and can be defined precisely in terms of

(1) ability to breathe
(2) ability to transfer oxygen effectively in the lungs
(3) ability to increase cardiac output to meet a given work load
(4) ability to transport oxygen to the working muscles
(5) ability to exert adequate muscular force to perform a given job.

A job to a person is simply a set of demands imposed on the body's physiological systems. In a sense, these demands are the physiological translation of the required responses from the body systems; the ability of the body to match these responses is the demands counterpart – work capacity. Job demands and human work capacity are typically described in terms of the following common descriptors (dimensions)

(1) reach demand/capability
(2) strength demand/capability
(3) energy expenditure demand/capability
(4) cardiac output demand/capability

The work 'demand' references the job requirements on a given scale, whilst 'capability' references the limiting physiological/physical value on the same scale.

Using common descriptors for both job demands and work capacity, we are now in a position to design and implement a pre-employment screening program. The development of such a program would involve the following

(1) determine the physical and physiological demands of the jobs for which applicants will be screened
(2) based on job demands defined in (1) develop a simulator (a functional screening test) that will assess each applicant's physiological efficiency as well as work capacity
(3) having defined the work capacity of each applicant, we proceed to assign all applicants to one of three groups
   (a) those with work capacity that far exceeds job demands,
   (b) those with work capacity that is far below job demands, and
   (c) those with work capacity that is very close to job demands.

With the applicants tested and classified into these groups, the screening is complete, and thus decisions on employment can be reached on a rational and an unbiased basis – *individuals, males or females (who at the time of screening are assessed to be functionally qualified), will not be exposed to undue risk when assigned the targeted jobs.* The architecture of the above screening program is rather simple and straightforward, and, indeed, the steps outlined are fundamental in many of the textbooks of ergonomics and work physiology. However, the success of such programs rests with two prerequisites – determination of job demands, and assessment of the functional capacity and physiological efficiency of the applicants.

Prediction of job demands and physiological response

The performance of a job, any job, from maintaining an erect posture to handling a heavy and bulky load, constitutes an external demand imposed on the human body to which a chain of coupled activities marks a predictable and quantifiable body response. First, the demand, regardless of its type or characteristics, will require muscular activity which may involve one or more muscle groups. Muscular work consumes energy that has to be supplied by oxidising the substrata in the body. The oxidising agent is the oxygen obtained from the atmosphere. To deliver the needed oxygen to working muscles, the body mobilises two primary systems – the respiratory system and the cardiovascular system.

The respiratory system delivers oxygen to the blood and clears out carbon dioxide (CO_2) produced in the oxidisation process. On the other hand, the cardiovascular system responds to the imposed demand by pumping more oxygenated blood to meet the energy requirements of the working muscles. The functions of the three body systems (muscular, cardiovascular and respiratory) in response to job demands are highly coupled and can be predicted (assessed) by means of several physiological measures. Primary physiological measures of interest can be grouped in accordance with their source of derivation: (1) measures based on gas analysis and (2) measures based on the bioelectric responses of the body muscular system. Gas analysis measures include oxygen consumption, ventilation rate, carbon dioxide produced, respiration rate and oxygen pulse. The bioelectric measures include heart rate, electrocardiograms, electromyograms (EMG).

The procedure of collecting and analysing the physiological response data is by now well defined and established and can be found in many work physiology textbooks. Incidentally, some of the major data collection and analysis procedures date from the 1920s and early 1930s; it seems that the fundamental approach used in collecting such data has not changed, at least in principle, since that time.

Over the years, physiologists have studied a host of jobs in the laboratory (under controlled conditions) and in industry (Passmore and Durnin 1955). From knowledge gained from all these studies performed by many researchers from different countries and studying a multitude of jobs the following assumptions can be made regarding job demands and physiological responses.

(1) At the submaximal work heart rate, oxygen consumption and ventilation rates are linearly related to each other regardless of the type or nature of the job performed.

(2) The presence or absence of thermal stress has no effect on the oxygen consumption associated with job performance.

(3) Heart rate is linearly related to the increase in thermal stress. When work is performed in hot environments, heart rate will increase linearly due to the combined effect of work stress and heat stress.

(4) Maximum heart rate that can be reached by an individual is independent of state of health or degree of fitness and depends only on age.

(5) Maximum oxygen uptake that can be maintained by an individual can be predicted from knowing the maximum heart rate (see assumption (1) above).

(6) Physiological responses of unfit or unhealthy individuals are markedly higher than for normal individuals performing comparable jobs.

(7) Physiological responses are linearly related to work intensity. This is true for all types of jobs performed under various conditions. This linear relationship is usually presented in the literature in terms of an efficiency factor (or the slope of the linear line), which is a function of each individual's attributes (degree of fitness, state of health, etc.).

The above assumptions are well defined in the literature and have been supported by numerous studies in work physiology and ergonomics. Wasserman and Whipp (1975) provide the most detailed comprehensive review in support of the stated assumptions. In addition, Buskirk *et al.* (1977) present the supportive data for the assumption concerning the effects of heat stress on physiological responses. Most recently, Swenton-Wall (1980) has ascertained once more the validity of the above assumptions through a comprehensive physiological assessment of several jobs in an aluminium reduction plant.

The implications of the above assumptions should be very clear – once the work output is known, the levels of corresponding physiological responses can be predicted. Next, knowing the physiological efficiency of the person, a determination can be made as to whether the person will be able to perform the job without being exposed to unacceptable risk. In other words, to develop a screening program, we need to define the work output and strength requirement for each job as well as the physiological efficiency of each applicant.

Work output and strength requirement

Work output

Performance of a job can simply be described in terms of the motions of body segments involved in its execution. The motion of each segment, in turn, can be categorised in terms of three fundamental characteristics – displacement, velocity and acceleration. The characteristics can be obtained experimentally either through photographic or electromechanical techniques (Ayoub (1972) summarises the techniques). Using motion characteristics, coupled with the principle of body dynamics, we can proceed and compute the mechanical work output versus time for a given job. In addition, information concerning the forces and torques acting on each articulation joint of the body during the motion can be obtained and presented as a series of profiles versus time. In general, these forces and torques may be expressed as

$$F_j(t) = f_1[\theta_i(t), \dot{\theta}_i(t), \ddot{\theta}_i(t), m_i, I_i, \ell_i, r_i,]$$
$$T_j(t) = f_1[\theta_i(t), \dot{\theta}_i(t), \ddot{\theta}_i(t), m_i, I_i, \ell_i, r_i,]$$

where θ_i = angular position (Euler angle) of the ith segment, $\dot{\theta}_i$ = angular velocity of the ith segment, $\ddot{\theta}_i$ = angular acceleration of the ith segment, m_i = mass of the ith segment, I_i = moment of inertia of the ith segment, ℓ_i

= length of the ith segment, r_i = distance of the centre of mass of the ith segment from its proximal point, T_j = torque acting on the jth joint, F_j = force acting on the jth joint, and f_1 and f_2 = functions derived from mechanics (Ayoub 1971).

Using results of the dynamic analysis, an estimate of job demand is obtained. Human effort during motion may be assessed in using a number of mechanical criteria (e.g. work, power angular impulse, linear impulse and stress at the articulation joint). Over the years, extensive studies have supported the conclusion that power developed at the different articulation joints is the measure which best describes human effort (Ayoub 1971). Power job demand can be expressed as

$$\int_{\theta_1}^{\dot{\theta}_2} \bar{M}d\dot{\theta}$$

where $d\dot{\theta}$ = small angular velocity of the body, and $\dot{\theta}_1, \dot{\theta}_2$ = initial and final angular velocities.

In lieu of the exact experimental procedure just described, two other approaches can be considered.

Using averages

This is by far the most widely used and referenced approach in the literature. It determines the work output in terms of the work done in changing the body posture and position of the tool or object handled through the motion. In using this approach, no attempt is made to assess the work output at any particular point in time, nor are the effects of dynamic forces considered. In essence, for a given job, the average work output is given by

$$Fd/T$$

where F = force due to body weight or work tool, object, etc., d = distance through which the force has moved the object, and T = time taken to move the mass through distance d.

In many applications, work output is computed based on the actual work done in moving a tool or object, while the work done in changing body posture is ignored. Because of this, a discrepancy in the literature concerning human work efficiency does exist, and a host of values have been reported. Therefore, care should be exercised when interpreting some of these efficiency values. In the same manner, using weight of the object/tool handled as an equivalent to strength demand of the job is basically substituting an average value for the peak strength demand.

Although simple to define and estimate, the limitations of using average values should be fully appreciated – an average value may or may not be representative of peak demand (work output or strength) associated with job performance. This could influence to a great extent the stress level (or risk) of a given job, and accordingly, the conclusions concerning pre-employment screening and selection.

Using models

Through modelling, the motion characteristics and related dynamic descriptors can be predicted for the best and worst performances of a given job. By knowing (1) the characteristics of the job (workplace geometry, initial and final points of the motion, the weight and size of the object handled, etc.), and (2) basic anthropometric data of the individual performing the job, an optimisation model can be developed (Ayoub and Elshafei 1974; Gruver *et al.* 1979). Optimising the model objective function subject to job and human constraints yields two classes of possible job motions – motion associated with best performance (job performed at minimum cost (mechanical energy)) and motion associated with worst performance (job performed at performed at maximum cost). With the extreme motions fully defined, two limits for both total work output and peak strength can be computed. These limits are then used to predict the expected range of physical and physiological responses of job performance. The attractiveness and perhaps the power of the modelling approach should be obvious; based on a limited and rather general number of job and workplace descriptors, a host of data concerning the dynamics of the job can be obtained.

Indirect methods

In contrast to all the above methods, work output can be estimated indirectly. To this end, indirect approaches to work output assessment do not focus on the mechanics of motion itself. Rather, 'secondary' physiological measures are taken of workers on the job and are later converted to work output via an extrapolation procedure. Both oxygen consumption and heart rate may be used in this regard. In particular, if the oxygen consumed by an individual at work as well as his physiological efficiency are known, then the work output for that job may be calculated. The validity of using oxygen uptake as a measure of energy is well documented in the literature (Brouha 1980; Durnin and Passmore 1967).

Another means by which one may assess work output is by using heart rate at work. As with oxygen uptake, if this quantity is known together with efficiency, the work output may be extrapolated. One note in this regard is that the effect of heat stress on heart rate must be taken into account. That is, if the heart rate of a worker in a hot environment is used in conjunction with his efficiency factor from a cool one, then without proper adjustment work output will be overestimated.

Strength demand

Dynamic strength demands of the job are estimated as follows.

(1) The maximum torque (dynamic) acting on the back is obtained from motion analysis of the job.
(2) Given the torque demand (back) for job position, the equivalent hand force required from a subject assuming a standard testing posture is determined. This is illustrated in Figure 12.6.

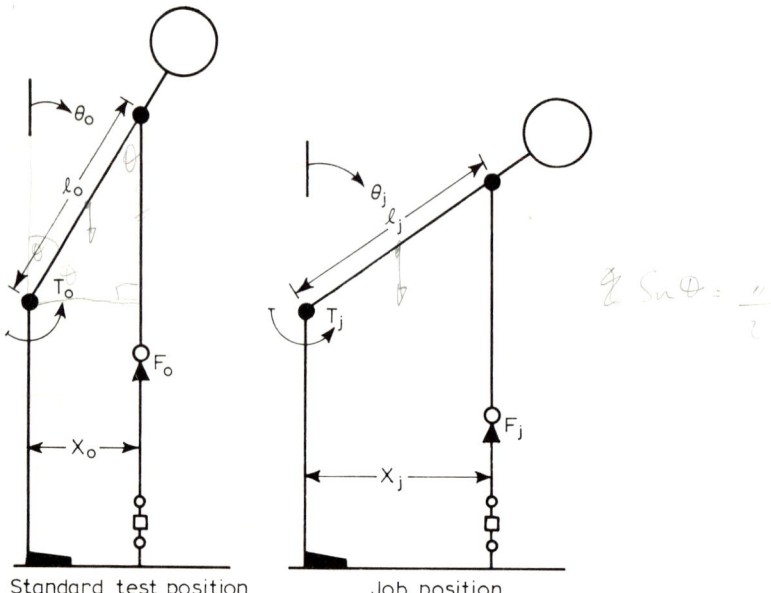

Standard test position   Job position

θ_o = angle of back in standard test posture (i.e., 35°)
θ_j = angle of back in job position
X_o = horizontal distance between hands and 'back pivot' in standard test position
X_j = horizontal distance between hands and back pivot in job position
ℓ_o & ℓ_j = length of back (from hip to shoulder)
T_o = torque acting on back in standard test position
T_j = torque acting on back in job position (i.e., job demand)
F_o = vertical force developed in standard test position
F_j = vertical force developed in job position

The torque acting on the back may be expressed as
Test position: $T_o = F_o \times \ell(\sin \theta_o)$
Job position: $T_j = F_j \times \ell(\sin \theta_j)$
Assuming $T_o = T_j$ (i.e. that back strength is constant), we obtain

$$F_j = \frac{\ell(\sin \theta_o) \times F_o}{(\sin \theta_j)}$$

In the standard testing position $\ell \sin \theta_o = 10$. Therefore F_j can be approximated

$$F_j = \frac{10 \times F_o}{X_j}$$

Figure 12.6 Predicting job position strength from strength in standard test positions

From Figure 12.6, it is apparent that the forces that may be exerted in a job position (known as job position strength) are easily predicted from a knowledge of the forces produced in a standard posture and the angle assumed at work. When the maximum torque achieved at work is used in assessing strength demands, a maximum or peak demand is identified. Average torque may be substituted in the above procedure when average strength demand is desired. For the standard back strength testing position, the following relationship is found between force (F) and distance (X) (Figure 12.6):

$$F_j = 10F_0/X_j$$

It should be noted that the relationship is similar to that reported by Chaffin et al. (1978). These investigators obtained their relationship through extensive testing of subjects assuming different postures.

In 'transforming' the torque obtained for a job into 'strength demand' (standard static posture), the assumption is implicitly made that at some point in the job cycle, the person should be able to produce the torque demanded by the job. Regardless of the posture assumed, this torque remains the same. However, the force output will vary from posture to posture, and in general an exponential relationship between force (exerted) and distance (from an 'ankle reference' to the point at which the force is exerted) will be found (Chaffin et al.1978).

Physiological efficiency

The assumption is always made (or perhaps implied) that a person seeking employment is free from any functional diseases which may impede or impair the person's physiological responses to job demands. This is simply not true, and in many cases, the presence or absence of any impairment cannot be ascertained without actually testing the person at submaximal workloads (exercise testing).

Malfunction of one component (link) in the gas transport systems (respiratory, cardiovascular, and muscular) will undoubtedly create additional stress on the other components within and among the systems. Intolerance to work is a common manifestation of inability of the gas transport systems to meet job demands. This can be attributed to respiratory or cardiovascular diseases (Wasserman and Whipp 1975).

The functional capacity (state of health) of an individual cannot be predicted *a priori*, nor can it be accurately determined based on some personal characteristics such as age, weight, height, etc. The practice of predicting work capacity of an individual by employing multiple regression functions developed based on a pool of subjects who may or may not be representative of the individual at hand is very questionable, if not unacceptable. An acceptable and more realistic alternative, however, would be to assess each individual while performing one of the three standard laboratory tasks – walking/running on a treadmill, exercising on a bicycle ergometer or stepping up and down with a certain frequency on a step of standard dimensions.

Of the choices available for simulating work output demands, the step test is recommended due to a number of considerations

    (1) equipment required for step testing is less expensive and easier to transport than either the bicycle ergometer or treadmill

    (2) the step test satisfies the requirement of having large muscle groups involved in exercise used to assess efficiency

    (3) people are more familiar with the stepping motion than they are with either pedalling or walking on a treadmill (Datta and Ramanathan 1969; Montogomery 1976).

The work output obtained from a step test is a function of three variables – body weight of the individual being tested, the height of the step and the frequency at which the individual steps up and down. The frequency recommended is 15–20 'total body lifts' per minute; i.e. the subject must raise (and lower) the entire body to step height 15–20 times per minute. Using two or more different workloads (with a step test), the individual's physiological efficiency (expressed as a relationship between physiological measures and work output) is defined. In addition, from the test data, the individual state of health can be ascertained (Jones *et al.* 1975). Figure 12.7 shows how step-test data can be used to screen three applicants for a job with known workload. Because the three applicants are the same age, their

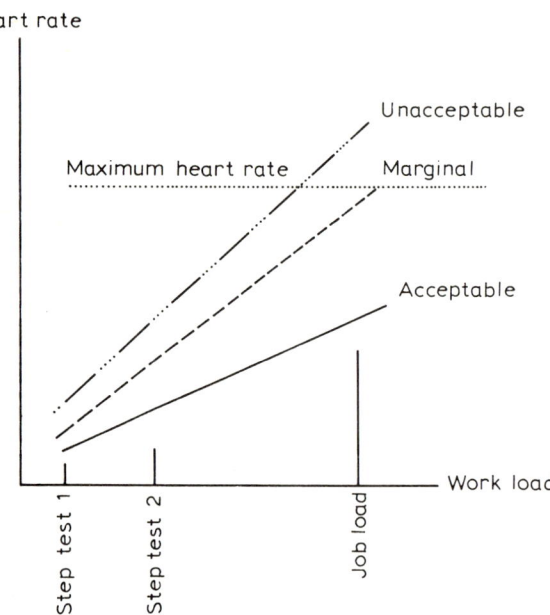

Figure 12.7 Three applicants, same age

maximum heart rates are taken to be the same. However, due to the marked difference in their physiological response on the step test, their employment potential varies, and they are classified as acceptable, marginal and unacceptable.

On the other hand, to evaluate the physical capability of an individual, strength testing offers a simple, yet accurate approach. An individual can be tested for arm, back and leg strength values in a matter of minutes. The positions to be used for arm and leg strength assessment are similar to those reported by Chaffin *et al.* (1977a). The posture for back testing is as suggested by Weiner and Lourie (1969). The assessment of human strength is a very delicate matter. Strength measures are sensitive to many psychological variables falling under the label of 'motivation' (Ikai and Steihaus 1961; Kroemer 1978). As such, it is necessary to standardise the testing procedure to the greatest extent possible. Using the test results, a complete strength profile can then be developed utilising the fact that strength (force that can be exerted) is proportionate to the distance between the hands (point of exertion) and the back (point of support).

In summary, step and strength testing of an individual yield the following

(1) physiological efficiency expressed in terms of the relationships between work output (work load) and heart rate
(2) strength profile illustrating the forces that can be exerted at any point in the workplace envelope
(3) degree of difficulty to be assigned to various levels of work output – perception of work stress.

Application

The approach towards pre-employment screening, previously detailed has been adopted for two aluminium reduction plants of the Reynolds Metal Company, Richmond, Virginia. Insofar as satisfying the requirements of EEOC Uniform Guidelines, the design and subsequent implementation of the programs are patterned around the concept of *content validity*. The jobs selected for the study, the methods and equipment used for job analysis are given below.

In general, the procedures employed involved

(1) assessing the work capacities of the present workers
(2) assessing the demands posed by each job.

The environment found in a reduction plant is a most difficult one in which to carry out a scientific investigation. In order to assure the success of a project with this degree of complexity, it was first necessary to undertake a series of pilot studies to acquaint investigators with the plant environment and testing equipment, as well as to familiarise both investigators and Reynolds personnel with the methods and procedures of the study.

Twenty-seven individuals served as primary subjects in this study. Eighteen others were directly involved in preliminary studies. The subjects were chosen from workers performing the following jobs

Flex raiser	Pin cleaner	Carbon setter breaker	Materials handler
Anode paster	Pin dragger	Stud-press operator	Pourer at holding furnace
Pin driver	Utility/Laborer	Carbon puller	

For each plant, data collection was carried out in two basic stages. The first of these was in the plant medical department and centred on the collection of data about the workers themselves. The second stage took place in the plant and revolved around the assessment of job demands.

Stage 1 – Medical department data

Upon arrival, each subject was given an overview of why he/she was being tested and what he/she was to expect. Next, the height, weight, sex and date of birth of each subject was recorded, along with his/her job title. Wet bulb globe temperature (WBGT) was also recorded at this time (barometric pressure was also noted). The data, as well as all other information about the subjects, were recorded on appropriate data collection forms. Physiological measures were obtained from each subject at rest, and while exercising on a step test (Figure 12.8) at workloads of $200\,\mathrm{kg\,m\,min^{-1}}$ and $300\,\mathrm{kg\,m\,min^{-1}}$, respectively. These measures include heart rate, oxygen consumption and ventilation rate.

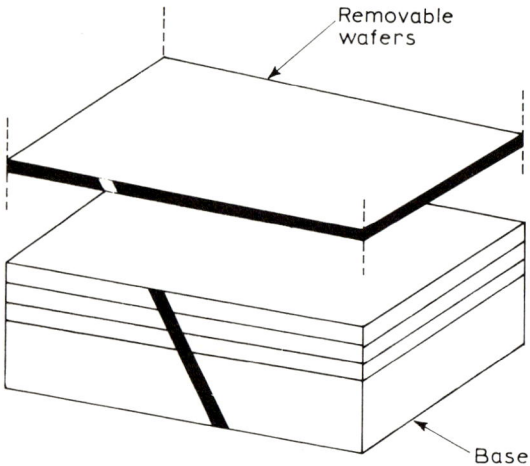

Figure 12.8 Illustration of the steptest

Oxygen consumption and ventilation rates were determined from gas analysis (expired air). Expired air was collected by using a combination of a face mask fitted with a one-way 'Y' valve (Koegel model), flexible hose, and a Douglas bag (Figure 12.9). For volume and oxygen concentration determination, a Beckman oxygen analyser (Model 0260), Max Plank gasometer, and Hewlett-Packard Pneumotachograph were utilised (see Figure 12.10).

During the pilot study, an attempt was made to use the OXYLOG (manufactured in England and commercially available) for gas collection and analysis. The OXYLOG is a small, lightweight unit that is easily carried by the subject. It is connected directly to a face mask (via hosing) and provides digital readings of oxygen consumption and ventilation rate. Unfortunately, after a few trial tests in the plants, the instrument was found to be unreliable, especially in the reduction environment.

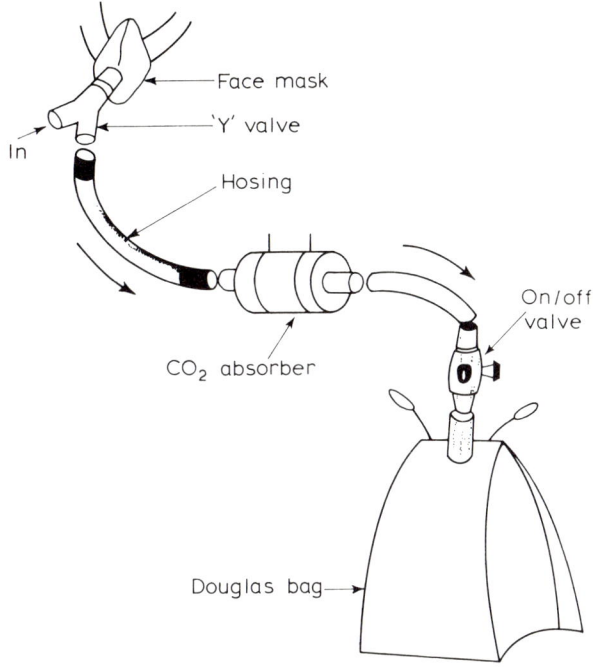

Figure 12.9 Illustration of the gas collection system

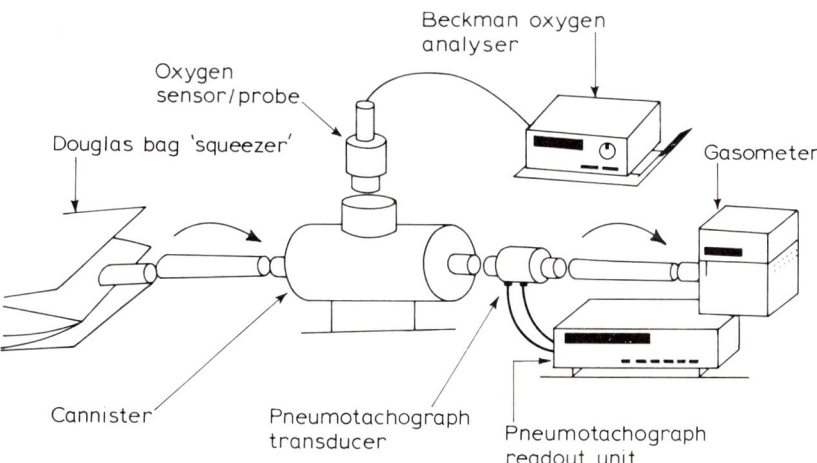

Figure 12.10 Illustration of the gas analysis system

EKG signals were picked up from subjects by three electrodes connected to disposable pads. From these electrodes, the signal was fed into a small unit containing an EKG amplifier and FM transmitter. The transmitter was wired directly to a mini-cassette tape recorder. Both the FM transmitter and taperecorder were placed in a small belt-pack worn by the worker (Figure 12.11). This set-up kept a record of the subject's EKG which could later be played back and analysed.

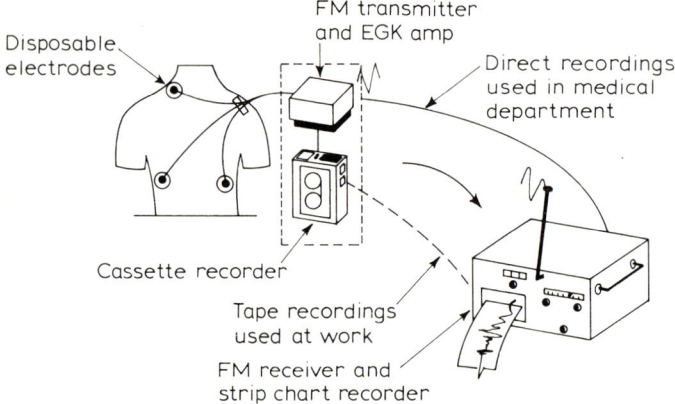

Figure 12.11 Wiring diagram for heart rate monitoring

For several reasons, it was important to assess the workers' perceptions of the physical demands of the jobs in their plants (to test the relationship between workers' perceptions of the job and actual job demands). For this purpose, workers were asked to rate the strenuousness of jobs in their plant in a pairwise fashion. Figure 12.12 shows the ranking of the jobs of the two plants in terms of the perceived difficulty.

Stage 2 – Plant data

Physiological measures were taken of workers while they performed their jobs in order to assess job demands. In addition, several workers were filmed as they worked on the more strenuous parts of their job cycle. The filmed data were used for biomechanical analysis of the jobs (i.e. determining the forces and work outputs required for each job).

The physiological measures collected at work included heart rate, oxygen consumption and ventilation rate. Where possible, data were collected for five minutes or more, and only after the worker had reached steady state. During gas collection, the Douglas bag was carried (on a back pack) by one of the investigators. This assured little interference with the subject performance.

Filming of workers was accomplished with a stereographic system consisting of two synchronised 8 mm movie cameras (Ayoub *et al.* 1970). Each job was monitored for approximately five minutes (this covered several cycles in most jobs; in all cases the most strenuous part of the job was recorded). Small buttons mounted on elastic straps were attached to

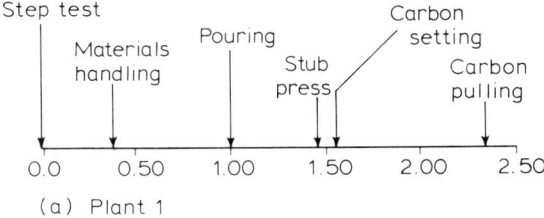

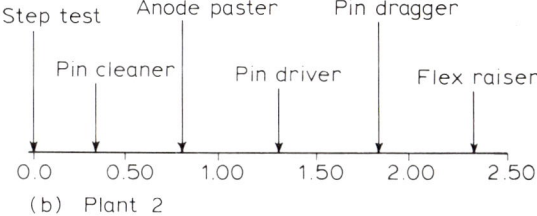

Figure 12.12 Scale of perceived job difficulty. (a) Plant 1, (b) Plant 2. The scales contain interval data only (not ratio). As such, scale values may not be taken as absolute; only differences between scale values are meaningful. In addition, the scales developed at both plants are independent, and bear no relation to each other; values cannot be compared between scales

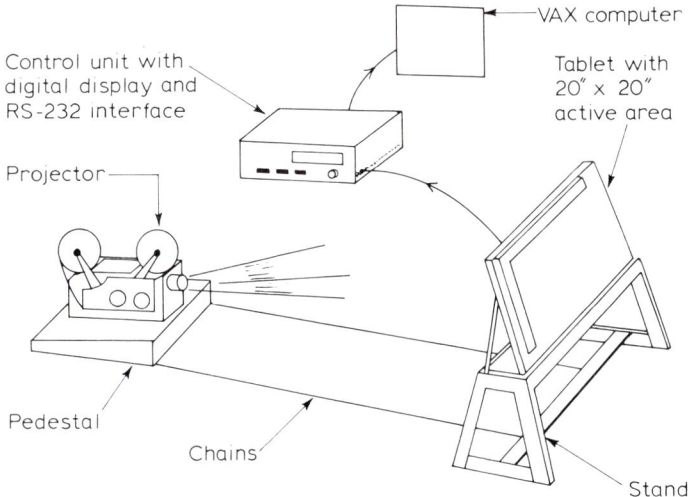

Figure 12.13 Illustration of the motion analysis system

wrist, elbow and shoulder joints to serve as markers. Pictures were taken with both cameras mounted on a specially constructed tripod. To analyse film data, a time-lapse projector (model 1100) and Graphpen digitiser (GP-6-30) were used (Figure 12.13). The output from the digitiser is sent to a DEC-VAX computer for storage and analysis; a sample output is given in Figure 12.14.

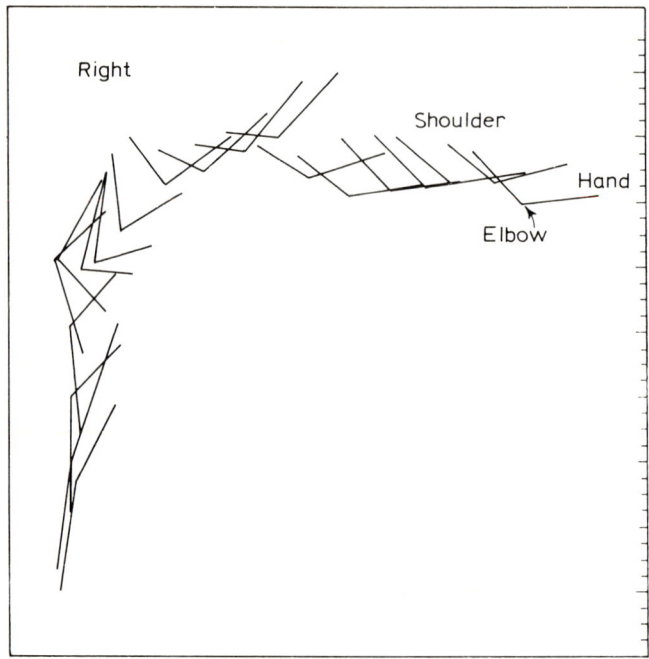

Figure 12.14 Paths of motion during the execution of anode pasting

Much equipment was required to carry out this study. Moreover, many of the items were delicate, and in some cases, had considerable bulk. For obvious reasons during recording in the plants, a cargo van was used to transport equipment and to hold the oxygen analysis apparatus. In addition, the van served as a preparation room for subjects (i.e., a place to hook up electrodes, etc.).

Assessment of strength

To assess the strength of each subject, a load cell mounted on an adjustable track, chain, bar and digital readout unit were used (Figure 12.15). The load cell is connected to a readout unit which displays the force in pounds. A peak hold feature may be adjusted to maintain the display for up to 30 s (30 s maximum decay time). The load cell used is manufactured by the Data Instruments Company (model JP) and the readout unit is an Inservco model M1411.

Implementation

If screening is to be based upon the concept of utilisation (both physical and physiological), both job demands and applicant work capacities must be known. The assessment (discussed in the preceding section) done for

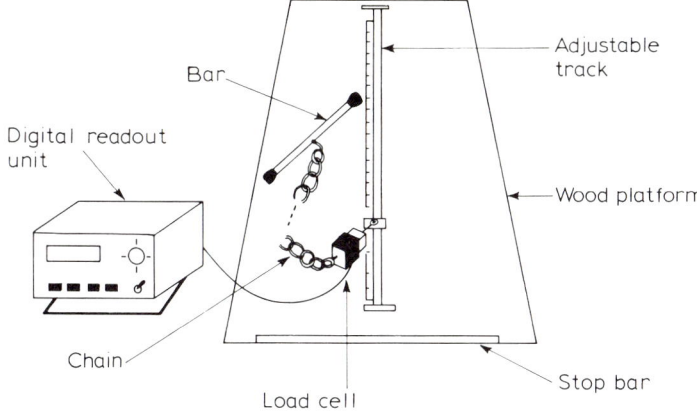

Figure 12.15 Illustration of strength testing apparatus

each job has provided detailed profiles of its demands. To have effective pre-employment screening, then, only the following steps remain

(1) establishing a methodology for assessing the physiological and physical capacities of each applicant
(2) projecting the physiological costs that applicants would pay if assigned to each job
(3) computing levels of utilisation for the cardiac and muscular systems
(4) accepting applicants whose levels of utilisation at work fall within safe limits and rejecting those whose levels of utilisation appear to constitute substantial risk.

Projecting the physiological (heart rate) cost of work

To project the cost that each applicant will pay for a given workload(s), it is necessary to obtain measures of heart rate at two different levels of output. Outputs of approximately 200 and 300 kg m min^{-1} are chosen for the reasons cited previously. Similarly, a step test with adjustable height was selected as the 'exercise tool'.

Establishing job demands – work output

Plant 1

Jobs examined at this facility fall into two broad classes – those in the potroom and those in pin cleaning. Screening for potroom work must be based on the highest demand job(s) found within. From the analyses done in this study, an output requirement of 500 kg m min^{-1} has been defined for the potroom. If applicants are screened using this criterion (500 kg m min^{-1}), they should be capable of performing all jobs found in the potroom. Additional data in support of using a 500 kg m min^{-1} work output as a basis for potroom screening come from the biomechanical analysis performed (see Table 12.3).

Table 12.3 *Job demands at plant 1*

A. Torque and work output demands of each job as determined by dynamic analysis

| Job | Torque | | | Work output (kg m min^{-1}) |
	Average	Maximum	Location	
Pin dragging	7.94	20.97	Hip joint	597.0
Flex raising	11.97	19.56	Hip joint	450.6
Pin driving	1.29	2.84	Shoulder joint	331.2
Pin cleaning	3.51	8.64	Hip joint	310.8
Anode pasting	0.97	2.43	Shoulder joint	75.1*

* This assessment of output is based exclusively on the 'door raising' phase of the job cycle

B. Strength demands of each job as determined by dynamic analysis

| Job | Strength demand Back reference posture | Strength |
	Average	Maximum
Pin dragging*	53.05	140.12
Flex raising*	83.33	136.17
Pin driving**	23.66	52.08
Pin cleaning*	25.32	52.33
Anode pasting**	16.93	42.42

 * Based on back torque
** Based on shoulder torque

The given workloads do not reflect the effect of thermal stress. It is realised, however, that heat as well as work output contributes to total workload (job demand). The effect of heat is to elevate heart rate, with increases in the range of 1 bpm per 1°C expected (for temperatures ranging from 25–45°c (77–113°F). Oxygen consumption, on the other hand, is not affected. In the screening procedure developed, 10 bpm are added to the predicted heart rate of each applicant to adjust for heat. This allows the applicant's utilisation level to be assessed for work in a 35°C environment. Although temperatures *may* reach levels above 35°C in the summer months, an adjustment of greater than 10 bpm is not justified based on the data presently available.

Plant 2

Jobs at this facility fall into three broad classes – those in the potroom, those in the case house and those in the carbon plant. The procedure followed in determining job demands was essentially the same as that used at Plant 1. The job demands for work output suggested for use in screening are 500 kg m min^{-1} for the potroom and carbon plant; 400 kg m min^{-1} for the cast house.

Strength demands

The strength requirements for each job were determined on the basis of the biomechanical analyses performed. Briefly, from the torque profiles of each articulation joint, a determination was made of the equivalent forces required from a person in a standard posture. The demands suggested for screening are as follows: arm strength = 40 lbs; back strength = 80 lbs; leg strength = not significant in the execution of these jobs. These demand values are essentially the same for both plants.

Establishing cut-offs

Applicants are selected or rejected on the basis of ability to perform work without overly taxing their bodies. That is, applicants are chosen only when their levels of utilisation are at or below certain critical values (or 'cut-offs').

Work output

Ability of applicants to meet work output requirements safely is based on level of cardiac (heart rate) utilisation. The cut-off value employed is 75%; applicants falling below 75% are accepted, those between 75% and 80% are classified as 'marginal', and those above 80% are unacceptable. Marginal individuals are given the benefit of possible 'measurement error' and are scheduled for re-testing at a later date.

The screening steps detailed above have been summarised and presented in a manual to be used by the medical personnel. Typically, an applicant can be tested and classified (i.e. acceptable, unacceptable or marginal) in about an hour. In classifying an applicant, a set of charts can be used to

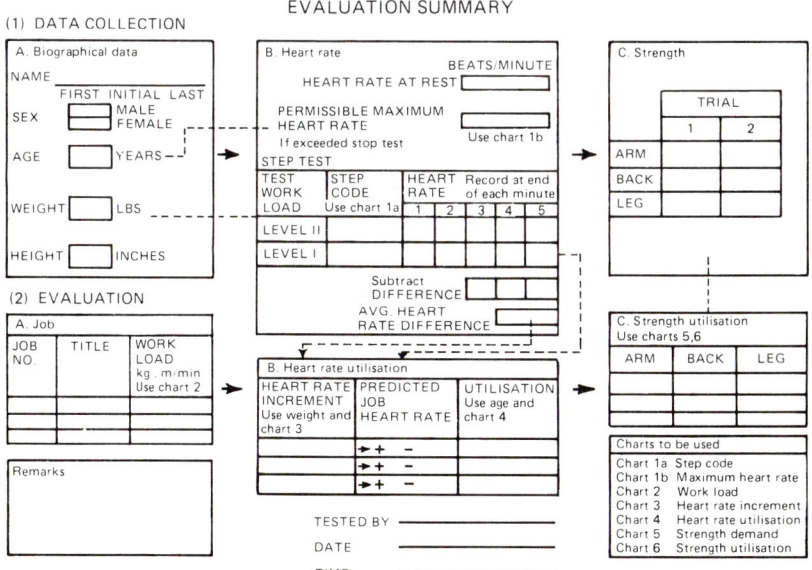

Figure 12.16 Chart used to record test results

determine levels of utilisation for both strength and heart rate. The form used for collecting test data and results is shown in Figure 12.16. Figures 12.17 and 12.18 show a sample of the charts used for determining heart rate utilisation. A large body of literature is available in support of these cut-off values (Astrand 1960; Micheal *et al.* 1961).

The ability of applicants to meet the torque requirements of work safely is assessed through strength utilisation. The cut-off employed in this program is 50%; applicants falling below 50% are acceptable, those between 50% and 60% 'marginal', and those above 60% are unacceptable. In contrast to applicants labelled as marginal due to heart rate, those falling in this class on the basis of strength may still be accepted for employment on a conditional basis.

The area of 'safe lifting limits' has been the subject of numerous studies over the years. The particular percentage of capacity which is reported as 'safe' has been largely a function of the methodology used in determining demands. When static weights have been used in determining demands, limits as low as 20% have been reported as necessary reliably to prevent injury (Herrin and Chaffin 1978). Researchers who have considered dynamic aspects of the lift (motions), however, support using criteria in the neighbourhood of 50% (Chaffin *et al.* 1977a). This difference suggests an additional 'margin of safety' which is needed to protect against the dynamics of a true lifting situation. In this study, a full fledged dynamic analysis has been performed and peak forces (torques) identified. As such, there is no need for a large 'margin of safety' and 50% has been selected for the cut-off.

Conclusions

This study has provided a detailed examination of a set of jobs and workers who perform them in an aluminium reduction plant. Jobs were analysed for work output and torque requirements. Workers' capacities for both physiological (energy expenditure) and physical work (strength) were assessed. From this study, the following conclusions can be supported.

(1) Job demands for work output can be assessed using both the physiological and biomechanical approaches. Each of these methods has its own advantages and disadvantages.

(2) The work outputs extrapolated from oxygen consumption and ventilation rate are highly similar. This justifies the use of ventilation rate as a basis for predicting work output.

(3) The capacities which an individual has for both physiological and physical characteristics. Some assessment of physiological function is necessary.

(4) The assessment of human strength (static) is a highly reliable procedure.

(5) Biomechanical analysis of the motions involved in work can be used to determine the strength demands of that job.

(6) Maximal capacities for heart rate, oxygen consumption and work output can be projected based on regression functions and extrapolation procedures.

Predicted job heart rate

Weight (lbs)

| Job workload 500 |
| weight 100–204 |

Difference between step test heart rates	100-3	104-7	108-11	112-5	116-20	121-4	125-9	130-4	135-9	140-4	144-7	148-52	153-7	158-61	162-5	166-9	170-3	174-7	178-82	183-7	188-92	193-6	197-200	201-4
5	28	27	26	25	24	25	24	23	22	22	21	22	22	27	26	25	25	24	24	23	22	24	24	24
6	32	31	30	28	27	28	27	26	25	24	24	25	24	30	29	29	28	27	26	26	25	27	27	26
7	36	34	33	32	30	31	30	28	27	27	26	27	26	33	33	32	31	30	29	28	27	30	30	29
8	39	38	36	35	33	34	33	31	30	29	28	30	29	37	36	35	34	33	32	31	30	33	32	32
9	43	41	39	38	36	37	35	34	32	31	30	32	31	40	39	38	37	36	35	33	32	36	35	34
10	47	45	43	41	39	40	38	36	35	34	33	35	33	44	42	41	40	39	37	36	35	39	38	37
11	51	48	46	44	41	43	41	39	37	36	35	37	36	47	45	44	43	41	40	39	37	42	41	40
12	54	52	49	47	44	46	44	42	40	36	37	39	38	50	49	47	46	44	43	41	40	45	43	42
13	58	55	52	50	47	49	47	44	42	41	39	42	40	54	52	50	49	47	45	44	42	47	46	45
14	62	58	56	53	50	52	49	47	45	43	42	44	43	57	55	53	52	50	48	46	45	50	49	48
15	65	62	59	56	53	55	52	50	47	45	44	47	45	60	58	56	55	53	51	49	47	53	52	51
16	69	65	62	59	56	58	55	52	50	48	46	49	47	64	62	60	58	56	54	51	50	56	55	53
17	73	69	65	62	59	61	58	55	52	50	48	52	50	67	65	63	61	59	56	54	52	59	57	56
18	76	72	69	65	61	64	61	58	55	53	51	54	52	70	68	66	64	61	59	57	54	62	60	59
19	80	76	72	68	64	67	63	60	57	55	53	57	54	74	71	69	67	64	62	59	57	65	63	61
20	84	79	75	71	67	70	66	63	60	57	55	59	57	77	74	72	69	67	64	62	59	68	66	64
21	87	83	78	75	70	73	69	65	62	60	57	62	59	80	78	75	72	70	67	64	62	70	69	67
22	91	86	82	78	73	76	72	68	65	62	60	64	61	84	81	78	75	73	70	67	64	73	71	69
23	95	90	85	81	76	79	75	71	67	64	62	66	64	87	84	81	78	76	73	70	67	76	74	72
24	98	93	88	84	79	82	78	73	70	67	64	69	66	91	87	84	81	79	75	72	69	79	77	75
25	102	97	92	87	81	85	80	76	72	69	66	71	68	94	91	87	84	81	78	75	72	82	80	78
26	106	100	95	90	84	88	83	79	75	71	69	74	71	97	94	90	87	84	81	77	74	85	82	80
27	109	104	98	93	87	91	86	81	77	74	71	76	73	101	97	94	90	87	84	80	77	88	85	83
28	113	107	101	96	90	94	89	84	80	76	73	79	75	104	100	97	93	90	86	83	79	91	88	86

Figure 12.17 Illustration of the chart used for predicting heart rate increment. The heart rate increment for a person weighing 179 pounds and having a 12 bpm difference between high and low levels of the step test is 43 bpm

Chart 4

Heart rate utilisation as a function of age and workload

Age (years)

Predicted job heart rate	19	21-22	24-25	27-28	30-31	33-34	36-37	39-40	42-43	45-46	48-49	51-52	54-55	57-58	60-61	63-64	66
100 101	51	52	52	53	53	54	54	55	55	56	57	57	58	59	59	60	
102 103	52	53	53	54	54	55	55	56	57	57	58	58	59	60	60	61	
104 105	53	54	54	55	55	56	56	57	58	58	59	60	60	61	62	62	
106 107	54	55	55	56	56	57	57	58	59	59	60	61	61	62	63	63	
108 109	55	56	56	57	57	58	59	59	60	60	61	62	62	63	64	65	
110 111	56	57	57	58	58	59	60	60	61	62	62	63	64	64	65	66	
112 113	57	58	58	59	59	60	61	61	62	63	63	64	65	66	66	67	
114 115	58	59	59	60	61	61	62	62	63	64	65	65	66	67	67	68	
116 117	59	60	60	61	62	62	63	64	64	65	66	66	67	68	69	69	
118 119	60	61	61	62	63	63	64	65	65	66	67	68	68	69	70	71	
120 121	61	62	62	63	64	64	65	66	66	67	68	69	69	70	71	72	
122 123	62	63	63	64	65	65	66	67	68	68	69	70	71	71	72	73	
124 125	63	64	64	65	66	66	67	68	69	69	70	71	72	73	73	74	
126 127	64	65	66	66	67	68	68	69	70	70	71	72	73	74	75	75	
128 129	65	66	67	67	68	69	69	70	71	72	72	73	74	75	76	77	
130 131	66	67	68	68	69	70	70	71	72	73	74	74	75	76	77	78	
132 133	67	68	69	69	70	71	72	72	73	74	75	75	76	77	78	79	
134 135	68	69	70	70	71	72	73	73	74	75	76	77	77	78	79	80	

Figure 12.18 Illustration of the chart used for assessing heart rate utilisation. From Figure 12.17, the heart rate increment is 43 bpm. Adding this increment to the heart rate obtained at the low level of the step test, we obtain the predicted job heart rate. For this example, job heart rate is 116 (i.e. the sum of 73 and 43)

(7) When job demands and human work capacity are expressed in terms of a common unit, both physiological and physical utilisations can be expressed for the individual at work. Further, utilisation is a valid index of the degree to which that individual will be 'taxed' by the job.

Reynolds has instituted the screening program at both plants. So far more than 70 applicants have been tested. Initial screening results and feedback from the plants are positive and very supportive of the design and architecture of the program.

In sum, the approach offered towards the design and implementation of pre-employment screening programs is different from available approaches in the following respects.

(1) It is integrative in nature, for it considers all aspects of physical and physiological characteristics of human work capacity.
(2) It is suitable for dealing with jobs characterised with brief exertions as well as sustained performance. Strength capability would be the critical capacity dimension for short/discrete jobs, while physiological attributes would be the limiting criteria for sustained performance.
(3) It remains simple to implement and to maintain. Further, its tests and interpretation of their results are straightforward and can be mastered with a minimum of training.

References

ASTRAND, I. (1960). 'Aerobic work capacity in men and women with special reference to age', *Acta Physiologica Scandinavica*, **49**, Supplement 169.

AYOUB, M. A. (1971). *A Biomechanical Model for the Upper Extremity Using Optimization Techniques*, unpublished doctoral dissertation, Texas Tech. University.

AYOUB, M. A. (1979). *Control of Manual Lifting Hazards Through Employee Training, Selection, and Placement*, Technical Report, Industrial Engineering Department, North Carolina State University, Raleigh, North Carolina.

AYOUB, M. A. (1980). 'An ergonomic approach for the design of preemployment screening and selection programs', *Proceedings – 1980 Spring Annual Conference*, American Institute of Industrial Engineers.

AYOUB, M. A. *et al.* (1970). 'A stereometric system for measuring human motion', *Human Factors*, **12**, No. 6, 523–535.

AYOUB, M. A. & ELSHAFEI, A. N. (1974). *Manual Materials Handling (Lifting): Optimization Models for Allocation of Resources and Assessment of Work Capacity* (OR Report No. 94), Graduate Program in Operations Research, North Carolina State University, Raleigh, North Carolina.

AYOUB, M. M. (1972). 'Human movement recording for biomechanical analysis', *Int. J. Production Res.*, **10**, No. 1 35–51.

AYOUB, M. M. *et al.* (1978). 'Modelling of lifting capacity as a function of operator task variables', (in *Safety in Manual Materials Handling*, Drury, C. G. (ed.)) National Institute for Occupational Safety and Health, DHEW(NIOSH) Publication No. 78–185, 120–130.

BROUHA, L. (1980). *Physiology in Industry: Evaluation of Industrial Stresses by the Physiological Reactions of the Worker*, Pergamon Press, Oxford.

BUSKIRK, E. R. *et al.* (1977). *Measurement of Work Metabolism*, National Institute of Occupational Safety and Health, DHEW(NIOSH), Cincinnati Publication No. 77–163.

CHAFFIN, D. B. *et al.* (1978). 'Pre-employment strength testing – an updated position', *J. Occupational Med.*, **20**, No. 6, 403–408.

CHAFFIN, D. B. *et al.* (1977a). *Pre-employment Strength Testing*, National Institute of Occupational Safety and Health, DHEW(NIOSH), Cincinnati Publication No. 77-163.

CHAFFIN, D. B. *et al.* (1977b). 'A method for evaluating the biomechanical stresses resulting from manual materials handling jobs', *Am. Ind. Hygiene Ass. J.*, **38**, 662-675.

DATTA, S. R. & RAMANATHAN, N. L. (1969). 'Energy expenditure in work predicted from heart rate and pulmonary ventilation', *J. Appl. Physio.*, **26**, No. 3, 297-302.

DURNIN, J. & PASSMORE, R. (1967). *Energy, Work and Leisure*, William Heinemann, Ltd, London.

GRUVER, W. A. *et al.* (1979). 'A model for optimal evaluation of manual lifting tasks', *J. Safety Res.*, **11**, No. 2 61-71.

HANDLEY, W. (ed.). (1977). *Industrial Safety Handbook*, (2nd Edition), McGraw-Hill Book Company, London.

HERRIN, G. D. (1978). 'A taxonomy of manual materials handling hazards', (in *Safety in Manual Materials Handling*, Drury, C. G. (ed.)), National Institute for Occupational Safety and Health, DHEW(NIOSH) Publication No. 78-185, 63-67.

HERRIN, G. D. & CHAFFIN, D. B. (1978). 'Effectiveness of strength testing for manula materials handling jobs', *Professional Safety*, (July), 39-43.

IKAI, M. & STEIHAUS, A. H. (1961). 'Some factors modifying the expression of human strength', *J. Appl. Physiol.*, **16**, No. 1, 157-163.

INTERNATIONAL LABOR ORGANIZATION. (1964). *Maximum Permissible Weight to be Carried by One Worker*, Occupational and Health Series No. 5, International Labor Office, Geneva, Switzerland.

INTERNATIONAL LABOR ORGANIZATION. (1967). *Maximum Weight Recommendation*, Occupational and Health Series No. 128, International Labor Office, Geneva, Switzerland.

JONES, N. L. *et al.* (1975). *Clinical Exercise Testing*, W. B. Saunders Co., Philadelphia.

KROEMER, K. (1970). 'Human strength: terminology, measurement and interpretation of data', *Human Factors*, **12**, No. 3, 297-313.

KROEMER, K. (1978). *The Assessment of Human Strength, Safety in Manual Materials Handling*, National Institute for Occupational Safety and Health, DHEW(NIOSH), Cincinnati Publication No. 78-185, 39-45.

LAUBACH, L. (1978). 'Human muscular strength', (in *Anthropometric Source Book Volume I: Anthropometry for Designers*), NASA Reference Publication 1024.

LINCOLN, T. (1968). 'The role of the occupational physician in the evaluation of applicants fo employment', *Southern Med. J.*, **61**, 359-362.

MICHEAL, E. D. *et al.* (1961). 'Cardiorespiratory responses during prolonged exercise', *J. Appl. Physiol.*, **16**, 997-1000.

MONTGOMERY, C. (1976). 'Pre-employment back X-rays', *J. Occupational Med.*, **18**, No. 7.

PASSMORE, R. & DURNIN, J. (1955). 'Human energy expenditure', *Physiol. rev.*, **35**, 801-840.

PRESENT, A. J. (1974). 'Radiography of the lower back in pre-employment physical examinations', *Radiology*, **112**, 229-230.

SNOOK, S. H. (1978). 'Psychophysiological indices – what people will do', (in *Safety in Manual Materials Handling*, Drury, C. G. (ed.)), National Institute for Occupational Safety and Health, DHEW(NIOSH) Publication No. 78-185, 63-67.

SNOOK, S. H. *et al.* (1978). 'Three preventive approaches to low back injury', *Professional Safety*, (July), 34-38.

STRAUB, G. F. (1923). 'The diagnosis of conditions causing backache', *J. Am. Med. Ass.*, **80**, 674-678.

SWENTON–WALL, P. (1980). *Evaluation of Physiological Job Demands in an Aluminium Reduction Plant*, Unpublished Masters Dissertation, North Carolina State University.

TICHAUER, E. R. (1978). *The Biomechanical Basis of Ergonomics*, John Wiley & Sons, New York.

WASSERMAN, K. & WHIPP, B. (1975). 'Exercise physiology in health and disease', *Am. Rev. Respiratory Disease*, **112**, No. 2, 219-249.

WEINER, J. & LOURIE, J. (1969). *Human Biology: A Guide to Field Methods*, F. A. Davis, Philadephia.

Chapter 13

The design of an accident investigation procedure

M. Edwards

Introduction

There is evident disagreement among ergonomists concerning the success with which ergonomics has been applied to real world problems (see Kvålseth 1980). This disagreement may, to some extent, be an artefact of geography since some countries appear to accept ergonomics more readily than do others. However, an additional explanation is ventured here. Application seems to be most straightforward in those instances where the ergonomist and his collaborator (engineer, designer, manager) share the same conceptual framework. Such applications are typically concerned with the design of individual items of hardware (consumer products, seating), with physical workload, or with the specification of physical environments (noise levels, thermal comfort zones). In general, the ergonomics requirements in these cases may be stipulated fairly simply and often in terms which are familiar to or analogous with those used by engineers.

Ergonomics application is attempted using methods broadly comparable with those of the physical sciences where data collected in the laboratory may be applied directly to the problem. Measurable physical and physiological characteristics are the focus of attention and the underlying model of man is mechanistic and reactive. Whether or not this approach is valid, its congruence with that of the engineer is apparent and serves to foster the application of ergonomics. This type of application lends itself to the compilation of ergonomics manuals and checklists for use by engineers and designers without the need for intervention by the ergonomist.

It is more difficult to effect application where there is no identity of orientation between the ergonomist and his collaborator. The centrality of man in the system is fundamental to the ergonomist but this perception is not shared by the engineer for whom the machine is paramount. Gagné (1962) has pointed out that 'system developers have been known to take the view that if only the hardware subsystem can be made to run, somehow human beings with proper characteristics will be found and "fitted into" the system'. The areas where there is no shared conceptual framework are typically concerned with man as an information processor, either through

186

the medium of hardware (consoles etc.) or directly from software (instructions, maps, manuals). Analyses of such problems are not easily expressed in ways immediately appealing to engineers.

The complex determinants of human response and the characteristically active and interactive nature of man's intercourse with his environment render invalid the direct application of laboratory findings to these problems (Chapanis 1976). They are not soluble by routine application of checklists but require an informed evaluation of all the relevant factors in the situation. This approach and the model of man on which it is based are not readily recognisable by the engineer. Thus the difficulties of implementing ergonomics solutions, or even of studying the ergonomics problems, hinge on the difference in orientation between the ergonomist and his potential clients. A modification of the orientation of the engineer away from the centrality of the machine to an appreciation of the centrality of man is a prior condition of the application of ergonomics in these areas.

The relationship between the ergonomist and his collaborators will also be affected by the source of the initiation of the project. Broadly, it is possible to distinguish between an ergonomist who has been engaged by a client to advise on a particular problem, and one who is seeking a fieldwork site in which to conduct a programme of research. The present study falls into the latter category.

Access to the organisations

A research proposal from a University was accepted by a funding body. The aim of the research programme was to design a procedure for use in industry for the investigation and reporting of industrial accidents which would attempt to account for human error. After the award of the research grant, approaches were made to two industrial companies with a view to obtaining their cooperation in the research programme. In each case, requests were directed to particular individuals who were already known to the University, namely the Chief Safety Officer of company A and the Chief Medical Officer of company B. Whilst these individuals could not themselves authorise access to the companies, they were in a position to exercise their not inconsiderable influence on those who could. Their willingness to do so depended on the conviction that their company would gain, or at least not lose, by involvement in the project. The nature of the funding body and its relevance to the topic of the proposed study prompted the Chief Safety Officer to agree to direct the request through the appropriate channels. In the case of the Chief Medical Officer, this factor, together with a conviction that human error was too often overlooked, appeared to have a bearing on his agreement to pursue the question of access.

The individual through whom access to a research site is achieved may have a significant effect on the course of the research programme. The contacts available to the researcher will be to some extent determined by his 'sponsor' and the investigation perceived as within the purview of that sponsor. This may have attendant advantages and disadvantages.

The present study consisted of four related activities. These were

the study of the accident reporting systems in operation in the companies,
the design of procedures utilising an ergonomics perspective for the investigation and reporting of industrial accidents,
the use of these procedures by relevant personnel within the companies,
an evaluation of the procedures.

Cooperation from the companies was essential for the first and third of these and desirable for the fourth.

Obtaining facilities for the study of the accident reporting system was easier in company A than in company B, while cooperation in the use of the procedures was achieved more quickly in company B than in company A. Possible explanations for this may be found in the differing concepts of research held by the two companies and in particular by the sponsors. The study of the system demanded little from the company, involving as it did only a passive involvement in the project and it also appeared to match the perceptions of the sponsor of company A of research as equivalent to carrying out a survey. Experience of research students from a variety of disciplines (mainly engineering) had sensitised the sponsor in company B to expect the presentation of a formal programme of activities from the research worker and thus agreement to provide access was by inference a commitment to participate in the programme.

Additionally, the institutional status of the sponsor in company B was greater than that of the sponsor in company A and his position in the hierarchy of the company at large was an influential factor.

The study of the accident reporting systems

The study of the accident reporting systems was set in the context of a study of the total safety systems operating in the companies. This included, for example, safety sampling, safety training, safety committees and accident review. The flow of information about injuries and accidents was charted; location of decision points in the system noted; key roles identified. The characteristics of the accident information and the structure of the taxonomies used to classify accidents were examined. The only difficulty in carrying out this part of the study was met in company A where it proved impossible to obtain agreement to interview the safety representatives (who are also trade union shop stewards). It was possible, however, to observe them in operation at meetings of the Safety Committees.

The major findings from the first part of the study are concerned with information display, taxonomy and the underlying model of accident causation which informed the thinking about industrial accidents at all levels of both companies.

A display is evaluated in terms of the extent to which it fulfils its function. Accident information is collected for a number of disparate reasons (to satisfy insurance companies, to comply with the law) but the objective with which this study was concerned was the collection of accident information as a basis for accident control. A list of up to 50 minor injuries stating name of injured person, injury and 'cause' does not convey information in a form where it is meaningful as a basis for decision. Narrative reports compiled by supervisors about lost time accidents varied along the dimensions of comprehensiveness, comprehensibility and legibility. Perhaps this is not unexpected in the absence of formal training for accident reporting and where no framework is provided for recording the essential features of the event.

The major classification of injury accidents in industry is in terms of the consequent absence from work of the injured person. This is a function of the legal requirement to report to a statutory body any accidents that result in the loss of three consecutive days work. The distinction between lost time accidents and minor injuries has its origins in an attempt to quantify injury severity in an unambiguous way. However, it is apparent that the relationship between injury severity and lost time (except in the case of a small number of traumatic injuries) has now broken down. The statistic of lost time accidents is more likely to reflect the influence of social and economic factors.

A dysfunctional consequence for safety of the breakdown of the distinction in terms of absence from work between serious and minor injuries is the tendency to focus investigation on one class of events not because of their intrinsic safety aspects but because of their statutory implications. It also has the effect of causing resentment among safety officers at the requirement to report to an outside body events which they consider to be trivial.

Minor injuries had been classified according to type of injury in company B. No classification of these events was attempted in company A. Lost time accidents were classified at each company. The taxonomies in use illustrated the difficulties associated with the necessity to classify events having nothing in common except their outcome, i.e. injury. The classification systems used comprised categories which were not logically compatible ('type' of accident including the activities of the injured person and the agents of injury) nor were they mutually exclusive ('working conditions' including 'ineffective light, heat and ventilation, slippy, etc. (sic!) floors' which may in fact be due to 'design and layout' which includes 'faulty design' or to 'construction' which includes 'faulty construction' or to 'direct supervision' which includes 'bad housekeeping').

Perhaps the most important finding was the model of accident causation that informed all discussion and action concerning accidents in both companies and among all personnel. This model is characterised by an emphasis on culpable human error, a view of accidents as arbitrary events having only a tenuous connection with other aspects of the work situation, a legalistic orientation and a concept of safety as a separate, optional, extra.

Culpable human error was seen as a major causative factor in accidents. Recorded preventive action by supervisors was most often of the kind 'told him to be more careful'; chairmen of safety committees (senior managers) expressed the view 'if we take care, we can avoid accidents'; safety personnel urged greater 'self discipline' to avoid the 'bulk of the accidents'. When causes other than culpable human error were sought, these were most often proximate factors, close to the accident in time and space. This had the effect of restricting preventive measures to these localised factors, emphasising the arbitrariness of the event rather than seeking the underlying causes. For example, a pool of spilled oil is identified as the cause, and prevention is equated with cleaning up the oil. The rectification of the final precipitating factor in an accident situation is likely to have limited value, and appeals to exercise greater care may be irrelevant if the apparent carelessness is more appropriately ascribed to sub-optimal machine design or to inadequate training procedures.

A number of factors combine to emphasise the legal aspects of accidents, with dysfunctional consequences for safety. The statutory framework within which accident reporting is embedded and which determines the activities consequent upon the incidence of lost time accidents has been alluded to above. The requirement to report these accidents to an outside body engenders defensiveness among safety personnel who perceive them as a 'black mark against the company'. This feeling of defensiveness is compounded if the injury is considered by them not to warrant the loss of working time.

Feelings of defensiveness may also arise if accidental injury becomes the subject of litigation in pursuit of a claim for compensation. The view has been expressed that the number of claims for compensation for industrial injury has increased in recent years largely as a result of the activities of the safety representatives which, it is felt by safety officers, diminish the possibility of carrying out an objective investigation into the circumstances of accidents. Frankness is not expected of the injured person in this situation, particularly if the safety representative is thought to have 'got to him first'. The requirement to disclose in court all documentation associated with the accident serves further to inhibit objective reporting. These postures are not confined to accidents which are the subject of litigation but are generalised to accidents as a whole. Under these circumstances, the clerical tasks of completing forms may become a substitute for active accident investigation, since they have in any case a certain priority by virtue of the statutory requirements which they satisfy.

There is a tendency to view safety as a separate and separable aspect of system function. This view is manifested in the separate provision of safety training in the induction training of new operatives; by the necessity to add guards to machines after they have been delivered rather than have them designed with safety as an integral component; by the conflict between safety needs and the maintenance of production levels (evident in the difficulties of scheduling statutory inspections); by the removal of guards by operatives who find them detrimental to high output. This leads to a

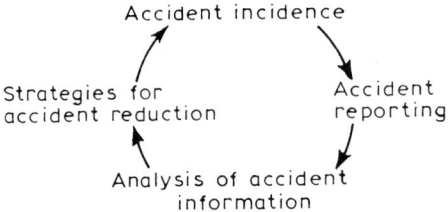

Figure 13.1 Accident reduction system

concept of safety as an optional extra added willingly by good management as evidence of benevolence and reluctantly by poor management in order to comply with the law.

An accident reduction system depends for its effectiveness on the operation of a feedback loop which controls the input to the system (Figure 13.1). Accident information was not being used, nor in many cases was it of sufficient quality to be used, for this purpose. Action to reduce accidents was *ad hoc*, based on an intuitive understanding of the hazards. The lack of good quality information prevented the development of empirically grounded safety policies, and also their evaluation.

The analysis of the safety system thus indicated two sets of problems. These were the culpable error model of accident causation and deficiencies in the accident information. The major disadvantage of the culpable error model is its limitations for developing strategies for accident reduction. What is required is a model which admits the complexity of accident causation but at the same time allows the development and operationalisation of effective strategies of accident reduction. Such a model is described below.

The system model

The *system model* of accident causation conceptualises accidents as symptoms of system failure. The appropriate study of these symptoms will pinpoint problem areas and indicate the kind of action required to correct the malfunction in the situation. This approach is based on the premise that what people do in a work situation is determined not only by their own capabilities and limitations but also by the machines they work with, the rules and procedures, both formal and informal, which govern their activities and the total environment within which these activities take place, i.e. the physical and social environments. The system (Figure 13.2)

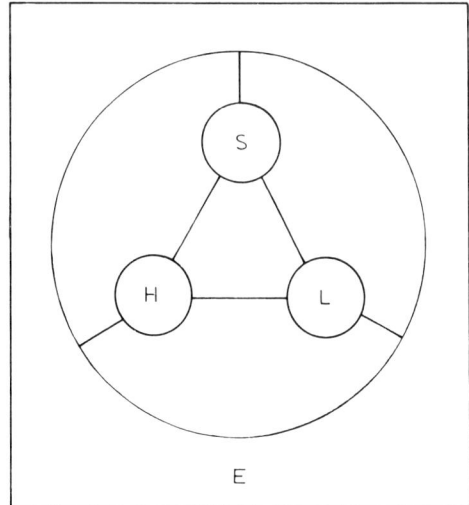

Figure 13.2 The SHEL system

made up of these elements, namely man (Liveware), machine (Hardware), rules and procedures (Software) and the physical and social environment (Environment) has been called the SHEL system (Edwards 1972).

The elements in the SHEL system are richly interactive. For example, machinery (H) designed for use on earth may require considerable adaptation for use in space or under the sea (E); i.e. the environment and hardware must be compatible. Training procedures (S) effective with young people (L) may be inappropriate for older workers (L). Machines (H) designed to operate on one voltage will not interface with machines (H) designed to operate on a different voltage. Of all the possible interactions between these system elements, it is mainly the ones involving the liveware, the people in the system, that are most relevant to the consideration of accidents. These occur at the man–machine (L–H), man–procedures (L–S), man–environment (L–E) and man–man (L–L) interfaces.

System failure may be due to failure in any one of the single elements in the system: a person may collapse without warning with catastrophic consequences for the system. More typically, however, system failure occurs because there is a mismatch at an interface between different system elements. Accidents as symptoms of system failure provide clues about the location of the source of failure, indicating where mismatches occur and consequently what action may be taken to reduce the mismatch.

It is clear that there are major differences between the system model and that based upon culpable human error. The concept of culpability has no place in the system model; safety is not a separate entity but the consequence of the optimal operation of the system; the distinction between accidents in terms of their outcome (absence from work, extent of injury) are no longer relevant and the system concept fosters the consideration of a multi-casual explanation ranging far beyond the obvious proximate factors.

The development of the procedures

The development of the procedures for accident investigation and reporting was based on the system model described above. It was recognised at the outset, however, that the number of questions that might be asked about an incident is far greater than that which might be included in an accident investigation instrument. Indeed, it is impossible to define a set of procedures for an activity, which, like all problem solving, is essentially a creative process. The aim was to provide a framework within which the relevant areas might be covered, albeit cursorily, and to reorient those involved in accident investigation to a different and more fruitful concept of accident causation.

Ideally, the incidents for which information should be collected include all injury and damage accidents, as these represent deviations from acceptable system performance. Initially, however, the procedures were designed for the investigation and reporting of injury accidents, with the aim of collecting information systematically about all injuries reported to the Medical Department, whether or not they subsequently became lost time accidents, such that each incident could be investigated thoroughly with all the incident reports comparable along the dimensions of the system model in order that patterns of system failure might be detected.

While the safety officer is concerned primarily with the investigation of lost time accidents, the supervisor has the responsibility to investigate all the minor injuries that are reported and to carry out the initial investigation of the lost time accidents. It seemed appropriate, therefore, to design procedures for use by supervisors to investigate all the injury accidents taking place within their areas. A questionnaire was prepared consisting of questions covering such areas as liveware factors (including training and experience, use of protective clothing, presence of distraction or stress) liveware–environment interface factors; liveware–hardware interface factors and liveware–software interface factors.

Negotiations for the use of the procedures

The two companies reacted differently to the proposal that company personnel should use these procedures in the investigation of accidents.

The Chief Safety Officer in company A had involved four safety officers, each responsible for a division of the company, in the first stage of the project. The initial meeting with the four safety officers to discuss the system model and the use of the questionnaire resulted in their insistence that unless the size of the questionnaire could be reduced to fit on one side of a page of A4 and some questions requiring 'subjective' responses were removed, there was no possibility that the instrument would be accepted by management or supervision. As to the SHEL model, they considered that it described accurately their current approach to accident investigation.

The questionnaire was redesigned by retaining the four areas of interest but reducing significantly the number of questions in each area. Supporting documentation was designed such that the procedures included, in addition to the questionnaire for recording the investigation of the accident, a coding frame, a scoring sheet for summating the results of a set of accident reports and a summary sheet intended for circulation at safety committee meetings to replace the exhaustive and unsystematic lists of name, number, injury and 'cause' which had formed the basis of the safety committee's discussion of minor injuries.

The questions regarded as unacceptable by the safety officers may be classified into two categories, namely those concerned with the individual and those concerned with the working environment. Questions relating to the individual to which objections were made had the aim of eliciting the investigator's impression of the extent to which aspects such as inattention, distraction and stress might be implicated in the accident. Such judgements are made in practice but there was a reluctance to accept their formalisation in a written document. Judgement was also the issue in relation to questions concerning the working environment.

The most critical of the constraints imposed by the safety officers was the requirement that it should extend over no more than one page. This posed the problem of the optimal utilisation of the space. In addition, attention had to be paid in the design to the tasks of both the user of the questionnaire (the supervisor) and the scorer (the safety officer).

After the modified version had been accepted, the four safety officers initiated discussion with their respective managements about the introduction of the procedures, which they agreed should be used by supervisors for the investigation and reporting of minor injuries. The Chief Safety Officer was not involved in these discussions. During the months that followed, it was apparent that only one safety officer was making any significant progress in advancing the project. For the rest, one safety officer discovered that it was the safety representatives rather than the supervisors who were receiving the documents concerning minor injuries in his division and that any investigation that took place was carried out by them. This posed a problem for the safety officer which could not be solved within the context of the project. One safety officer was taking on increasing commitments to a Division in the North of England which eventually became his only responsibility. One safety officer felt that a period of major reorganisation, with its attendant redundancies, was not the best time for introducing yet another change. After a period of four months, it was agreed by the management of one Division that the procedures should be introduced for a trial period of six months. This Division was characterised by relative stability of employment and the services of a safety officer whose interest and concern for the reporting of minor injuries pre-dated the start of the project. A further delay was necessary while the agreement of the safety representatives to the change was obtained. Six months after the first discussions, the procedures were implemented.

The design of the questionnaire was not the only, or the most important, area where constraints were exercised over the management of the project. The adoption of the procedures was to be an 'all or none' response and thus it was not possible to carry out a small-scale pilot study. In spite of an early indication that some aspects of the accident report were inadequate, no changes were possible until the end of the initial trial period of six months.

The successful operation of the procedures was felt by the research worker to depend heavily on the appropriate training of the supervisors in their use, with particular emphasis on the system model. However, it was made clear by the safety officers at the first discussion of the procedures that they considered it neither appropriate nor desirable for the research worker to be involved either in the preliminary discussions with management and safety representatives, or with the training of the supervisors in the use of the procedures.

Proposals were submitted to company B for the use by safety officers of a questionnaire, based on the original design for company A, for the investigation and reporting of lost time accidents and for the use by supervisors of a shorter form (two sides of a page) for minor injuries. The meeting at which these proposals were made was attended by the Chief Medical Officer, the Chief Safety Officer and the senior Safety Officer of that part of the company in which the initial study had taken place. Because of the difficulties arising from the industrial action of supervisors with reference to safety matters, it was considered inopportune by the company to pursue the proposal for their involvement in the use of the procedures. However, it was decided that a speedy decision would be made with regard to the investigation of lost time accidents by safety officers after further consultation within the company.

The outcome was an agreement to complete an accident record form for every lost time accident that occurred within the company for a period of three months, or until the total number of reports amounted to 50. Nine safety officers were involved.

The research worker was invited to attend one of the regular meetings of the safety officers to outline the rationale of the procedures, to explain with the aid of specially prepared guidelines (a copy of which was given to each safety offcer) how to complete the form and to answer any questions they might wish to ask.

The safety officers all claimed that they were already using the system model. With regard to the form, they expressed grave reservations about the questions which appeared to them to demand of their answers either inference or judgement. They took the view that neither of these activities was permissible in relation to accident investigation. The approach of the safety officers appeared to be influenced strongly by the possibility that what they had written would be tested in a Court of Law and they should not report anything that was not a fact or a recorded statement of an individual (the injured person, witnesses). In practice, safety officers are obliged to make judgements and inferences when investigating accidents. However, these are not formally recorded and therefore do not constitute evidence for the courts or any other interested party. Furthermore, because they are not recorded, the assumptions on which they are based are not made explicit (e.g. culpable error, malingering).

While it could not be claimed that the safety officers received training in the use of the accident form, there was at least the opportunity to discuss some of their reservations and to explain some of their difficulties.

The use of the procedures

In company A the management of the Division instructed the supervisors to investigate each minor injury in their areas which was reported to the Medical Department and to record their findings on the report form. At the beginning of each month, the reports of the previous month were collected and, during the six months of the trial period, passed to the research worker for coding, scoring and summarising. A brief summary was written by the research worker with the aim of elucidating the findings of the monthly set of reports. The involvement of the research worker had the aim of devising the best method of carrying out these activities and modifying the supporting documentation for this purpose.

At the end of the six-month trial period, agreement was obtained from the safety committee for the continued use of the procedures, at which time the improved design of the accident report was put into circulation and the safety officer was trained to code, score, summarise and analyse the information on the reports.

In company B, the safety officers were supplied with copies of the accident analysis form, one to be completed for every lost time accident occurring in their areas. The use of the forms continued over a period of six months in order to obtain the target of 50 accident records. There was no move to retain them after this period.

Evaluation

The evaluation of the use of the procedures in the two companies indicated the limited achievement of the aims and underlined the problems associated with the introduction and management of change.

The aim of the study was two-fold, namely to change the model of accident causation from one in which the explanatory principle was culpable error to the system model in which accidents are considered symptomatic of system defects and to ameliorate the accident information system in order to facilitate the identification and rectification of system defects.

The means by which these aims were to be achieved was the use of specially designed procedures for accident investigation and reporting. The procedures were considered not only as a vehicle for collecting accident-relevant information, but also, by encouraging the consideration of questions not hitherto considered systematically in relation to accidents, to be instrumental in modifying the narrow, culpability-based approach to a broader appreciation of the factors which shape human behaviour.

With respect to the model, a major problem was the belief by those engaged in accident investigation that this was the approach that they were already using, and that the system model was not a new concept for them. In fact, the system model demanded for its acceptance a significant modification in their approach to accident causation and such modifications are not accomplished easily. Not only is there a requirement for cognitive restructuring but the emotional and motivational aspects must be taken into account. Furthermore, the legal framework was not amenable to change and this was clearly a source of difficulty as far as the adoption of the system model was concerned.

It became clear that the use of the procedures alone was not to be effective in changing the model but that discussion based on particular investigations could go some way at least to raise questions about the culpable error model. Discussions with the senior safety officer in company B were a continuing feature of the project and the value of these discussions had become apparent in the modifications of attitudes that took place during this period.

The application of the model was more central to the activities of the safety officers than to those of the supervisors as the former were expected to investigate accidents in greater depth (and less frequently). The supervisors in company A collected each month information about a large number of injuries (on average 50) which were reviewed at the monthly meeting of the safety committee in addition to being examined by the safety officer. It was possible to compare the use of the procedures with the method that had been in operation previously.

One of the objectives of systematising the collection of accident information was to obtain an insight into the pattern of accidents on which to base a programme of accident reduction. In spite of the inevitable defects of a new and untried system, it was possible to draw some conclusions from an analysis of the accident reports completed by the supervisors in company A.

The nature of the technology made it predictable that the bulk of minor injuries would be cuts and these were shown to make up half the total, the largest single injury group. It was clear from the reports that the supervisors experienced difficulties in encouraging the use of protective clothing by operatives. However, the reports indicated that half the injuries which should have been prevented by the use of protective clothing were still incurred when it was being used. If this information was valid, then it suggested that the protective clothing issued was inadequate for its task, either because of the material from which it was constituted or the extent of the coverage it provided. In addition, the advice of supervisors to wear protective clothing at all times was likely to be devalued by the high incidence of injury when it was worn. Thus, any reluctance on the part of operatives to wear protective clothing is reinforced by evidence that it does not give complete protection. The accident information underlined the importance of matching protective clothing to the task. While it would not be accurate to suggest that the safety officer was unaware of these problems regarding protective clothing before the study, the collection of accident information defined the problems more precisely both for him and for the members of the safety committee and indicated the sort of policies most likely to be effective in solving them.

The accident reports required the supervisor to record the action he took to prevent recurrence of the incident. The responses of the supervisors to this question provided a valuable indicator of their general approach to accidents and their own role in accident prevention. Reported preventive action was classified into five categories, two of which may be regarded as positive and the rest negative. Positive preventive action included action aimed at reducing the accident potential in the situation and the advice to wear protective clothing. Negative preventive action included advice to take more care, 'none' recorded on the report, and the absence of any response to this question on the report. Altogether, positive responses made up one-third of the total. Preventive action is the key to accident reduction and the large proportion of responses which did not contain positive action was a cause for concern.

In general, the attitudes of supervisors were characterised by complacency and passivity with respect to minor accident incidence. Some accidents were regarded as 'inevitable' and negative responses were recorded when relevant positive action was suggested by other information in the report, such as the use of the correct tool or the reduction of environmental hazards.

There was evidence in the reports of ineffectiveness on the part of supervisors. One trainee without protective clothing injured himself three times within one month and after each injury the supervisor reported instructing him to use protective clothing. Phrases such as 'he will not wear standard issue' and 'once more stressed need to wear protective clothing' suggested that supervisors had difficulties in providing leadership.

It was clear from the first part of the study that the supervisors played a major role in the accident information system and were also in a position to play a key role in accident reduction. Supervisors are regarded by higher management as being responsible for ensuring that safety is maintained in the workplace; this view is endorsed by the safety officer; safety representatives consider that it is the duty of supervisors to exert their authority in the furtherance of safe conditions in the workplace. However, there was evidence that the supervisors experienced difficulties in carrying out the behaviours expected of them. The repeated (and frequently unheeded) advice to wear protective clothing, the uncritical acceptance of injury from certain tasks and the tolerance of sub-optimal standards in the workplace all suggested a mismatch between expectations and performance.

The expectations of management concerning the performance of the supervisors was not congruent with the behaviour of management towards the supervisors. Regarding the introduction of the new procedures, the safety officer considered it necessary to obtain agreement from management and safety representatives. Supervisors, however, were not consulted although they were most affected by the change. Neither did management provide an opportunity for any induction training in the use of the accident reports by either the research worker or the safety officer. The introduction of the new procedures was characterised by confusion and misunderstanding. The accident reports required considerably more time and effort than had previously been expended on accident investigation and the success of such a procedure depends crucially on the motivations of those involved. Only three out of a total of 25 supervisors were eligible to attend the meetings of the safety committee and for the majority of supervisors, no provision was made to feed back the monthly minor injuries summary in a way which recognised their unique contribution. The supervisors' relationship with the safety representatives was ambiguous. While nominally responsible as members of the workforce to the supervisor, the safety representatives exercised more power than the supervisor and had relationships with management which were outside the hierarchical structure within which the supervisor operated. At the same time, the safety representatives had no more responsibility for safety than any other member of the workforce.

The difficulties of the supervisors were highlighted by the use of the procedures which demonstrated the need for the enhancement of the supervisor's role to ensure safe conditions in the workplace.

To summarise the effectiveness of the use of the procedures in company A, while there was evidence that the culpable error model was highly resistant to change, considerable improvements were made in the methods of collecting and utilising accident information relating to minor injury. These methods continued to be used after the completion of the project period. The difficulties of the supervisors, however, were not recognised.

In company B, nine safety officers completed 50 accident record forms. A comparison of the information in the accident record forms with that in the official reports showed that the former contained considerably more detailed information. However, a comparison of the methods used to investigate accidents (e.g. number of individuals interviewed, number of visits to the site of the accident) suggested that for some safety officers the collection of this information was a more demanding task.

Each record form included details of the preventive action recommended by the safety officers. In nearly one-third of the incidents, no action was recommended; 10% recommended hardware modifications and 60% consisted of statements about what individuals (employees, supervisors) should do or what should be done in general. These recommendations specified goals ('supervisors must enforce safety rules'; 'window maintenance to be improved') but they did not provide detailed advice on how these goals were to be achieved. Applying the SHEL model to the recommendations, it was shown that the majority were concerned with the L–S interface. However, they did not have the aim of modifying this interface, but instead restated the rules ('employees should use hoists').

The completed accident record forms demonstrated an uncritical acceptance of the effectiveness of training schemes, of the suitability of the design of workstations and the primacy of the machine. The recommendations showed a lack of innovation on the part of the safety officers and a failure to perceive accidents as a valuable source of information about the state of the organisation and the problems it faces.

The amelioration of the accident information and reduction system was not achieved in any lasting way in company B nor was the system model of accident causation adopted. The main benefit of the exercise was that it demonstrated to senior safety officers the validity of the conclusions of the first part of the study. The restriction of accident information to that required for statutory purposes had had the effect of concealing both the inadequacies of the accident control system and the limitations of the training received by safety officers for carrying out accident investigation.

The conclusions drawn from this study were that organisational change is a prerequisite for the adoption of the SHEL model, as this model demands the transfer of safety matters from the periphery to the centre of managerial attention. If the safety officer is to make recommendations that are both innovative and effective, and which are to have an impact on managerial decision making, then an enhancement of his status is necessary. He must recognise that his first commitment is to safety, and see his loyalty to the company not in terms of defence against compensation claims but in the achievement of high standards at the workplace. This implies the professionalisation of the role of safety officer, which, in turn, implies the requirement for professional training commensurate with the task.

Conclusion

At the outset, the project appeared to have as its object the relatively straightforward aim of improving the design of the accident information system, with the implementation of the 'package' expected to follow. However, as this discussion has shown, the ergonomics problems were not confined to the form of the accident documentation but extended into the field of strongly entrenched attitudes with the ergonomics solution seen to depend for its success on the implementation of organisational change.

The likelihood that any attempt to change a part of the system under investigation will have implications for other parts of the system should, of course, come as no surprise to ergonomists who deal in system concepts. Why, then, should we expect 'packages' to be readily implemented? Indeed, the ease of application may be in inverse proportion to the significance of the ergonomics contribution. Reference was made in the introduction to the need for a shared conceptual framework between ergonomist and collaborator if application is to be accomplished. It is because of the systemic effects of the application of ergonomics solutions that a shared conceptual framework is necessary.

Acknowledgement

The project discussed in this chapter was funded by a grant from the Health and Safety Executive to the Department of Engineering Production, University of Birmingham.

References

CHAPANIS, A. (1976). 'Engineering psychology', (in *Handbook of Industrial and Organisational Psychology*, Dunnette, M. (ed)), Rand McNally, New York.
EDWARDS, E. (1972). 'Man and machine: systems for safety', Proceedings of the BALPA Technical Symposium, *Outlook on Safety*, 21–36.
EDWARDS, M. (1981). *The Study of the Feasibility of the Development and Use of a Systematic Analysis Technique for the Investigation of Industrial Accidents'*, Final Report to the Health and Safety Executive.
GAGNÉ, R. M. (1962). 'Human functions in systems', (in *Psychological Principles of System Development*, Gagné, R. M. (ed)), Holt Rinehart and Winston, New York.
KVÅLSETH, T. O. (ed.). (1980). 'Special issue on "ergonomics in action-from theory to practice"', *Ergonomics*, **23**, 685–853.

Chapter 14

Ergonomics applied to slipping accidents

L. Strandberg

Ergonomics in occupational accident prevention

Among ergonomists there is no need to point out that occupational *injuries* should be prevented primarily through improvements in the working environment. Even if higher skills and safer behaviour can be achieved through education and training of risk-exposed workers, permanent counteraction of common risk factors requires changes in equipment design and in work organisation. This philosophy is widely accepted for occupational *diseases* and corresponding contributing factors (agencies) in the environment such as improper working postures, vibration, noise, pollutants, radiation, etc. However, in spite of their dominating numbers in occupational injury statistics, occupational *accidents* are often looked upon differently, only as results of 'human error' or 'poor workmanship'. Then, one does not consider contributing factors in the working environment such as poor visibility, slippery surfaces, deceptive machine dynamics, superhuman task demands, unsatisfactory guarding, etc. This common attitude is probably reinforced by learning effects: one or a few risk factors may be present in a job task without any accident occurring the first thousand times (Swain (1972) for further details on the nature of human 'error').

Thus, accident potentials may be strongly under-represented in the lists of perceived environment deficiencies that are handed over for action to the ergonomics specialist from, e.g. worker representatives. Consequently, if the ultimate goal is to reduce injuries in general, possible needs for accident prevention must be taken into account by the ergonomist. No other specialist is better suited for this responsibility.

Accident description models

Comparison of contributing factors

While well-defined description models are needed to *quantify* the accident contribution from certain factors, the hazard *identification* is usually an unstructured and creative process more dependent on the model's flexibility than on its unambiguity. The degree of accident contribution or involvement from certain objects, events or activities may be quantified in a number of dimensions and on different levels. Unfortunately, the superficial levels, commonly adopted for accident statistics, will display results that are misleading in many ways. This effect can often be derived from the statistics' intrinsic accident description model, allowing one, and only one 'cause' to be registered per case.

Even if it is unintentional, such models counteract the more fruitful philosophy of an accident as a *multi-causal* phenomenon. A man–machine system which allows serious injuries to occur due to one single error, should not exist in a civilised world. If it does, the system, not the human being, must be changed.

The prevention strategy is strongly dependent on the analysis techniques and accident description models that are used for data collection and for comparison of contributing factors. Therefore, four common types of accident description models will be applied on the following accident as an illustration.

Example of an accident

A railway bridge was under construction. Snow had fallen during the night, but most had melted during the day. On one side of the river was a shed for the workers which was heated from early morning. On the other side was a container for equipment. A worker used the lifeline and a girder to cross the river – the lifeline was kept in the container during the night.

Wearing slippery shoes, he slid on an obscured patch of snow and fell. The lifeline broke, probably because of a sharp edge on the bridge structure, and the man fell into the river. The water was cold and the man drowned. There was a lifeboat, but this was padlocked to a tree and a colleague was unable to help.

Single type models

Every fatal accident in Sweden is classified in one (and only one) group according to the so called E-list for 'External cause of injury' in *ICD* (International Statistical Classification of Diseases, Injuries and Causes of Death, see WHO 1967) which seems to offer at least the following alternatives for the above accident.

E885 Fall on same level from slipping, tripping or stumbling. This includes slipping on ice, mud, oil, snow; stumbling, tripping over carpet, kerb, rug, small object. It excludes attack by animal (E906).
E882 Fall from or out of building or other structure. This includes a fall from balcony, bridge, building, flagpole, tower, turret, viaduct, wall, window and excludes collapse of a building or structure (E916).
E910 Accidental drowning and submersion. Includes immersion and swimmer's cramp and excludes in transport accidents (E800–E845), in cataclysm (E908, E909).

Apparently, the choice between E885, E882 and E910 must be made subjectively by the registering personnel, as the E-list groups are considered to be mutually exclusive. Though the event 'slipping' may contribute to a lot of accidents that are registered in other groups, it is only mentioned under E885. So, the actual involvement of each listed factor will not be revealed by statistics, that is based on the single type model.

The same principle was applied to the previous Swedish occupational injury statistics. (The present information system is based on a sequential model, see below.) The previous statistics presented 16 mutually exclusive groups of 'main cause of accident', see Table 14.1. Then slipping was

Table 14.1 *Previous Swedish occupational accident tabulation and numbers for one year (from* Occupational Injuries 1975, *Official Statistics of Sweden, National Social Insurance Board, Stockholm, 1979)*

Classification of accident causes	Number of occupational accidents 1975 distributed by 'main cause'		
00 Motors, generators and transmissions (not incorporated into a machine)	313		
01 Machines and splinters, etc. coming therefrom	16 797		
02 Lifts, cranes and other hoisting appliances; conveyers	4 704		
03 Vehicles, ships, aircraft	8 996		
04 Hand tools (including power tools) and implements, and splinters coming therefrom	21 333		
05 Hot or cold substances (solid, liquid, gaseous)	765		
06 Electric current	363		
07 Explosions, bursts, fires, etc.	650		
08 Toxic or corrosive substances	1 488		
09 Falling to a lower level	9 552		
Thereof: falling from elevation		9 034	
falling into hole		518	
10 Falling on one and the same level	9 902		
Thereof: slipping		5 646	(5%)
other		4 256	
11 Falling objects not handled by the injured person; landslides, sliding materials, collapsing supports, etc.	4 520		
12 Treading on, knocking against or being struck by objects not handled by the injured person	11 657		
13 Lifting, carrying and similar activities on the part of the injured person	19 508		
14 Animals	539		
15 Other accident causes	4 336		
00–15 All 'causes'	115 423		

considered to be only a subgroup of 'falling on one and the same level'. (No. 10 in Table 14.1), although slipping must have been involved in lower level falls (09), machine (01) and carrying (13) accidents as well.

The almost arbitrary spreading of one accident antecedent in different groups is partly due to the single type model's incapability of treating the accident as a sequence of unintentional events with several involved agencies. In addition the type or 'cause' groups juxtapose

intentional activities (walking in the accident example; No. 13 in Table 14.1),

unintentional events (slipping, falling; Nos 07, 09, 10, 12),
involved objects, etc. (bridge, snow, lifeline, water; Nos 00–04, 14),
injury types (drowned; Nos 05, 06, 08).

Due to similar criticism of the ANSI single type model (included in
'American National Standard Method of Recording Basic Facts Relating
to the Nature and Occurrence of Work Injuries'), Safety Sciences (1977)
applied a sequential model to 1077 injury reports involving slips, falls or a
work surface. Even if these reports were taken from a small sample, not
being quite representative for the US establishments, the analysis points at
a number of details important in the prevention of falling accidents.

Table 14.2 *Accidental falls and other causes of death 1975 (from Official Statistics of Sweden)*

External cause of death according to ICD, 8th revision. (See WHO manual, Geneva, 1967. [ICD: International Statistical Classification of Diseases, Injuries and Causes of Death])	*Number of people dying 1975* *Age interval (years)*			
	0–14	15–64	>64	All ages
Fall on or from stairs or steps	0	37	56	93
Fall on or from ladders or scaffolding	0	16	11	27
Fall from or out of building or other structure	3	28	7	38
Fall into hole or other opening in surface	0	3	1	4
Other fall from one level to another	7	23	37	67
Fall on same level from slipping, tripping or stumbling	0	78	237	315
Fall on same level from collision, pushing or shoving by or with other person	0	1	3	4
Other and unspecified fall	0	36	1 097	1 133
Accidental falls. ICD Nos E880–E887. Sum of above	10	222	1 449	1 681
Motor vehicle accidents. ICD Nos E810–E823	108	781	347	1 236
All accidents. ICD Nos E800–E949	209	1 695	2 025	3 929
All causes of death	1 422	18 726	68 054	88 202

Because of the characteristics of single type models' statistics, we know
that their number of, e.g. slipping and falling accidents are underestimates.
In spite of that, the number is high. See Table 14.2, where slipping,
tripping or stumbling is the largest specified subgroup. Note that people
older than 64 years were victims in more than 1400 of the 1681 fatal falling
accidents during 1975. For further details see SCB (1977). According to
occupational injury statistics (RFV 1979) each non-fatal accident in the
subgroup 'slipping' causes an average of thirty days sickness absence.

Sequential models

A sequential model for official statistics

Since 1 January 1979, occupational accidents (with one or more working
days' absence) in Sweden are registered as sequential and with multiple

so-called agencies. Registration and evaluation take place in a computer-based information system ISA, Informationssystemet om Arbetsskador (Andersson and Lagerlöf 1978; Lagerlöf 1980). About 100 descriptors per accident are registered.

With ISA an accident is registered in reverse chronological order and three types of unintentional events are utilised.

One *injury event* (IE),
One *contact event* (CE),
Preceding events (up to three preceding events, PE, per accident may be registered). See Table 14.3.

The ISA classification lists consist of about 20 IE, 30 CE and 60 PE types exemplified in Figure 14.1. Further details are presented by Andersson and Svanström (1980) and by Strandberg (1980b).

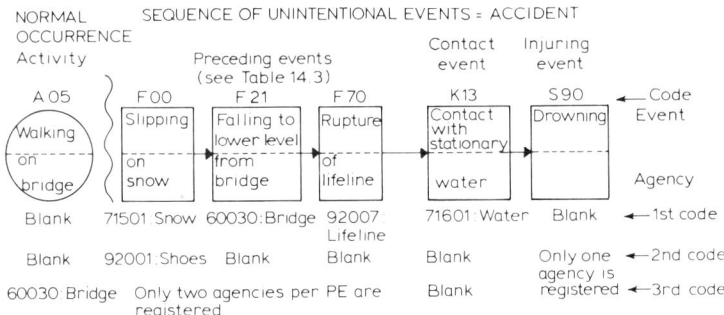

Figure 14.1 ISA sequential model representation of the accident described on page 202

The *activity* occupying the injured person prior to the accident is then assigned one of 14 numbers. The activity does not need to have a causal relationship with the accident (= the sequence of unintentional events).

The technical equipment, machinery components, materials, etc. which are involved in the accident (and affecting the course of events) are registered as *agency* numbers making up an extensive list of several hundred items. Each registered agency is connected with the appropriate event and to the activity according to strict rules.

In official statistics (see, e.g. SCB 1981), ISA presents surveys on main events and principal agencies. From each case, one main event and one principal agency is selected by a computer program. The selection is completely reproducible with well-defined criteria.

ISA data on slipping accidents

The large number of registered accidents (more than 100 000 each year), the sequential model and the ISA registration strategy yield a quite reliable basis for statistical evaluation of 'blackspots' among activities, events, objects, injury types, etc. The (PE) event 'slipping' was included in about 12 500 (11%) of the 113 000 occupational accidents registered by ISA on

Table 14.3 ISA selection of preceding events

	Code	preceding event	Code	preceding event
(F)	F0, 1	*Loss of balance or other loss of personal control*	F44	Electrical flash-over, short-circuit
	F00	Slipping, skidding on foot	F45	Lightning
	F01	Tripping	F46	Boiling (violent and inadvertent)
	F02	Push	F49	Other event, unclear
	F03	Loss of consciousness, falling asleep, giddiness	F5, 6	*Collapse, overturning, inundation, unhooking etc.*
	F04	Something giving way underfoot, loss of support and rocking or tipping of underlying surface	F50	Collapse of goods in bulk
			F51	Object coming loose
	F05	Lurching, jerks in vehicles, etc.	F52	Object turning over, stack collapsing
	F06	Misjudgement of support, 'treading on air'	F53	Object collided with or pushed down
	F07	Sliding, loss of hold	F54	Unhooking, etc.
	F08	Getting stuck	F55	Goods rolling or sliding
	F10	Jerk or blow with hand-held machine	F56	Shifting, rocking
	F11	Disruption of communications	F57	Recoil, ejection
	F19	Other event, unclear	F58	Folding, collapse
	F2	*Personal fall*	F60	Uprooting of stump
(F)	F20	Fall at same level	F61	Inundation
(F)	F21	Fall to lower level	F62	Overfilling
(F)	F22	Fall from moving vehicle	F63	Splashing in vessel
	F23	Jump	F64	Escape of liquid
	F29	Other type of fall, unclear	F65	Waves splashing over
	F3	*Loss of control of vehicle*	F69	Other event, unclear
	F30	Puncture	F7	*Rupture, distortion, oscillation*
	F31	Disturbance of other technical function	F70	Rupture, distortion
	F32	Swerving, evasive action	F71	Oscillation, swaying
	F33	Skid	F79	Other event, unclear
	F34	Driving in a dip, driving into an object, animal, etc. (leading to loss of control)	F9	*Other or unclear preceding event*
			F91	Inadvertent machine or vehicle movement, e.g. inadvertent start, double stroke. Also failure to stop when turned off or braked
	F35	Penetration of driving surface	F92	Confusion
	F39	Other event, unclear	F93	Disrupted material flow, e.g. entrapment, pile-up, congestion
	F4	*Fire, explosion, etc.*	F94	Other functional disruption, e.g. 'sticking' of machine part, control equipment, etc.
	F40	Fire	F99	Other event, unclear
	F41	Explosion		
	F42	Blasting, implosion		
	F43	Shooting		

(F) Codes marked F must always be preceded by another F-marked event

1979. Of these 12 500 slipping accidents, only 5200 (42%) event sequences included 'fall at same level'. So, with a single type model (where slipping is treated exclusively as a subgroup of fall at same level) the importance of proper slip-resistance may be seriously underestimated. See Table 14.1 from the previous statistics, where slipping was identifiable in only about 5600 (5%) of all 115 000 occupational accidents. In fact, 26% of 5300 'fall to lower level' accidents during 1979 were preceded by slipping. Only one other PE ('loss of support of underlying surface') was involved to the same extent (26%) in falls to lower level, while 'treading on air' (8%) and 'tripping' (7%) initiated the fall less frequently. Note that such data are important to falling accident prevention, as the countermeasures are different for different initiating events.

Focusing on the 12 500 slipping accidents during 1979, their PE, CE and IE registrations tell us that

((a)–(c) from PE data)
(a) 97% had no other PE registered before the slipping event
(b) 45% had no personal fall or jump registered
(c) 11% included 'fall to lower level'.

((d)–(f) from CE data)
(d) 79% resulted in contact with agencies at rest
(e) 13% resulted in strenuous or violent body movement
(f) 6% resulted in contact with agencies in motion (including vehicles, machine parts, carried objects, etc.).

((g)–(h) from IE data)
(g) 68% terminated in injuries from external forces
(h) 30% terminated in injuries from body overloading (e.g. spraining, twisting, pulled or broken muscle).

According to activity data
(i) 57% of the slipping accidents occurred during movement on foot (without any object being carried)
(j) 13% occurred during manual carrying or lifting
(k) more than 5% occurred during cleaning.

While the average accident involvement of slipping was 11% during 1979, certain occupations had a much larger slipping involvement, namely

(l) 25% for cleaning personnel (slipping was involved in about 570 of all their 2300 accidents)
(m) 19% of 8400 accidents injuring transport workers (where errand-drivers were on top with slipping in 38% of their 280 accidents)
(n) 18% of 5200 accidents injuring household and serving personnel.

Agency registrations indicate that about 8% of the slip-up accidents occur in vehicles, 12% on stairs and 35% due to snow or ice. About 50% of all slipping accidents occur indoors.

Some sequential model limitations

Most of the ISA events cover only a few seconds before injury or damage. Sequential models with larger time span have been used by Fischhoff *et al.*

(1978) to illustrate opportunities for prevention, which are often neglected due to their temporal and spatial distance from the accident.

A sequential model has also been suggested by Benner (1977) for pure case studies and hypothesis generation. However, the sequential model may give the impression that a given accident outcome (injury or damage) can always be blocked by a single countermeasure, i.e. preventing the occurrence of a single event in the accident sequence. This erroneous interpretation is likely to occur if the sequential model's *temporal relationship* between specific events is confused with a general causal relationship. Less apparent cases than our accident example may then result in too-restricted actions – in analogy with one ridiculous conclusion from Figure 14.1: drownings are well prevented by skid-resistant shoes.

Logic diagram models

In the logic diagram analysis (LDA), fault-trees are used to clarify the *causal relationship* between different conditions and events contributing to a specific (injury or damage) 'top' event. Usually, the logic diagram is too complicated for statistical registration, but it may be a flexible tool for hazard identification and *qualitative* case analysis by ergonomists. To avoid confusion, the basic diagram elements should be few. In Figure 14.2 four elements are presented for consideration. Note that the LDA is performed from top to bottom, whilst the causal flow goes upwards.

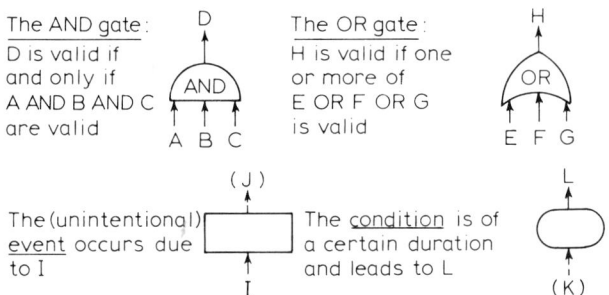

Figure 14.2 Logic diagram elements. The term *logic* refers only to the commonly used denomination Logic Diagram Analysis (LDA) and not to a valuation of the model as more logical than others

In general, the *condition* is subject to preventive actions, whilst the *event* is quickly occurring as a logical consequence of certain conditions or other events. Therefore, the LDA branches should not be left open but analysed further until preventable conditions have been formulated at the bottom of the diagram.

Each AND gate input is *necessary* for its output. Therefore, the output event will be prevented if only one of the inputs is blocked or eliminated. The OR gate's inputs, on the other hand, are only *sufficient* for the output. Thus, prevention of the OR output requires blocking of all the inputs. For example, Figure 14.3 illustrates that slip-resistant shoes would have prevented the slipping event (AND gate output) but perhaps not the falling

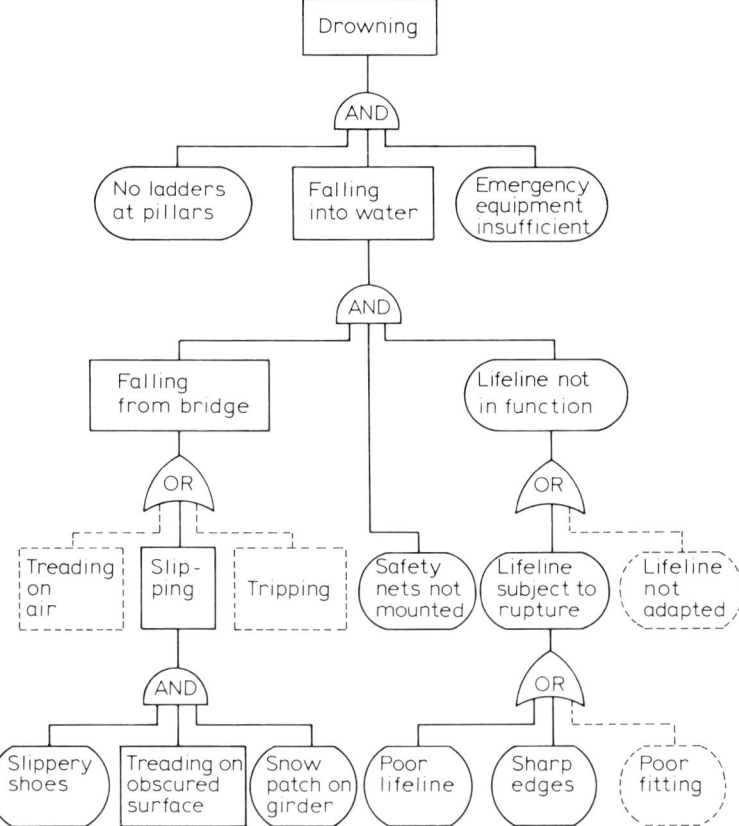

Figure 14.3 Logic diagram suggestion for the accident described on page 202.
Dashed elements did not contribute in this case

event (OR gate output), which may follow tripping or treading on air, as
well.

In retrospective accident analysis the OR gate can be used when it is
unclear which of several causal elements (i.e. conditions or events)
contributed to the actual accident. The OR gate inputs should also include
such causal elements that are highly probable – even if they were not
involved in the actual accident. In this way, the LDA results from one case
study can be used for more general preventive actions. The aim of
generalisation is essential to the 'safety analysis'. Therefore it comes
frequently in conflict with the 'responsibility analysis', with its emphasis on
assigning individual blame, and its exclusive orientation towards the one
and only accident course, which actually occurred.

Fault-trees are also used for *quantitative* predictions of the probabilities
of crucial faults in some technical systems. However, if some causal
element has been forgotten, the calculated fault probability value may be
much too low (cf. Fischhoff *et al.* 1978). Therefore, one cannot rely upon
LDA absolute probability values for man–machine systems, as they are
affected by many unpredictable causal elements. Thus, quantitative LDA

should only be used on man–machine systems for comparisons between technical designs, with known and equivalent ergonomic characteristics.

Dynamic models

Logic diagram analysis is also limited by its incapability to describe the dynamic interaction between continuous variables. For example, nothing is indicated in Figure 14.3 about the definition and tolerable limit of shoe slipperiness or what slipping severity will produce an unrecoverable fall. Such questions cannot be answered without analysis of gait, slipping and falling dynamics; and without the answers, it is impossible to point at and to eliminate the most important hazards before accidents have happened. Measurement methods and limit values are needed for (acute) accident hazards as well as for pollutants and other (chronic) health hazards.

Although slip resistance seems to be a purely physical phenomenon and qualitatively well-known, its measurement and limit values have been argued upon for decades. Consequently, there are numerous slip-resistance meters and measurement methods, some of which will be discussed in the next section.

Probably, the confusion on slip-resistance measurements will be reduced when the dynamics of slipping and falling have been explored in more detail. Whilst the dynamic model is widely accepted for vehicle skidding, very few dynamic measurements have been performed in controlled experiments with walking and skidding human subjects. In the last part of the next section such data will illustrate the accident prevention potential of dynamic models and work (i.e. gait) analysis techniques.

Slip-resistance as a safety performance quantity

Accident prevention through product safety standards

In the previous section statistics and retrospective accident analysis indicated the circumstances where slipping was most frequent. However, successful prevention in practice requires measurement techniques and criteria for the objective selection of satisfactory slip-resistant shoes and walking surfaces. Such safety standards are generally needed for products with large accident involvement.

Standardisation of product *design* is often a safety prerequisite in man–machine systems. Operator 'errors', or rather unforeseen actions, are more likely to occur if similar products deviate, for example, in their design and positioning of controls. (Imagine the safety of an automobile with the brake pedal to the right of the accelerator.)

However, design standards may prevent sound product development. Therefore, safety *performance* standards should be preferred whenever possible. See, e.g. Jaksch *et al.* (1974) for automobiles, Strandberg (1978) for road tankers or Wilson and Kirk (1980) for household products. 'The problem is to identify such safety-relevant performance qualities and to develop reliable, objective procedures for their measurement'. (Dugoff *et al.* 1971). Unfortunately, this problem has been underestimated by many investigators of slipping accidents, who did not consider slips and falls to be complicated phenomena from both tribological and biomechanical aspects. Therefore, the literature exhibits quite a few slip-resistance measurement methods which 'demonstrate how an exciting and original approach can be invalidated or seriously damaged by inattention to basic principles of research methodology' (Haddon *et al.* 1964).

Current slip-resistance meters

Many methods and types of apparatus intended for slip-resistance measurements have been found in the literature (see Table 14.4). Notice that Table 14.4 concentrates on pedestrian friction meters. Many facilities for general tribometric measurements (see, e.g. Moore 1972; Czichos 1978) are excluded, as well as most road friction meters (see Ohlsson 1979). In addition, numerous spring force meters, inclined planes and sliding distance measurements (rows (a), (e) and (f) in Table 14.4a) have probably been utilised for friction coefficient evaluation without having been traced in the literature.

It should also be emphasised that Table 14.4 is a list of meters, not of methods. Many slip-resistance measurements are not represented, because they have been based on subjective evaluation, practically without apparatus (see, e.g., CSMA 1970). On the other hand, one meter may represent a number of operational definitions of slip-resistance, due to differences in the testing procedure applied by different experimenters. Changing the operation means changing the concept (Bridgman 1927).

The versatility of different meters has been compared and commented on by many investigators. See, e.g. National Research Council (1961); Bring (1964); Reed (1975); Brungraber (1976), or other references in Table 14.4c where several apparatuses appear in the right-hand column. No method or apparatus has achieved international acceptance for universal slip-resistance measurements. A universal procedure seems to be a Utopia, if all demands (from field to laboratory tests, from general walking surface evaluation to shoe component optimisation, from dry to lubricated conditions, from spot to area measurements, from average to variation measures, etc.) must be met by one apparatus, where the cost/benefit ratio is reasonable from the user's point of view. Therefore, neither the measurement methods themselves nor their outputs (seemingly 'objective' product data) should be accepted without examination of their inherent slip-resistance definition as discussed below.

Slip-resistance definition based on tribology and biomechanics

Many of the apparatuses mentioned in Table 14.4 and the corresponding methods may have their *reliability* (capability to yield reproducible results) improved, if operating variables are minutely selected and controlled. In addition, unexpected result variations may be explained if more tribometric characteristics are considered apart from the friction coefficient output (Czichos 1978). However, in order to determine and improve their *validity* (output relevance or correlation with real slip-resistance during walking), one must know more about the forces and motions during human slips and falls.

Table 14.4a Apparatus (numbered in Table 14.4b) for slip-resistance measurements. Grouping according to output quantities and working principles that have been interpreted from statements in the references (Table 14.4c). Notice that apparatus in italics (30, 31, 46, 48) appear in two positions

Output quantity			Static friction coefficient only		Dynamic friction coefficient only		Both static and dynamic friction coefficient				Row index
							Sliding velocity not controlled		Sliding velocity controlled		
Basic quantity	Working principle		Force application time not controlled	Force application time controlled	Sliding velocity not controlled	Sliding velocity controlled	Force application time not controlled	Force application time controlled	Force application time not controlled	Force application time controlled	
	Spring or the like		38 58		55	30 31 48	4 11 21 35 36 56 61		2 3		a
	Mass		46 52								b
Force	Electronic		49	45	9 12	1 6 7 30 31 42 44 47 48 50 53 57 62	13 37 40	32	8 34 39 54	43	c
	Inclined 'leg'		14 15 16 17 19 20 23 33 41	18							d
Angle	Inclined plane		10 22 51 59 60								e
	Sliding distance				5 27 28 46						f
Energy	Pendulum overshoot angle				24 25 26 29						g
Column number			1	2	3	4	5	6	7	8	

Table 14.4b *List of slip-resistance meters and references touching upon them*

Apparatus		References
No.	Name is established in references if in bold type (Description within brackets)	Position in matrix Table 14.4a	Major references in bold type

No.	Name / description	Position in matrix Table 14.4a	Major references
1	CEBTP portable pedestrian skidmeter	c4	C25 **M20**
2	**HPS** – horizontal pull slipmeter	a7	B70 **B90** B110 C40 D10 I10 I20 I30 J10 N20 P30 **R30 R50** S05 S10
3	**Topaka**	a7	B40 D10 R30 **W20**
4	Ewerdahl horizontal pull (stationary dynamometer, pulley and sledge)	a5	B50 **E50**
5	Ericsson (rail slope accelerated sledge)	f3	**B50**
6	(Lathe driven horizontal pull)	c4	B50 **S70**
7	Moving table (0.07 ms^{-1} constant speed)	c4	**E40**
8	**UFTM** – universal friction testing machine	c7	L10 **R20 R30** S05
9	von Rosenberg (rotary specimen, motor current measurement)	c3	B50 **R60**
10	Standard for metal roof colour (inclined plane with subjects)	e1	**A10** A20
11	Roos af Hjelmsäter (manually turned specimen)	a5	**B50** E30
12	(Rotary brushes, motor current measurement)	c3	A05 B50 **N10** P20
13	(Subject pushing bar, standing on piezoelectric force-plate)	c5	**B30** B50
14	**Hunter**	d1	B50 B60 B90 E20 **H10** N10 P20
15	**James** ASTM D 2047-75	d1	A40 B20 B40 B50 B60 B70 B90 B110 C40 D10 E10 E20 G10 J10 N10 P20 P30 R30 R50 S10
16	**Dura**	d1	**B20** B50 N10 P20
17	**Carlsöö – Mayr** (manually pushed carriage)	d1	B60 C10 **C20** E20 F20 K10 O10 S90
18	**NBS – Brungraber**	d2	B35 B70 B80 B100 **B110** S05
19	Liberty mutual – 1958	d1	B50 D10 **F10** R30
20	Liberty mutual – 1940	d1	**G40**
21	Schuster horizontal pull	a5	B40 **S20**
22	Mercier's inclined plane	e1	**M40**
23	(Four joint platform)	d1	B50 **G30**
24	**Sigler**	g3	B40 B50 B60 B70 B90 D10 **E20** J10 J20 N10 P20 S30 S40 **S50**
25	**British Portable Tester**	g3	**A30** B60 B70 B90 C40 E20 **G20** M10 N10 P20 P30 R30 R40
26	NCSA bicycle wheel	g3	B50 **N10** P20
27	Travelers insurance tester (puck thrown from pendulum)	f3	B50 **N10** P20
28	Wilson, Mahoney (rail slope accelerated sledge)	f3	R30 **W30**
29	Leroux rugosimeter	g3	**N10** P20
30	Egan moving platform	a4 & c4	**N10** P20
31	Robinson-Kopf. (Instron pulled HPS)	a4 & c4	R30 **R50**
32	Bring (three degrees of freedom moving shoe and strain gauge force plate)	c6	B60 **B120**

Table 14.4b *(continued)*

Apparatus		References
No. *Name is established in references if in bold type* (*Description within brackets*)	*Position in matrix Table 14.4a*	*Major references in bold type*
33 Pangels	d1	B50 B60 **P10**
34 Hoechst (horizontal pull with accelerometer)	c7	B35 **B40** B90
35 (Weighted bag)	a5	D10 P20
36 Model 80 floor friction tester	a5	B110 **T10**
37 Wrapping friction meter	c5	**S80**
38 Ramsay, Senneck (shoe with suspended weight and hand lever)	a1	**R10**
39 AFNOR (oscillating table, stationary shoe)	c7	**A03 T20** T30
40 Cloven friction tester	c5	**N30** N40
41 Agricultural university of Norway floor tester	d1	**N40**
42 **Skiddometer** trailer **BV6** (axle torque from braked rolling wheel)	c4	**A50**
43 Coenen (three degrees of freedom moving shoe and piezoelectric force plate)	c8	**C30**
44 **Skiddometer** trailer **BV11:3** (axle torque from braked rolling wheel)	c4	**M30**
45 SATRA (two degrees of freedom moving shoe)	c2	**S60**
46 Kollsman bathtub surface tester	b1 & f3	B70 **B100**
47 **Skiddometer BV5** truck mounted (axle torque from braked rolling wheel)	c4	N50
48 Skiddometer pushed manually (axle torque from braked rolling wheel)	a4 & c4	**V10**
49 Walking grid friction meter	c1	**O10**
50 Baumgärtel, Richter (beam bending moment from rotating disc)	c4	**B10** B40
51 BG/FA Bauliche Einrichtungen (inclined plane)	e1	B25
52 (Specimen pulled by weight)	b1	**B50** E30
53 ASTM D 1894-78 (tensile tester crosshead with horizontal slider)	c4	**A35** P30
54 PFI (axle torque from circular segment rolling with slip)	c7	**F05** P22 P24 P26
55 Penn state dragtester	a3	**A25**
56 Bigfoot	a5	S05
57 FIS (Forschungsinstitut für Schuhtechnologie) Tribometer	c4	S15
58 FIS Rutschwiderstandtester (pendulum wheel acting on horizontal slide)	a1	S15
59 FIS inclined plane	e1	S15
60 Fliesen-Beratung inclined plane	e1	F07 F08
61 Fliesen-Beratung dynamometer	a5	F07
62 Zatloukal Instron	c4	Z10

Table 14.4c *References with description of apparatus for slip-resistance measurements*

Reference No. Author, year, title, publication	Description of apparatus number (see Table 14.4b)
A03 AFNOR, (1977). Chaussures de sécurité résistance au glissement, AFNOR S73–102	39
A05 American Telephone and Telegraph Company, (1958). Bell system practises, measurement of slip-resistance of resilient floors, Principles and evaluation.	12
A10 Arbetarskyddsstyrelsen, (1974). Färg för målning på yttertak av plåt, meddelande 1974:24 (in Swedish)	10
A20 Arbetarskyddsstyrelsen, (1979). PM angående industriellt målad takplåt, Arbetarskyddsstyrelsen (in Swedish).	10
A30 ASTM, (1974). Standard test method for measuring pavement surface frictional properties using the British Portable Tester, ASTM E303–74.	25
A35 ASTM, (1978). Standard test method for static and kinetic coefficients of friction of plastic film and sheeting, ANSI/ASTM D1894–78.	53
A40 ASTM, (1954). Proposed method of test for measuring the static coefficient of friction of waxed floor surfaces. ASTM Bulletin.	15
A50 Auto-Products AB, Skiddometer BV6, Brochure, Auto-Products, Stockholm.	42
B10 Baumgärtel, K. and Richter, E-F., (1963). Messung des Reibungskoeffizienten von Metallen und Kunststoffen, Zeitschrift für Instrumentenkunde.	50
B20 Berkeley, B. and Burns, J. D., (1957). Floor wax slip testing. Soap.	15 16
B25 Berufsgenossenschaften, (1979). Merkblatt Keramische Bodenbeläge für Arbeitsräume und Arbeitsbereiche mit erhöhter Rutschgefahr, Fachausschuss Bauliche Einrichtungen, Bonn.	51
B30 Blanvin, M., (1961). Contribution a l'étude de l'adhérence sol-semelle, Cahiers de notes documentaires Institut National de Sécurité.	13
B35 Braun, R. and Brungraber, R. J., (1977). A comparison of two slip-resistance testers, ASTM STP649.	18 34
B40 Braun, R. and Roemer, D., (1974). Influence of waxes on static and dynamic friction. Soap/Cosmetics/Chemical Specialties.	3 15 21 24 34 50 55
B50 Bring, C., (1964). Friktion och halkning, Byggforskningen, Rapport 112 (in Swedish).	4 5 6 9 11 12 13 14 15 16 19 23 24 26 27 33 52
B60 Bring, C., (1978). Provning av halksäkerhet, KTH Institutionen för Byggnadsteknik, Meddelande nr 115 (in Swedish).	14 15 17 24 25 32 33
B70 Brungraber, R. J. and Adler, S. C., (1977). Technical support for a slip-resistance standard, National Bureau of Standards, ASTM STP 649.	2 15 18 24 25 46
B80 Brungraber, R. J., (1975). Portable tester for measuring the static coefficient of friction between a floor surface or the like and a shoe sole or heel material or the like, United States Patents 3,975,940.	18
B90 Brungraber, R. J., (1976). An overview of floor slip-resistance research with annotated bibliography, National Bureau of Standards – Technical note 895.	2 14 15 24 25 34

Table 14.4c *(continued)*

Reference		Description of apparatus number (see Table 14.4b)
No.	Author, year, title, publication	
B100	Brungraber, R. J. and Raper, T. J., (1977). A comparison of two testers in evaluating the slip-resistance of bathtub and shower base surfaces. National Bureau of Standards.	18 46
B110	Brungraber, R. J., (1977). A new portable tester for the evaluation of the slip-resistance of walkway surfaces, National Bureau of Standards, Technical note 953.	2 15 18 36
B120	Byggstandardiseringen, (1980). Remiss SS 923515 Golvmaterial – bestämning av friktionstal vid halkning, Byggstandardiseringen (in Swedish).	32
C10	Carlsöö, S. and Mayr, J., (1967). Mätning av halkrisk, Land och Sjö (in Swedish).	17
C20	Carlsöö, S. and Mayr, J., (1968). Die Bestimmung des Gleitens und des Gleitrisikos beim normalen Gang, Fliesen-Beratungsstelle E. V.	17
C25	CEBTP, A.F.P.V: appareil de frottement à petite vitesse du CEBTP, Brochure, Centre Expérimental de Recherches et d'Etudes du Batiment et des Travaux Publics.	1
C30	Coenen, W., (1980). Prüfung und Beurteilung der Gleitsicherheit von Schuhen unter praktischen Gesichtspunkten, Arbeitssicherheit.	43
C40	Cramp, A. P. and Masters, L. W., (1974). Preliminary study of the slipperiness of flooring, National Bureau of Standards.	2 15 25
D05	DIN 51097, (1977). Bestimmung der rutschhemmenden Eigenschaft, Nassbelastete Barfussbereiche, Deutsche Industrie Normen 51097.	60
D10	Doering, R. D., (1974). Defining a safe walking surface, National Safety News.	2 3 15 19 24 35
E10	Ekkebus, C. F. and Killey, W., (1973). Measurement of safe walkway surfaces, Soap/Cosmetics/Chemical Specialties.	15
E20	Eliasson, A. L., Hubalkova, A., Kuschyk, H. and Ohlsson, K., (1978). Golvprojekt – Halksäkerhet. Bakteriologiska mätningar, Miljövårdsprogrammet, Lunds Universitet (in Swedish).	14 15 17 24 25
E30	Eriksson, F., (1948). Redogörelse för försök att bestämma golvmaterials egenskaper ur halkfaresynpunkt och för litteraturstudier i samband därmed, Statens Provningsanstalt (in Swedish).	11 52
E40	Esmay, M. L. and Segerlind, L. J., (1964). Analysis of frictional characteristics of stairway-tread covering materials, American society of agricultural engineers.	7
E50	Ewerdahl, S. (1938). Halksäkerhet hos golvbeläggningsmaterial, Byggmästaren (in Swedish).	4
F05	Fischer, W. and Mattil, K., (1979). Neues Verfahren zur Bestimmung des Verschleisses und des Gleitverhaltens von Sohlenwerkstoffen, Gummi, Asbest, Kunststoff no. 6.	54
F07	Fliesen-Beratungsstelle, (1976). Untersuchung der rutschhemmenden Eigenschaft an keramischen Bodenbelägen, Fliesen – Beratungsstelle E.V. – Untersuchungsinstitut Grossburgwedel.	60 61
F08	Fliesen-Beratungsstelle, (1976). Rutschhemmende Eigenschaft keramischer Bodenbeläge in gewerblichen Betrieben, Fliesen – Beratungsstelle E.V. – Untersuchungsinstitut Grossburgwedel.	60

Table 14.4c *(continued)*

Reference		Description of apparatus number (see Table 14.4b)
No.	Author, year, title, publication	
F10	Frederik, W. S. (1958). Description of a new portable slip testing machine, CSMA Proceedings of the 44th midyear conference.	19
F20	Frycklund, H., Klittervall, T. and Lindberg, S-E., (1972). Halkrisker på golv inom livsmedelsteknisk och kemisk industri, Examensarbete, Arbetsmedicinska Institutet (in Swedish).	17
G10	Gavan, F. M. and Vanaman, J. B. (1968). Significant variables affecting results obtained with the James friction machine, Materials Research and Standards.	15
G0	Giles, C. G., Sabey, B. E. and Cardew, K. H. F. (1965). Development and performance of the portable skid resistance tester, Rubber Chemistry and Technology.	25
G30	Gough, V. E. (1953). A simple direct-reading friction meter, Journal of Scientific Instruments.	23
G40	Gurney, S. W. (1940). Is the floor too slippery?, National Safety News.	20
H10	Hunter, R. B. (1930). A method of measuring frictional coefficients of walk-way materials, National Bureau of Standards Journal of Research.	14
I10	Irvine, C. H. (1967). A new slipmeter for evaluating walkway slipperiness, Materials Research and Standards.	2
I20	Irvine, C. H. (1976). A simple method for evaluation of shoe slipperiness, ASTM Standardisation News.	2
I30	Irvine, C. H. (1976). Evaluation of some factors affecting measurement of slip resistance of shoe sole materials on floor surfaces, Journal of Testing and Evaluation.	2
J10	Johnsson, B. S. (1958). A discussion of some factors influencing slip resistance measurements, CSMA Proceedings of the 44th Midyear Conference.	2 15 24
J20	Joy, W. H., Pollnow, F. J., James, S. V. and Gurney, C. W. (1951). Field testing of waxed floors for slip resistance, Soap.	24
K10	Klittervall, T. (1978). Det går att göra mera för att minska halkolycksfallen, Arbetsmiljö (in Swedish).	17
K20	Kummer, H. (1963). Penn State Drag Tester, Highway Research Record No 28, Highway Research Board.	55
L10	Little, A. D. (1975). UFTM Evaluation, NIOSH, Contract no. 210-75-0032.	8
M10	Mahone, D. C. (1962). Pavement friction as measured by British portable tester and by the stopping-distance method, Materials Research and Standards.	25
M20	Majcherczyk, R. A different approach to measuring pedestrian friction the CEBTP skidmeter, ASTM STP 649.	1
M30	Mattsson, M. and Runqvist, H. (1971). Friktionsmätvagn BV 11:3 beskrivning och instruktion, Statens Väginstitut, Internrapport nr 44 (in Swedish).	44
M40	Mercier, A. A. (1930). Coefficient of friction of fabrics, Bureau of Standards Journal of Research.	22
N10	National Research Council. (1961). Causes and measurement of walkway slipperiness, National Research Council – Publication 899.	12 14 15 16 24 25 26 27 29 30
N20	National Safety News. (1974). Shoe sole slipperiness standard status, National Safety News.	2

218

Table 14.4c *(continued)*

Reference No.	Author, year, title, publication	Description of apparatus number (see Table 14.4b)
N30	Nilsson, C. (1976). Golv i djurstallar rapport från ett NJF-symposium, Lantbrukshögskolan Institutionen för Lantbrukets Byggnadsteknik (in Swedish).	40
N40	Nilsson. (1978). Golv i djurstallar del 2. Sveriges Lantbruksuniversitet Institutionen för Lantbrukets byggnadsteknik (in Swedish).	40 41
N50	Nordström. O. and Ohlsson, E. (1971). Description of friction test vehicle no 5 of the National Swedish Road and Traffic Research Institute, Report no 2.	47
O10	Olsson, G., Gullander, A., Hansson, J-E. and Isaksson, A. (1973). Jämförelse av galler ur halkrisksynpunkt. Arbetarskyddsstyrelsen, Uppdragsrapport Dnr 90/73 S (in Swedish).	17 49
P10	Pangels, R. (1962). Keramische Bodenbeläge mit hohem Gleitschutz, Wand und Decke.	33
P20	Pfauth, M. J. and Miller, J. M. (1976). Work surface friction coefficients: A survey of relevant factors and measurement methodology, Journal of Safety Research.	12 14 15 16 24 25 26 27 29 30 35
P22	PFI. (1974). Wirklichkeitsnahe Verschleissmessung an Sohlenmaterialen, ABC der Schuhfabrikation no 9.	54
P24	PFI. (1974). Wirklichkeitsnahe Verschleissmessung an Sohlenmaterialen, ABC der Schuhfabrikation no 10.	54
P26	PFI. (1975). Device for measuring sole wear, Schuh-Technik no 1.	54
P30	Pooley, R. W. (1977). Measurement of frictional properties of footwear sole and heel materials, ASTM STP 649.	2 15 25 53
R10	Ramsay, H. T. and Senneck, C. R. (1970). Anti-slip studs for safety footwear, Research Report 274 Ministry of Technology Safety in Mines Research Establishment. Applied Ergonomics, 1972.	38
R20	Reed, M. E. and Mahon, R. D. (1977). Description of the National Institute for Occupational Safety and Health (NIOSH) Universal Friction Testing Machine, ASTM STP 649.	8
R30	Reed, M. E. (1975). Standardization of friction testing of industrial working surfaces, NIOSH 76–123.	2 3 8 15 19 25 28 31
R40	Road Research Laboratory. Instructions for using the portable skid-resistance tester, Road Research Laboratory.	25
R50	Robinson, W. H. and Kopf, R. E. (1969). Evaluation of the horizontal pull slipmeter, Materials Research and Standards.	2 15 31
R60	von Rosenberg, G. (1959). Beitrag zur Bestimmung der Gleitsicherheit von wachsgepflegten Fussböden, Fette/Seifen/Anstrichmittel, No 3.	9
S05	Safety Sciences. (1977). Collection and analysis of work surface accident profile data, NIOSH, Contract no. 210-76-0150.	2 8 18 56
S10	Santos, F. (1966). Factors in detecting and correcting floor slipperiness, National Safety News.	2 15
S15	Schreier, W. and Wusterhausen, E. (1978). Gleitverhalten von Schuhwerkstoffen und Schuhen, Leder Schuhe Lederwaren no 1.	57 58 59
S20	Schuster, K. (1966). Glätte- eine Undersuchung für die praktische Unfallverhütung, Die Berufsgenossenschaft.	21

Table 14.4c *(continued)*

Reference		Description of apparatus number (see Table 14.4b)
No.	Author, year, title, publication	
S30	Sigler, P. A. (1943). Relative slipperiness of floor and deck surfaces, National Bureau of Standards, Building Materials and Structures, Report BMS 100.	24
S40	Sigler, P. A., Geib, M. N. and Boone, T. H. (1948). Measurement of the slipperiness of walkway surfaces, National Bureau of Standards.	24
S50	Sigler, P. A. (1950). Safe floor and floor finishes, Soap and Sanitary Chemicals.	24
S60	Skoforskningsinstitutet. (1979). SATRAs forskning i halkning vid gång, Skoforskningsinstitutet, Örebro (in Swedish).	45
S70	Sponseller, H. P. and Gavan, F. M. (1963). A machine for measuring dynamic friction, Materials Research and Standards.	6
S80	Statens Tekniska Forskningscentral Trävarulaboratoriet. (1977). Bestämning av friktionskoefficienten hos emballagematerial för sågvaror, Undersökningsrapport A 12781/77, VTT, Finland (in Swedish).	37
S90	Strandberg, L. (1979). Feluppskattning för Carlsöö-Mayr's friktionsmätare, PM 1979-05-16, Arbetarskyddsstyrelsen (in Swedish).	17
T10	Technical Products Co. Model 80 floor friction tester, Brochure, Technical Products Co.	36
T20	Tisserand, M. (1972). Etude des qualités d'adhérence des chaussures montantes de sécurité, Travail et Sécurité.	39
T30	Tisserand, M. (1977). Adhérence des semelles des chaussures d'atelier, Travail et Sécurité.	39
V10	VTI, -, Funktionsbeskrivning av handdragen skiddometer, Statens Väg- och Trafikinstitut (in Swedish).	48
W20	Williams, W. D., Smith, J. A. and Draugelis, F. J. (1972). Topaka: a new device and method for measuring slip-resistance of polished floors, Soap/Cosmetics/Chemical Specialties.	3
W30	Wilson, A. and Mahoney, P. (1972). Measuring frictional properties of soles and heels, Rubber World.	28
Z10	Zatloukal, J. (1973). The surface friction of shoe materials relevant to shoe making operations, Technical Development Department, Gottwaldov.	62

In a validity check of his method (apparatus No. 39 in Table 14.4), Tisserand (1969), found that its rank order correlation with subjective judgements of slip-resistance was negligible for static measurements and very high for dynamic measurements. Also tribometric research on rubber-like materials (e.g. Moore 1972) confirms the need for *dynamic* data from human gait and slipping. The large number of unvalidated apparatus may be explained by many meter designers' tendency to equate slip-resistance with static friction, because no sliding motion has been detected (irrespective of its existence) in their studies.

On the basis of tribology and practical experience, it seems to be of specific importance, that slip-resistance meters should reproduce the following operating variables from crucial gait phases.

(1) Contact time and normal force time derivative, for proper influence from surface patterning and its drainage capability.
(2) Foot angle, for testing the most important part of the shoe.
(3) Contact force application point at the shoe, ditto.
(4) Vertical force, for proper pressure in the contact area.
(5) Sliding velocity, for proper dynamic friction forces.

The reproduction of such variables must be based on proper biomechanical knowledge on human walking (Cunningham 1958; Harper *et al.* 1961; Lamoreux 1971; Jacobs *et al.* 1972; Mochon and McMahon 1980.

According to these references and similar literature, the above-mentioned variables (1)–(4) are quite well explored for walking on non-slippery surfaces. Though dynamic measurements of slip-ups in the laboratory have been presented (see Perkins 1978; Bring 1978), their motion data are based on stroboscope (30–100 Hz) or high-speed photography (up to 300 Hz). However, evaluation and synchronisation with force data seem to be quite time consuming, and other techniques are thus needed for studies of short-duration and low-velocity skids. The most interesting sliding velocities are up to the friction force peak, which occurs at about $0.02–0.5 \text{ ms}^{-1}$ for rubber-like materials (elastomers) (Conant and Liska 1960; Ohlsson 1979). As actual velocities during walking must be evaluated by differentiation (which amplifies noise) of shoe position data, a comparatively high sampling rate and sophisticated evaluation methods are necessary.

Therefore, a computerised and high-frequency gait analysis system, recently developed by Gustafsson and Lanshammar (1977) has been implemented for laboratory studies of human walking and skidding in a research project presented by Strandberg (1980a) and by Strandberg and Lanshammar (1981). The aim of the Mechanics of Skidding project is to accumulate sufficient knowledge about the biomechanics of slipping accidents and to evolve (or point at existing) adequate methods of measuring slip-resistance. These goals have been considered necessary for the development of safer shoes and walkways.

Computer analysis of slip-ups in the laboratory

Method and equipment

The first stage of the Mechanics of Skidding project mentioned above was a pilot study of normal gait. Without the subject's knowledge, a soap patch was applied or removed between various experiments. Four subjects and four different shoe models were used. Dynamic data from more than 100 experiments were recorded with the Gustafsson and Lanshammar gait analysis system (see also Strandberg and Lanshammar 1981). In this minicomputer system an optoelectronic device, Selspot, was used for kinematic data collection and ground reaction data were obtained from a Kistler force plate. Two Selspot cameras were used to obtain kinematic data for both legs. Landmarks (light emitting diodes) were placed on the shoulder, hip joint, knee joint, ankle joint, heel and toe base for both sides. The measurement area was approximately 3 m × 3 m. Data were collected at the rate of 315 Hz. The standard deviation of the measurement noise was 0.002 m and the systematic coordinate error was estimated to be less than 0.02 m.

The displacements of different body segments and of the shoes were calculated from the measured coordinate data. The velocities were calculated by numerical differentiation of the displacement data. Angles and angular velocities were obtained by application of trigonometric relations. From the force plate data, the vertical and horizontal components of the floor reaction forces as well as the application point of the resulting force were calculated.

For the Mechanics of Skidding project the gait analysis system has been combined with a rail-suspended safety harness (to prevent injuries in the event of falls), some devices to conceal the force plate surface (where soap was sometimes applied) from the subject, a video recorder (for tracking of experiments, force plate soaping, etc.) and additional computer software. Some results from the first project stage will be presented below (see Lanshammar and Strandberg (1980) for further details).

Every fall preceded by forward skid on heel

In 39 so-called *skids* out of 124 experiments, forward sliding of the stance leg shoe was detected shortly after heel strike. 23 skids ended in a *fall* (stopped by the safety harness). The remaining 16 skids became *slip-sticks* where the subject either was unaware of the sliding motion ('mini slip' in 4 cases) or regained balance – without apparent gait pattern disturbances ('midi slip' in 9 cases) and during large compensatory swing-leg and arm motions ('maxi slip' in 3 cases).

Though quite a few backward sliding motions were observed just before toe-off they never resulted in falls – not even loss of balance. Therefore, the 85 experiments not involving skids are called *grips*, irrespective of backwards sliding.

Dynamic data on human skidding and practical conclusions

The different phases of one complete gait cycle – one stride or two steps – are usually defined by the events *heel-strike* and *toe-off* (see Figure 14.4). The time ratio between the phases and their duration depend on many parameters (see, e.g. Grieve and Gear 1966; Andriacchi *et al.* 1977). One of them is the step frequency or cadence, which was 90, 100, 110 or 120 steps per minute in the experiments. Consequently, the different time durations may be non-dimensionalised, e.g. by division with the duration of one stride. However, this did not seem to reduce the corresponding variances in Table 14.5. Therefore time data are presented here directly in seconds.

In most of the recorded experiments the heel was sliding upon heel strike. The sliding motions were often unnoticed by the subject and occurred even without lubricant. Thus, the *dynamic friction properties*

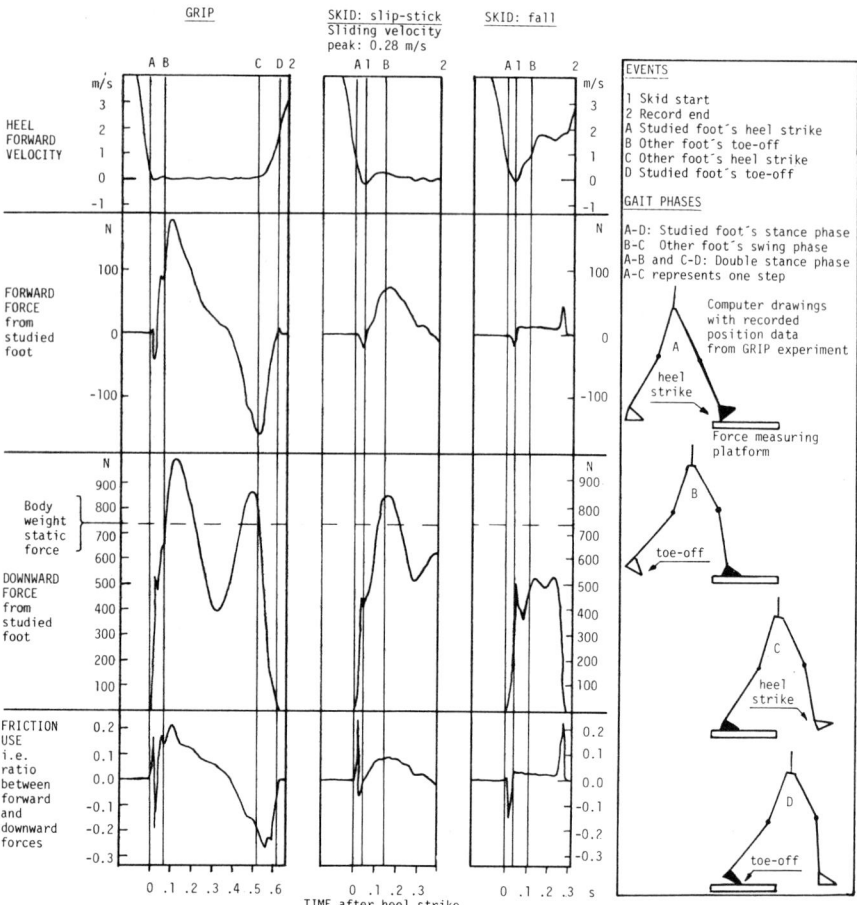

Figure 14.4 Selected diagrams from three experiments with the same subject
(HL in Tables 14.5 and 14.6)

seem to be more important than the static ones for avoiding slips and falls.
This conclusion contradicts the opinion of some investigators, claiming that
the static friction coefficient is the most relevant parameter to pedestrian
friction. However, a tribology expert stated that 'there is really no such
thing as a static coefficient of friction for most materials. Any frictional
force applied to them will produce some creep, i.e. motion' (Rabinowicz
1956). Even if the causal relationship should be reversed (motion produces
frictional forces) the relationship itself is accepted among tribologists.

In most of the slip-sticks, the peak velocity of forward slip remained
below $0.5\,\mathrm{ms}^{-1}$ (see Table 14.5). This indicates that the *friction properties
are most important to fall prevention for sliding velocities well below
$0.5\,ms^{-1}$*. However, the safe sliding velocity value depends, for example, on
walking speed, step length and anthropometric parameters. These relationships are now being studied with mathematical gait models.

The so called *friction use* (forward force divided by downward force) for
the slip-sticks stayed usually within the interval 0.1–0.2 during forward

Table 14.5 Skidding time, sliding velocity and distance, and absolute value of 'friction use' (ratio between forward and downward shoe forces). Mean value ± standard deviation for different skid types

Measured quantity Skid type No. in subgroup	Slip-sticks				5 AL	Falls with different subjects			All
	4 mini	9 midi	3 maxi	16 total		10 BÖ	8 HL	23 total	39 skids
Skid start* time after heel strike (ms)	48±39	55±15	44±13	51±22	61±25	45±18	37±14	46±20	48±21
Skidding time at peak velocity (ms)	33±17	52±20	52±34	47±22	Record ended mostly before peak.				
Peak velocity of forward slip (mms^{-1})	230±40	490±220	560±500	440±280	Above walking speed (1–2 ms^{-1}).				
Forward sliding distance (mm)	12±4	51±47	(86±37)†	(48±45)	†Record ended before skid stop.				
Friction use (absolute value) at skid start	0.12±0.07	0.10±0.07	0.04±0.03	0.09±0.07	0.04±0.02	0.13±0.05	0.04±0.04	0.08±0.06	0.09±0.06
Friction use 50 ms after skid start	0.15±0.02	0.14±0.04	0.06±0.02	0.13±0.05	0.02±0.02	0.12±0.06	0.04±0.02	0.07±0.06	0.09±0.06
Friction use 100 ms after skid start	0.13±0.03	0.15±0.06	0.08±0.04	0.13±0.05	0.02±0.01	0.11±0.05	0.03±0.02	0.06±0.05	0.09±0.06

* Skid start is defined by the first minimum in heel forward velocity if sliding continues after heel strike

slip. So in these experiments *0.2 appeared to be a sufficient dynamic friction coefficient.* However, even this limit depends on gait characteristics, which probably are strongly influenced by the friction experienced before the actual spot. Therefore, it seems reasonable to include *friction variation measures* as well as spot values and area averages in a slip-resistance safety criterion.

The friction characteristics mentioned above seem to be achievable in practice, even on slippery surfaces: irrespective of the test method (French standard with apparatus No. 39 in Table 14.4) and its inherent slip-resistance definition, Tisserand (1972; 1977) found encouraging improvements in the dynamic friction coefficient of 24 sole material samples from 1976 (best value: 0.27) compared to 22 samples from 1971 (best value: 0.19). The oscillation table tests were performed with working shoes from the French market applied flatly by a 600 N normal force to an oily steel surface. The friction force records were taken at $0.2\,ms^{-1}$ sliding velocity. In the 1976 tests ten shoes were regarded as good (dynamic friction coefficient above 0.15) compared with three shoes in 1971. However, Tisserand's friction force values may be higher than during walking due to (unknown) differences in normal force application time. This will be illustrated in the next paragraph, returning to the gait experiments.

In the 85 grips the friction use peak (mean value 0.17 ± 0.04 standard deviation) occurred about 90 ms (91 ± 25) after heel strike. Table 14.5 shows that the average skid started about 50 ms after heel strike. Thus, the *patterning of shoe heel and walking surface must be capable of quickly penetrating any lubricant patches.* A full scale test of this property must reproduce a vertical force time derivative in the $10\,kNs^{-1}$ order of magnitude, according to the vertical force value at skid start in Table 14.6. Therefore, the ability to control force application time was considered in the apparatus overview (Table 14.4a). The influence from force application time has been discussed by Braun and Roemer (1974).

After evaluation of the 39 skids, the values of foot angle (see Table 14.6) and contact force application point at the shoe indicate that the *dynamic slip resistance for the rear edge of the shoe heel is of the utmost importance for fall prevention.* Due to their false cueing, one cannot recommend shoes with soles which are more slip resistant than the heels. The near-falls, i.e. the maxi-slips, had an average sliding distance of about 0.1 m (see Table 14.5). Similar results have been arrived at by Perkins (1977). So if slip-resistant tapes, etc. are applied where people walk normally, the *gap between each tape should not exceed a few centimetres.*

Notice that the data above should be regarded as indications of the order of magnitude of each variable, and *not* as precise descriptors for a normal population of people, shoes and walking surfaces.

Conclusion

As opposed to occupational diseases, occupational accidents are unfortunately often considered to be caused solely by human error. Therefore, *accident* prevention is particularly dependent on ergonomists, who are

Table 14.6 Force and motion data from heel strike and skid start* in grips and skids. Mean value ± standard deviation.

Event	Vertical force (% body weight)	Foot angle (degrees)		Heel edge forward velocity (mms^{-1})							
				Subject AL		Subject BÖ		Subject HL		Subject KÖ	
	39 skids	85 grips	39 skids	14 grips	9 skids	19 grips	13 skids	47 grips	15 skids	5 grips	2 skids
Heel strike	0 by definition	22.0 ± 5.3		250 ± 430	840 ± 640	680 ± 520	1680 ± 1090	140 ± 270	60 ± 220	190 ± 170	100 ± 30
Skid start	64 ± 16		5.5 ± 5.9		80 ± 20		320 ± 290		100 ± 40		80 ± 20

* Skid start is defined by the first minimum in heel forward velocity if sliding continues after heel strike

aiming at improvements in the working environment, instead of unfruitful attempts to reduce natural variations of human behaviour. However, the large number of accident hazards in the working environment require proper techniques to identify the most relevant safety qualities and to develop objective procedures for their measurement.

Since accidents are multi-causal phenomena, all events and agencies from each accident cannot be lumped together into one 'accident type' upon registration for *statistical analysis,* without leading to serious underestimates of particular hazards in the statistical output. This was illustrated with official statistics on slipping accidents. The single type model, applied to previous occupational injuries, revealed less than half the annual number of slippings compared with the presently applied sequential model.

Logic diagram analysis (LDA) was touched upon as a feasible tool in *case studies,* where the causal relationships are to be clarified. Although LDA and fault trees are used for risk quantification in some purely technical systems, their man–machine system models should be considered to be primarily qualitative.

The accident analysis models above, consider each hazard as either existing or non-existing, thus giving no support for the assessment of limit values to crucial properties in the environment, such as slip-resistance. With dynamic *work analysis* models, on the other hand, the physical quantities that are frequently involved in accidents, can be sufficiently characterised for the outline of danger measurement methods and safety performance criteria.

Very few of the 62 slip-resistance meters listed here have been validated and compared with biomechanical data on human walking, slipping and falling. Therefore, no objective slip-resistance data should be accepted without examination of the inherent slip-resistance definition of the actual meter and method.

The results from laboratory experiments with human subjects indicated that real slip-resistance corresponds much better to the dynamic friction coefficient than to the static one. Since the subjects never fell if the sliding velocity peak remained below $0.5\,\mathrm{ms}^{-1}$, slip-resistance testing seems to be more relevant, if the relative motion is kept within the $0–0.5\,\mathrm{ms}^{-1}$ interval.

The experiments also pointed at quite a high normal force time derivative in the $10\,\mathrm{kNs}^{-1}$ order of magnitude. This must be reproduced by the slip-resistance meter if the lubricant drainage capability of shoes and floors is to be properly tested.

Due to foot angle recordings, the rear edge of the shoe heel appears to be of utmost importance for fall prevention. Although the heel slid (often imperceptibly) in most of the 124 experiments, no apparent gait pattern disturbances occurred when the sliding distance was below $50\,\mathrm{mm}$. Thus, the gap between slip-resistant tapes, etc. should not exceed a few centimetres.

Acknowledgements

The project 'Mechanics of Skidding' started in 1978 with grants from the Swedish Work Environment Fund. The project continues from 1980 with grants from the funds for special work environment projects at the Swedish National Board of Occupational Safety and Health. Some of the material in this chapter has been reproduced from the Journal of Occupational Accidents with kind permission from Elsevier Scientific Publishing Company.

References

See Table 14.4c for additional references on slip-resistance meters.

ANDERSSON, R. & LAGERLÖF, E. (1978). *The Swedish Information System on Occupational Injuries*, Memorandum, Arbetarskyddsstyrelsen, National Board of Occupational Safety and Health, Stockholm.

ANDERSSON, R. & SVANSTRÖM, L. (1980). *Accidents at Work – Analysis and Countermeasures*, [in Swedish], Almqvist & Wiksell Förlag AB, Stockholm.

ANDRIACCHI, T. P. *et al.* (1977). 'Walking speed as a basis for normal and abnormal gait measurements', *J. Biomechanics*, **10**, 261–268.

BENNER, L. A., Jr. (1977). 'Hypothesis generation for rare events research', (in Proceedings of a workshop on rare event/accident research methodology, Pezoldt, V. J. (ed.), 25–28, Report No. NBS SP-482, National Bureau of Standards, Washington.

BRAUN, R. & ROEMER, D. (1974). 'Influence of waxes on static and dynamic friction', Soap/Cosmetics/Chemical Specialties, Dec. 1974, 60 ff.

BRIDGMAN, P. W. (1927). *The Logic of Modern Physics*, Macmillan, New York.

BRING, C. (1964). *Friction and Slipping*, The National Swedish Council for Building Research, Stockholm.

BRING, C. (1978). *Testing of Slipperiness*, [in Swedish], Ph. D.dissertation, Royal Institute of Technology, Stockholm.

BRUNGRABER, R. J. (1976). 'An overview of floor slip-resistance research with annotated bibliography', NBS Technical Note 895, National Bureau of Standards, Washington.

CSMA. (1970). 'Tentative method for comparative determination of slip resistance of floor polishes', *CSMA Bulletin*, No. 245–70, Chemical Specialties Manufacturers' Association.

CONANT, F. S. & LISKA, J. W. (1960). 'Friction studies on rubberlike materials', *Rubber Chemistry & Technology*, **33**, 1218–1258.

CUNNINGHAM, D. M. (1958). *Components of Floor Reactions During Walking*, Institute of Engineering Research, University of California, Berkeley.

CZICHOS, H. (1978). *Tribology*, Elsevier Scientific Publishing Co., Amsterdam.

DUGOFF, H. *et al.* (1971). *Measurement of Vehicle Response in Severe Braking and Steering Maneuvers*, SAE paper 710080.

FISCHHOFF, B. *et al.* (1978). 'Handling hazards', *Environment*, **20**.

FISCHHOFF, B. *et al.* (1978). 'Fault trees: sensitivity of estimated failure probabilities to problem representation', *J. Exp. Psychol*, **4**, 330–344.

GRIEVE, D. W. & GEAR, R. J. (1966). 'The relationships between length of stride, step frequency, time of swing and speed of walking for children and adults', *Ergonomics*, **5**, 379–399.

GUSTAFSSON, L. & LANSHAMMAR, H. (1977). *ENOCH – an Integrated System for Measurement and Analysis of Human Gait*, Ph. D. Dissertation, UPTEC 77 23 R, Institute of Technology, Uppsala University, Sweden.

HADDON, W., Jr. *et al.* (1964). *Accident Research. Methods and Approaches*, Harper & Row, New York.

HARPER, F. C. *et al.* (1961). *The Forces Applied to the Floor by the Foot in Walking*, National Building Studies Research Paper 32, HMSO, London.

JACOBS, N. A. *et al.* (1972). 'Analysis of the vertical component of force in normal and pathological gait,' *J. Biomechanics*, **5**, 11–34.

JAKSCH, F. J. *et al.* (1974). *Volvo's Safety System Integration in Production Automobiles: Crash Avoidance Engineering*, Paper presented at FISITA 15th International Congress, Paris, 13–17 May.

LAGERLÖF, E. (1980). *Opportunities Provided by the New Accident Statistics*, Memorandum, Arbetarskyddsstyrelsen, National Board of Occupational Safety and Health, Stockholm.

LAMOREUX, L. W. (1971). 'Kinematic measurements in the study of human walking', *Bull. Prosthetics Research*, BPR 10–15.

LANSHAMMAR, H. & STRANDBERG, L. (1980). *Slipping Accident Mechanics – Stage 1*, [in Swedish], Investigation report 1980: 30. National Board of Occupational Safety and Health, Solna.

MOCHON, S. & McMAHON, T. A. (1980). 'Ballistic walking', *J. Biomechanics*, **13**, 49–57.

MOORE, D. F. (1972). *The Friction and Lubrication of Elastomers*, Pergamon Press, Oxford.

NATIONAL RESEARCH COUNCIL. (1961). *Causes and Measurement of Walkway Slipperiness*, Federal Construction Council, Technical Report No. 43, National Academy of Sciences, NRC, Publication 899, Washington.

OHLSSON, E. (1979). *Friction Measurements on Runways and Roads*, [in Swedish], National Swedish Road and Traffic Research Institute, Report No. 177. Linköping.

PERKINS, P. J. (1978). 'Measurements of slip between the shoe and ground during walking', (in *Walkway Surfaces: Measurement of Slip Resistance*, Andersson, G. & Senne, J. (eds)), ASTM STP 649, American Society for Testing and Materials, 71–87.

RFV. (1979). *Occupational Injuries 1975*, [in Swedish with summary, list of terms, etc. in English], Official Statistics of Sweden. Riksförsäkringsverket, National Social Insurance Board, Stockholm.

RABINOWICZ, E. (1956). 'Stick and slip', *Scientific American*, **194**, No. 5, 109–118.

REED, M. E. (1975). *Standardization of Friction Testing of Industrial Working Surfaces*, US Department of Health, Education, and Welfare, Publication No. NIOSH 76–123, Ohio.

SCB. (1977). *Causes of Death 1975*, [in Swedish with summary, list of terms, etc. in English], Official statistics of Sweden, Statistiska centralbyrån, National Central Bureau of Statistics, Stockholm.

SCB. (1981). *Occupational Injuries 1979*, preliminary report, [in Swedish with summary, list of terms, etc. in English], Statistical reports HS 1981:7. Arbetarskyddsverket, National Board of Occupational Safety and Health & Statistiska centralbyrån, National Central Bureau of Statistics, Stockholm.

SAFETY SCIENCES. (1977). *Collection and Analysis of Work Surface Accident Profile Data*, prepared for National Institute for Occupational Safety and Health under contract No. 210–76–0150, San Diego, California 99121, USA.

STRANDBERG, L. (1978). *Lateral Stability of Road Tankers*, National Swedish Road and Traffic Research Institute, Report No. 138A. Linköping.

STRANDBERG, L. (1980a). *The Mechanics of Slipping Accidents*, Investigation report 1980:29E, National Board of Occupational Safety and Health, Solna.

STRANDBERG, L. (1980b). *Accident Investigation for Safer Products. A Pilot Study: Severe Vehicle Occupational Accidents*, [in Swedish with English summary], Investigation report 1980:36, National Board of Occupational Safety and Health, Solna.

STRANDBERG, L. & LANSHAMMAR, H. (1981). 'The dynamics of slipping accidents', *J. Occupational Accidents*, **3**, 153–162.

SWAIN, A. D. (1972). *Design Techniques for Improving Human Performance in Production*, Industrial & Commercial Techniques Ltd., 7 High St. Camberley, Surrey GU 15 3QU, England, Jan, (revised July 1977).

TISSERAND, M. (1969). *Critères d'Adhérence des Semelles de Sécurité*, Institut National de Recherche et de Sécurité, Nancy France.

TISSERAND, M. (1972). 'Etude des qualités d'adhérence des chaussures montantes de sécurité', *Travail et Sécurité*, Nov.

TISSERAND, M. (1977). 'Adhérence des semelles des chaussures d'atelier', *Travaile et Sécurité*, April.

WHO (1967). *Manual of the International Statistical Classification of Diseases, Injuries, and Causes of Death*, World Health Organization, Geneva.

WILSON, J. R. & KIRK, N. S. (1980). 'Ergonomics and product liability', *Appl. Ergonomics*, **11**, No. 3, 130–136.

Chapter 15

Simulators for training

R. B. Stammers

Introduction

Simulation is used in three main roles in ergonomics. Firstly in the development of man–machine systems where various forms of simulation are used. These range from mock-ups of control panels to complex computer models of system functions. The aim is to predict optimal equipment design and task assignments, etc. In a second role, simulators may be used for performance or physiological measurement when data collection is not possible or is difficult in the real situation. The aim in this case is to collect data that best approximate to the real situation. In the system development case, the emphasis is on low-cost alternatives to building the real thing and then trying it out. In the second case, the concern is more with simulators that give data that are a valid approximation to the real thing and therefore puts an emphasis on high face validity of the simulator.

This paper will be concerned with a third area of simulation, that used for training. In this case, there is a range of situations that have been used for training, the focus of interest is on the transfer of learning that occurs from practice on the simulator to practice in the real task. This deceptively simple statement covers a broad range of topics and covers some controversial areas. It is hoped to review these issues in this paper. A broad or a narrow view can be taken of training simulators. The narrow view focuses on the using of equipment for training, and if that equipment bears a strong resemblance to the real thing, it is called a *simulator*. In this case, it is possible to compartmentalise the area as a small part of the general topic of training. A broad view, albeit fraught with dangers, takes on a bigger task. If training is concerned with the transfer of learning from one situation to another, the important features of that training situation can be closely examined. Any situation that departs from the real world task demands and exerts some control over the learning progress of the trainee can be termed a *simulation*. This broad view can be seen to cover most of the activities that are usually considered under the heading *Training*. The broad approach and the use of the term simulation does force important issues into the open, and leads to an emphasis on the learning process and its enhancement. Whether the broad or narrow view is taken is perhaps not so important at this stage of the development of the subject. This paper will take a somewhat limited view by focusing on equipment-biased situations but will attempt to keep a broad perspective.

A training simulator has been defined by Gagné (1962) as

(1) attempting to represent the real situation;
(2) providing control over that situation for the users;
(3) deliberately omitting features of the real situation.

These characterising features have been used to emphasise two extreme positions that can be taken about simulators. The first concentrates on the achievement of a high degree of realism in the representation. The second draws attention to Gagné's points (2) and (3) and talks in terms of minimum realism or 'fidelity' to produce adequate transfer of training.

The first position puts forward the premise that the more realistic simulators are, the more acceptable they will be to their users and purchasers. The position is also influenced by the idea of achieving the best possible job with available technology. In addition, there is often the attitude that a real situation remains the best place to learn a task, and that a highly realistic simulator is the next best thing.

The alternative position puts an emphasis on the research that has shown that high fidelity is not always needed for effective learning. In addition, it highlights the idea that the real situation is often not particularly suitable for learning, e.g. there may be a lack of feedback to the learners of their performance.

Both positions can be seen as only limited solutions at the present time. The focus on high fidelity is producing some highly expensive simulators whose validity is not always questioned. The second approach would seem to offer more in the long run than at present. There are many research questions needing to be answered. However, progress has been made and in later parts of this paper a way forward, on the basis of establishing valid training principles from research will be outlined. In the meantime, it is perhaps appropriate to return to the reasons for having simulators in the first place.

Reasons for simulation

Simulation training will be used because some tasks are critical or the context in which they occur is dangerous or stressful. It will also be used because of the nature of human learning, particularly its proneness to error in early stages. Simulators will also be used because of the interaction between these system and learning factors. In certain situations errors or inadequate performance can be tolerated within an 'on-the-job' training regime. Other contexts will preclude the acceptability of such inadequacy because of the consequences in terms of the costs of waste material, lost production, danger to life and limb and environmental questions. An additional context determinant of simulation training is where the real life task is inaccessible for training purposes. This will be the case for a system that is not yet working, or one where it is impossible to provide adequate on-the-job training controls. Other context reasons include the need to avoid inclement weather affecting training or other environmental factors. There are a number of reasons therefore, from a purely systems viewpoint, that point to the need for simulator training. Added to these reasons, can be considerations of cost effectiveness. It may be feasible to run a real system for training purposes but the costs incurred in this activity may be unacceptable. For example, it is possible to start up and shut down a piece of industrial plant to enable operators to practise the procedures involved. It is, however, vary rare that such an activity can be tolerated solely for training purposes. Without a simulator these tasks will be practised infrequently and fortuitously, with no guarantee that trainees will undergo any structured experience in relation to the activities.

From what was said in the previous section, it is very often these system reasons that are given as justification for the existence of a simulator. However, consideration of important learning variables will also show the need for a controlled learning environment. It is necessary to exert control over the trainee's interaction with the task in the training exercise. The control may be over the degree of complexity of the task that the trainees encounters. Are they, for example, given a simple task to begin with, or parts of the overall task, or a general outline of the system before being given the full complexity of the task? Through the use of some form of simulation it is possible to 'structure' experience. Other control procedures that may be exerted during training exercises are to provide guidance and prompting, in order to prevent errors occurring. Additionally, various forms of feedback will be given to the learner in order to shape and direct performance. This provision of feedback, extrinsic to the actual task characteristics has often been isolated as a key training variable. Appropriate feedback for learning of the task may not always be present in the real system, and it may be for this variable alone that some form of simulator practice is desirable.

Another control aspect of the trainee's interaction with the task demands is where a simulator offers the opportunity of changing temporal characteristics of the situation. In some situations it is necessary to speed up task features so that trainees can make efficient use of their time in training. For example, a start-up procedure may in real life take several hours to complete, various parts of the plant having a slow response to operator inputs. A simulator enables practice of these elements in fast time. In a more general sense, a simulator enables the experiencing of a range of plant conditions, e.g. faults, in a much faster sequence than they would be encountered with daily experience with the real plant. In other situations where a task involves high speed, practice in the simulator will allow an initial slowing down of the task to enable response sequences to be learned. The proviso here is that the simulator should be adaptive in some way so that practice at the full speed on the actual task can ultimately be achieved.

There is also the question of stress and the extent to which it can be controlled and prepared for within a simulator. A number of sources of stress for a trainee have been cited (e.g. Duncan and Shepherd 1975). There is the stress of the task context, this can be hazardous or novel for the learner. Interacting with this source of stress, there will be that coming from the trainee's perception of his performance and its adequacy and from the potentially high negative pay-offs in the task situation. Thus, as well as potential task context stress there is the task-induced stress of performing a complex task at the early stages of learning.

All, or a combination of these factors, leads to large-scale activity in a simulator area. At the present time, there is a major emphasis in the area of flying training with other developments in marine operations, industrial process control and power generation. Whilst there is a concentration at the high technology end of the market, the development of general principles of simulator training should be of value to all training endeavours. To take the nuclear power context as an example, the need for simulators for training has been clearly established (e.g. Stammers 1979). A complex interaction of system and learning variables points to the need for simulators in this area. In the post-Three Mile Island atmosphere, there has been an even stronger emphasis placed on their importance (Hickey 1980; 1981). Modern plant offers limited opportunities for observation and practice of the tasks of control and the consequence of human error here is now more clearly recognised. It is hoped that the pressures here to do something are not so great as to put an emphasis on high fidelity simulators only, and that appropriate efforts will be put into research on the underlying psychological variables. It is encouraging that this area has been given some attention (e.g. Rasmussen and Rouse 1981).

In consideration of nuclear power, a further reason for simulator use emerges, this is the topic of performance measurement. In many situations, the justification for the use of a simulator as a training device also means that it is difficult to measure competency in the real situation. If certain tasks are only infrequently practised then the assessment of competency in them is, in turn, difficult. The use of simulators for this purpose then emerges as an important area. It also gives a different, yet persuasive, reason for high fidelity simulators. Whilst it may be persuasive, evidence on the validity of other predictive measures should also be sought. It can also be added that in the aviation area simulators are commonly used for re-validation procedures. In conclusion, simulators can be justified on a number of grounds to do with both system, contextual and learning factors. The extent to which a simulator design exercise can be carried out systematically is the next concern.

The problem of simulator design

Like any other area of design, the development of training devices remains a fairly unsystematic and diverse activity. Many reasons for this may be put forward; the complexity of the factors involved, the high cost and consequence of human error, and it must be said, the lack of firmly established principles from the psychology of training. In order to turn the activity into a systematic and efficient design process, the establishment of such training principles needs to be put on a sounder footing. Thus the question of simulator design can be approached indirectly from a consideration of simulator evaluation studies. Whilst there are a fair number of these now, they do not as yet fit into a coherent pattern of results that are easily translatable into principles of training. However, progress has been made and systematic interpretation and translation of training research would save money in unnecessary experimental studies, and in pointing to areas of neglect and lack of knowledge.

The problems of evaluating simulators reduce to the difficulties of assessing any training programme. Firstly there are a variety of people involved in the use of the system. In turn what is an acceptable measure of the device will range from detailed performance measures to the subjective assessment by skilled users. In addition there are contrasts to be drawn between the internal validities of the training and, the transfer, relearning and retention measures that can be taken in the real task context. The problem of deciding on a suitable measure of transfer performance has been long standing (Hammerton 1967; 1977) and the problem has been readdressed by Roscoe (1971; 1972) who suggests the use of the transfer effectiveness ratio. This attempts to show the value of a training device in relation to transfer effectiveness at different stages of learning. This allows for assessment of the cost effectiveness of different amounts of simulation training.

In turn the problems of experimentation in this area, with inevitably complex experimental design has led to innovative research on economical approaches (Simon 1973). The complexities of the area are being grappled with and the various measures of training devices are being explored (Caro 1977) and complex models for the *prediction* of device success are being developed (Wheaton *et al.* 1976). All these developments suggest the development of an important conceptual framework in the future.

Evaluation studies tend to fall into one of two categories. At its most basic, an evaluation exercise would determine whether the simulator meets the requirements set for it and whether it actually produces acceptable levels of performance. This approach would be most commonly adopted in a practical context where 'a simulator' has been built. Evaluation in a research context is likely to lead, in the long term, to more generally useful results. This typically takes the form of the comparison of a range of training situations and the extent to which their different features have brought about effective transfer of learning to the real situation. These studies are most usually concerned with answering questions of degrees of realism in simulators and the extent to which they are important for learning. There are, however, a number of problems associated with evaluation studies. These have been recently addressed by Adams (1979). He criticises the two standard methods of simulator evaluation. Firstly, there is the transfer of training approach that has already been mentioned. He sees difficulties with this approach, particularly in those situations where it is impossible or near impossible to objectively measure transfer of learning. An example of this would be in-flight training with a single-seat aircraft. The other common approach is the rating of simulators by experts, trainees or those who commission the simulator. There are obvious problems with such subjective measures and the extent to which someone who is skilled or has only superficial knowledge of a simulator can assess its *training* value. Adams suggests an alternative approach to evaluation which is to base it upon the extent to which a training device includes established psychological principles. This basically returns to the starting point in this section, where the existence of such an *established* set of training principles can be questioned. One of Adams' principles concerns the importance of knowledge of results or extrinsic feedback. This has already been mentioned as one of the most central principles of training. Whilst this is not open to question, there have been many studies that have shown this to be a complex area. Whilst most of them concern fairly simple skills, they have shown that such variables as the optimum timing, specificity and frequency of feedback is, in turn, dependent upon many factors relevant to the situation and the learner. Thus, even a very basic principle such as this must draw upon a very detailed knowledge base to be useful. However, the Adams' approach should be the ultimate goal to be aimed for. It is clearly wasteful as a design process to build two simulators with different features and to carry out experiments to decide what is best. A set of guiding principles that will enable the best possible simulator to be developed on the basis of current knowledge should be the objective. It is the extent to which current knowledge enables this process to occur efficiently that should be closely examined and the above mentioned approach of both clarifying and organising existing knowledge and setting out to determine the gaps in that knowledge is the important role that theoretically-based research can play.

The fidelity issue

A central topic within simulator design concerns the degree of realism or fidelity of the simulator. This is a complex and confused issue, complex because of intricacy of any real-life situation and the problems of the extent to which they can be represented in an off-the-job training situation. It is confused as an area because of the lack of useful tools for analysing the complexity because of unclear terminology. A distinction is often drawn between equipment fidelity and psychological fidelity. Equipment fidelity refers to the extent to which a simulator physically resembles the real situation. This would be in terms of both face validity, its appearance, displays, etc., and in terms of its functional validity in the sense to which it 'reacts' in the way the real equipment does. It can be seen that there is a range of physical fidelity from complete realism in the sense that an operator could not tell the different between operating a simulator and the real plant through to very rudimentary mock-ups, models and diagrams of equipment that are commonly used in the early stages of training. The concept of psychological fidelity is more ill-defined. It is usually taken to refer to the extent to which the simulator produces behaviour that is the same as that required in the real situation, perfect psychological fidelity would be found in a simulator that yielded a hundred percent transfer of learning to the real situation. Problems occur with this concept on a number of grounds. There is the problem of measurement of transfer of learning in some situations and psychological fidelity may therefore be determined subjectively through rating of the simulator by a skilled person. Another problem with the concept is that in most cases, the only way the psychological fidelity can be determined is in an *a posteriori* manner by measuring performance transfer. It should, however, emerge as the central concept in the area once the subject is more fully developed. Once a body of knowledge is established that will enable predictive statements about learning to be made, then psychological fidelity will be a useful term. The two views of fidelity then should become closely related in the future, but at the present time they are often confused.

Given that the fidelity question is a complex one, it is not surprising that an immediate solution to it is not available. Nonetheless, given that it is an essential problem in the area, it must be tackled in some way. What is needed is a number of working approaches that can advance the subject by tackling practical problems with a view to developing the theoretical and conceptual basis of the subject. The area of training has benefitted greatly from the recognition of the importance of task analysis as an essential precursor to the design of any training programme.

This usually occurs in the context of a 'systems' approach to training and there are many basic texts in the area that outline these approaches (Butler 1972; Goldstein 1974; Stammers and Patrick 1975). Task analysis, however, only shows us the nature of the training problems that are present and does not by itself solve them. It needs to be closely linked with the developing technology of training which will relate training principles to particular forms of task demands. In relation to this, the various forms of training media have to be isolated, and their strengths and weaknesses outlined. In relation to the development of simulators, there is a need to focus on the total task situation in order to determine the important features to be built into the simulator. There follows a suggested approach to this problem, an approach which attempts to tackle some of the complexity in the area.

It sets out with two purposes in mind, one is practically orientated, which is to do with the analysis of complex situations in order to determine important features for simulation. The second envisaged use is that it should form the basis for the structuring of research results and ultimate derivation of training principles. It is, at the present stage, very likely to be incomplete and imperfect. However, taking the line developed by Miller (1967) in the context of task taxonomies, it may be best to develop a tool and emphasise its utility, then try it out in practice to refine and perfect it. In the past, analysis of situations in relation to simulator design have tended to focus on the stimulus (or display) aspects of tasks and the response (or control) aspects alone. Whilst these are of key and central importance, it is felt that close examination of situations will reveal other important dimensions. These dimensions themselves can now be considered.

(1) Stimulus/displays

The concern here is with the physical resemblance of displays used in a simulator in relation to the real world situation. The range is from very straightforward simple displays of dials, etc. to the complex visual work projections that are used in some vehicular simulators. It is important to remember that as well as their physical appearance, many displays have important dynamic characteristics that have to be learned about.

(2) Responses/controls

Here the dimension is the degree of realism of various forms of input devices and their operation. The emphasis is on face validity of the controls.

(3) Display–control interations/intrinsic feedback

These features are difficult to completely separate from factors (1) and (2) but, in the main, involve the linkage between displays and controls, their interactions and the sources of natural feedback from the task that they provide.

(4) Task complexity

The above factors could be held to concern mainly qualitative fidelity in the sense that the whole or part of the task is represented in terms of equipment. By task complexity is meant the degree of representation of the rule structure of the task or the quantitative fidelity. For example, it would concern the extent to which all functions of a piece of equipment are simulated. It is possible to present all of the possible faulty conditions, all of the systems states, or is only part of the real system represented? This could be held to be quantitative fidelity. It is possible, therefore, to have part of the task represented in high fidelity and other parts in low fidelity, thus this dimension concerns the extent to which the total task complexity is put before the trainee.

(5) Temporal aspects

This dimension is concerned with the extent to which the natural temporal features of the real task are altered in the simulator. It would involve the extent to which tasks are slowed down or speeded up to enhance the learning of the task. It can be seen that variations of this dimension, along with some others, often make the simulator deliberately different from the real situation. This alteration is carried out in order to enhance learning rather than to represent the real situation directly.

(6) Environmental stresses

The topic of stress, in terms of simulators, has already been mentioned. It can be seen that a number of sources of stress are eliminated in the provision of simulators. At the same time, it should be mentioned again, that if such stress is a feature of real life tasks then training must prepare individuals, in a controlled way, to cope with them. The topic of stress is a controversial one and one issue that emerges is often couched in terms of the ethics of applying stresses to individuals. The question that arises is how far is it ethical not to prepare individuals for the potential stress that they may encounter in task situations?

(7) Situational pay-offs

An additional source of stress, not included in the above dimension, is the fact that simulators are built in order to prevent the results of inadequate performance impinging on the individual or the system. Again, the need to eliminate such hazards from training is obvious but the stress factors mentioned above need to be considered. The interaction of these two variables is important but it is possible to envisage situations where the individual was subject to stress from various sources even though the consequences of his actions were not important in terms of the system.

(8) Social environment

A minor factor in most training systems and a major one in some, is the adjustment from the social environment of training to that of the work situation. Although not always a major problem, if a broad view is taken of simulation training then, under certain circumstances, this could be the key variable for the efficiency of training provided.

(9) Instructional control

Like the temporal dimension considered above, this is a somewhat different dimension to that normally considered in this area. Particular features are built into simulators that are not there in the real task. Aspects such as guidance and extrinsic feedback have already been mentioned. Some simulators enable playback of a situation, or the freezing of the task at a particular point in time. The simulator can be, in some ways, more complex that the real-life situation. If these aspects of the simulators are fixed and inflexible then performance within the simulator can be different from that in the real-life task situation. The ideal simulator situation is an adaptive one whereby external support to performance during training is removed as the learning progresses. Thus, design guidelines can be produced that will isolate important features to be incorporated in order to exert instructional control. Their optimal fading needs consideration to produce performance, at the end of training that involves the trainee interacting with what resembles the ultimate task demands.

The hope is therefore that a dimensional analysis of this kind will help in handling some of the complexity of the area and enable the production of a simulator that follows a more systematic analysis of the demands of the real situation. Examples of work in the fidelity area can now be considered.

Some fidelity studies

Experimental work in this area has a long history and is of a somewhat scattered nature. In this section, no attempt will be made to provide a comprehensive review of work, rather a few studies that illustrate the range of work in the area will be mentioned. In recent years, cognitive psychology has begun to have an influence upon instructional activities. A number of areas have felt this influence and one in particular concerns the extent to which exercises involving rudimentary training material can be substituted for practice in real or simulated tasks. A study by Prather (1973) used a 'mental practice' technique: subjects listened to tape recordings of instructions while they imagined flying an aircraft in a particular landing manoeuvre. This was shown to be a useful addition to the normal training received by these pilots. Brecke *et al.* (1976) working in a similar area, demonstrated that cognitive pre-training in the verbal rules and instructional cues relating to the task, made learning of perceptual motor skills efficient. These results suggest not so much that simulators could be replaced entirely by activities such as mental practice, but illustrate ways in which a total instructional system of which a simulator is a part, might increase its efficiency. They also show that situations seemingly far removed from high fidelity simulators can have an effective part to play in training.

A study of a ninety-two step procedural task using a control panel has been often cited. The series of experiments (Cox *et al.* 1965; Grimsley 1969a; 1969b) demonstrated that for such a procedural task, low fidelity in terms of both stimulus and response dimensions in simulators, produced the equivalent levels of training to high-fidelity situations. Low fidelity in this case extended down to a reduced size diagram of the equipment. The use of low fidelity training devices for such procedural tasks is now well established and the term procedural trainer/mock-up is often used in the area.

It is perhaps not surprising that it is the area of aviation that has received the most attention in terms of simulation fidelity. A number of writers have drawn attention to the concern for high fidelity in some areas and have questioned this as a universal principle of training (Hopkins 1975). In this area, a major concern is over the value of motion cues in flight simulators. This can be seen as an area of stimulus or stimulus-response interaction fidelity. There remains a fair amount of controversy over the training value of such cues. Experimental results are not clear, suggesting that the issue is a complex one. A number of studies have shown limited usefulness of motion cues during training (Cyprus 1978; Martin and Waag 1978). On the other hand, a study of a particular flight manoeuvre by De Berg *et al.* (1976) showed the importance of an interaction of visual and motion simulation to the extent that it produced important cues for the pilot. An important point in this area was made by Gundry (1976), he pointed out the difference between the alerting role of disturbance 'motion' and the feedback function of 'manoeuvre' motion. An additional point is that the presence of motion need not be of absolute fidelity to the real task to have some training value. This area has been re-addressed recently by Caro (1979), he has suggested that this line be developed further to analyse more closely the exact role that motion cues play in the control of an aircraft and to translate these into requirements for simulation.

Another current concern in this high technology area involves comparison of the relative effectiveness of different visual displays for aircraft. There are high-fidelity terrain-model-based systems that are expensive to build, show only one scene, yet can be highly realistic. On the other hand, there are computer-generated display systems which lose out somewhat in realism but are much more flexible in the range of visual scenes they can present.

Another sort of study in the fidelity area is that which emphasises one aspect of effective training in the context of a low-fidelity simulator. The aim here is to produce an effective trade-off between dimensions of learning situations in order to produce the most efficient training system. A good example of this approach is the work of Shepherd (1977) who has produced a training simulator for the diagnosis of failures in process control plants. The simulator consists of the back projection of life-size photographs of control panels. These panels can illustrate various stable or faulty states. The advantage of the system comes about through its being able to show the trainee many examples of fault conditions via a random access slide projector. This enables the comparison of many conditions that are potentially confusable within a collapsed time span. Even the most sophisticated full-scale simulator would take some time to be put into these various conditions. Another advantage is that it allows extensive practice of an important task component in isolation. A final advantage is the very low cost of such a system. The reason for the intensive practice is to attempt to enhance the retention of skill and its retrieval under stressful conditions by giving practice of the relevant diagnostic aspects of the task. In many simulator-training situations, the importance of training for stress reduction and the building of confidence has been emphasised. The Shepherd system suggests that this may be done most cost effectively with the low-fidelity simulator.

It is hoped that the further analysis of studies such as these, with a view to developing training principles, will lead to the solid body of knowledge that is needed for the more effective design of simulators. The emphasis on cost effectiveness should lead to a close examination of low-cost training situations and the extent to which they can produce effective learning. This topic comes up again if the impact of computer technology on training is looked at in greater detail.

Computer-assisted learning and simulators

The traditional distinction that could be made at one time between training activities called 'computer-assisted learning' and training activities under the heading 'simulators' is now having to be broken down (Stammers 1981). Even from the early days of simulator development computers have had a large part to play, and it becomes difficult to envisage simulators of any complexity that do not have some form of computer involvement. In the computer-assisted learning (CAL) context, various forms of simulation have been used in instructional exercises. They usually involve simulating some process or activity from which data are collected to be used within other learning exercises. It is rare that any attempt is made to represent task hardware. It can be seen, therefore, that a clear distinction between CAL and simulators is hard to defend in a general sense, to this can be added a number of contemporary developments in the area that show that perhaps a much broader view of the particular training system is needed.

One factor is the increasing involvement of instructional features in complex simulators which would be under computer control. They would include complex instructor terminals (Smode 1974) and such facilities as already mentioned, playback, freeze, slow and fast time. In addition in complex training environments computer management functions may be used to sequence or organise particular conditions. Trainees may be scheduled through a variety of experiences, the difficulty of tasks given to various trainees can be balanced. A second factor is that, as mentioned above, results from experiments showing transfer from low fidelity simulators have suggested that inexpensive pieces of equipment or computer terminals themselves may provide effective training stations. There are now a number of demonstrations of effective training from computer-based instructional systems. Equipment has been represented on a visual display screen and this can be enhanced with the provision of textual information and extra information not typically there in the usual training situation or a simulator (Crawford and Crawford 1978; Stern 1975; Trollip 1979). These studies are good examples of where the instructional control dimension comes to the fore and interacts with the low-fidelity representation of the task equipment to yield an effective training environment. This becomes particularly important when one considers some other developments. Within many contexts, e.g. aviation, control rooms, etc., the task equipment itself is increasingly taking on the form of visual display units and specialised input devices. So there is the curious situation of computer-assisted learning terminals perhaps bearing a high degree of resemblence to the task equipment! Added to this, is the growing concern over the importance of effective training in high-technology systems. This, in turn, places an emphasis much more on the cognitive skills involved in some tasks, e.g. fault location in complex systems, than on the physical skills involved in manual control. On the topic of problem-solving behaviour, there is a fair body of evidence on the use of computer-based training (Patrick and Stammers 1981). It becomes very difficult to categorise training in this area as being either CAL or simulator training. Whilst traditional distinctions between training methodologies are blurred by developments of this kind, this is perhaps, in the long run, a healthy thing if it focuses on the important psychological dimensions of tasks and causes reflection upon the most appropriate forms of training.

It should also lead to a much broader view of large-scale training problems with, as mentioned above, a high-fidelity simulator perhaps having a role to play at the final stages of training and in competency measurement. A range of training activities with various forms and levels of simulators would feed into this ultimate stage, the progress of the individual through the system being one of a progression through a range of training contexts that lead to the building-up of a flexible and persistent set of skills.

Conclusions

Whether or not a broad or narrow view of simulation is taken, it can be seen that at the present time, hardware technology and probably software technology as well somewhat outstrip the development of human factors technologies. This does not mean that there should be a lack of confidence in the extent to which ergonomists and others can be associated with developments. It should be clear that they have their own specialist skills to contribute to this area. The concern should be to develop our own technology to the point where we can make the most effective use of the systems that are now available to us to produce cost effective and efficient training systems to match the efficiency of the services that these systems can provide.

References

ADAMS, J. A. (1979). 'On the evaluation of training devices', *Human Factors*, **21**, 711–720.

BRECKE, F. H. *et al.* (1976). *The Role of Verbal Prescriptive Rules in Cognitive Pretraining for a Flying Task*, Tempe, Arizona: College of Education, Arizona State University, Tech. Rep. 60201. (AD-AO38626).

BUTLER, F. C. (1972). *Instructional Systems Development for Vocational and Technical Training*, Educational Technology Publications, Englewood Cliffs, N. J.

CARO, P. W. (1977). *Some Factors Influencing Air Force Simulator Design*, Alexandria, Virginia: Human Resources Research Organization', Rep. No. HumRRO-TR-77-2 (AD-AO43 239).

CARO, P. W. (1979). 'The relationship between flight simulator motion and training requirements', *Human Factors*, **21**, 493–501.

COX, J. A. *et al.* (1965). *Functional and Appearance Fidelity for Training Devices for Fixed-Procedures Tasks*, Alexandria, Va.: Human Resources Research Office, Tech. Rep. No. 65-4 (AD 617767).

CYRUS, M. L. (1978). *Motion Systems Role in Flight Simulators*, Brooks Air Force Base, Texas, Air Force Human Resources Laboratory, Rep. No. AFHRL-TR-78-39 (AD-AO59744).

CRAWFORD, A. M. & CRAWFORD, K. S. (1978). 'Simulation of operational equipment with a computer-based instructional system: a low-cost training technology', *Human Factors*, **20**, 215–224.

De BERG, O. H. *et al.* (1976). 'The effect of simulator fidelity on engine failure training in the KC-B5 Aircraft', (in *Proceedings of the Visual and Motion Simulation Conference*, Dayton, Ohio). New York: American Institute for Aeronautics and Astronautics, pp. 83–87.

DUNCAN, K. D. & SHEPHERD, A. (1975). 'A simulator and training technique for diagnosing plant failures from control panels', *Ergonomics*, **18**, 627–641.

GAGNÉ, R. M. (1962). 'Simulators' (in *Training Research and Education*, Glaser, R., (ed.)) University of Pittsburgh Press, (Reprinted 1965, Wiley, New York).

GOLDSTEIN, I. L. (1974). *Training: Program Development and Evaluation*, Monterey, Ca: Brooks/Cole.

GRIMSLEY, D. L. (1969a). *Acquisition, Retention and Retraining: Effects of High and Low Fidelity in Training Devices*, Alexandria, Virginia: Human Resources Research Office, Tech. Rep. No. 69-1 (AD 685074).

GRIMSLEY, D. L. (1969b). *Acquisition, Retention and Retraining: Group Studies on Using Low Fidelity Training Devices*, Alexandria, Virginia: Human Resources Research Office, Tech. Rep. No. 69-4 (AD 686741).

GUNDRY, J. (1976). 'Man and motion cues', (in *Proceedings of Royal Aeronautical Society, Third Flight Simulator Symposium, Theory and Practice in Flight Simulation*), London, April.

HAMMERTON, M. (1967). 'Measures of the efficiency of simulators as training devices', *Ergonomics*, **10**, 63–65.

HAMMERTON, M. (1977). 'Transfer and simulation' (in *Human Operators and Simulation*), Institute of Measurement and Control, London, pp. 1–6.

HICKEY, A. E. (ed.) (1980). *Simulator Training of Nuclear Reactor Operators*, Bedford, Mass: American Institutes for Research.

HICKEY, A. E. (ed.) (1980). *Simulation and Training Technology for Nuclear Power Plant Safety*, Bedford, Mass: American Institutes for Research.

HOPKINS, C. O. (1975). 'How much should you pay for that box?', *Human Factors*, **17**, 533–541.

MARTIN, E. L. & WAAG, W. L. (1978). *Contributions of Platform Motion to Simulation Training Effectiveness. Study I – Basic Contact*, Brooks Air Force Base, Texas: Air Force Human Resources Laboratory, Rep. No. AFHRL-TR-15 (AD-AO58416).

MILLER, R. B. (1967). 'Task taxonomy: Science or technology?', *Ergonomics*, **10**, 167–176.

PATRICK, J. & STAMMERS, R. B. (1981). 'The role of computers in training for problem diagnosis', (in *Human Detection and Diagnosis of System Failures*, Rasmussen, J. & Rouse, W. B. (eds.)), Plenum Press, New York, pp. 589–604.

PRATHER, D. C. (1973). 'Prompted mental practice as a flight simulator', *J. Appl. Psychol.*, **57**, 353–355.

RASMUSSEN, J. & ROUSE, W. B. (eds.) (1981). *Human Detection and Diagnosis of System Failures*, Plenum Press, New York.

ROSCOE, S. M. (1971). 'Incremental transfer effectiveness', *Human Factors*, **13**, 561–567.

ROSCOE, S. M. (1972). 'A little more on incremental transfer effectiveness', *Human Factors*, **14**, 353–364.

SHEPHERD, A. (1977). 'Fidelity of simulation for training control panel diagnosis', (in *Human Operators and Simulation*), Institute of Measurement and Control, London, pp. 129–135.

SIMON, C. W. (1973). *Economical Multifactor Designs for Human Factors and Engineering Experiments*, Culver City, Ca: Hughes Aircraft Co., Rep. No. HAC-P73-326A. (AD-AO35108).

SMODE, A. F. (1974). 'Recent developments in instructor station design and utilization for flight simulators', *Human Factors*, **16**, 1–18.

STAMMERS, R. B. (1979). *Simulation in training for Nuclear Power Plant Operators*, Karlstad, Sweden: Ergonområd AB, Rep. No. 12.

STAMMERS, R. B. (1981). 'The computer terminal as a simulator', *Eur. J. Ind. Training*, **5**, No. 7, 27–29.

STAMMERS, R. B. & PATRICK, J. (1975). *The Psychology of Training*, Methuen, London.

STERN, H. W. (1975). *Transfer of Training Following Computer-Based Instruction in Oscilloscope Procedures*, San Diego, Ca: US Navy Personnel Research and Development Centre, Rep. No. TR-76-1. (AD-AO12637).

TROLLIP, S. R. (1979). 'The evaluation of a complex computer-based flight procedures trainer', *Human Factors*, **21**, 47–54.

WHEATON, G. R. *et al.* (1976). *Evaluation of the Effectiveness of Training Devices: Literature Review and Preliminary Model*, Arlington, Virginia, US Army Research Institute for the Behavioural and Social Sciences, Res. Memo 76-6. (AD-AO76809).

Chapter 16

The implementation of ergonomics

T. O. Kvålseth & B. Shackel

Introduction

In this chapter we consider the factors which influence the implementation of ergonomics, specifically which factors influence a firm's use of ergonomics for the design of work stations and work environments and what is the relative importance of such factors? Answers to these questions have some definite practical implications for the development of ergonomics knowledge and of appropriate practical methodology as well as for the education of ergonomists. The answers are not likely to be simple and unique since the process of ergonomic implementation is a complex one in which cultural, social and political factors play important roles (Chapanis 1975; Shackel 1963; 1975). Our views are presented in the context of western industrial society, and the empirical data base collected to substantiate some of our propositions will be limited to one particular industrial society, that of Norway.

Of the many factors which may influence the implementation of ergonomics, some appear to be important specific issues and some seem to be wider factors.

Important specific issues

The specific issues are concerned with the scope of ergonomics and the characteristics of ergonomists which appear influential.

(1) *Science versus technology.* There have been advocates that ergonomics should concentrate upon gathering knowledge and establishing principles and theories about people at work and leisure, and other advocates that ergonomics should primarily apply knowledge from the human sciences usefully to practical situations. We think ergonomics must do both and therefore be both science and technology.

(2) *Researchers versus practitioners.* Differences of orientation can evolve by inclination, training and experience; but those involved in industrial practice should also be competent in research methods,

because industrial problems often need some applied research. Both types of ergonomists are needed.

(3) *Training of ergonomists.* The curricula contents, the techniques and skills taught, and the orientation (e.g. towards research or industrial practice) all need regular review and development.

(4) *Presentation of ergonomics data.* More attention still is needed to the demand for useful data to be presented in usable form for use by designers/engineers/production organisers, etc.

(5) *Position and status.* The contribution made by the ergonomist and its acceptance depends to some extent upon his/her position and influence as an individual and as a professional in relation to the organisation.

(6) *Personality and social skill.* Similarly, although the ergonomist bases his/her advice upon scientific knowledge and methods, the success of his/her work (especially as a member of a team or in contact with clients) must depend to some extent upon personality and relevant social skills.

Wider influencing factors

The issues briefly discussed here seem to us the more influential factors, although it must be emphasised that our suggestions are based on subjective appraisal of past and present experience, with the empirical evidence confined to that presented in the next section.

(1) There are major factors inherent in the structural situation which will determine the extent of ergonomics relevance and implementation. These may be summarised as follows (see Shackel 1966 for a fuller discussion):

(a) extent of human involvement re type of product (i.e. how much human usage);

(b) extent of human involvement re production process (i.e. how labour intensive, how skilled, etc.);

(c) any special aspects of situation re environmental variables (for example, hot work);

(d) any special aspects of situation re health and/or safety (for example, passenger transport);

(e) size of organisation (re method of acquiring ergonomics help);

(f) legislation (whether laws or standards compel attention to ergonomics issues).

The next three factors all provide an interesting paradox. Each adds to the growing need for ergonomics in practice and each also helps to cause some of the difficulties for its application.

(2) Complexity and sophistication of modern industrial technology sets higher demands upon the human operatives and controllers; but complexity also causes designers to be too busy with technical problems either to deal with the human factors properly or to learn enough about how to deal with them.

(3) Time and distance barrier: the complexity also separates designer and user, and thus usually prevents effective feedback. Therefore the

ergonomist is an essential link who has often to operate as a sort of preventive and predictive feedback channel. However, both complexity and time and distance factors make this more difficult for the ergonomist to do.

(4) Separation of responsibilities and cost consequences: another problem which seems to follow from the complexity is that often the designer, manufacturer/marketer, buyer and user are separate. They may well be in separate organisations and certainly will have separate aims and criteria. The designer (engineer) will aim for a good machine solution; the manufacturer/marketer will aim to cut the capital cost (but not necessarily the running costs); the buyer will aim to pay a low price and will expect savings to come from the purchase (perhaps by staff reductions); the user will aim to minimise his personal loss (of skill, earnings, etc.) due to the new machine, or method of working, and the true cost of training and of inefficiency, if the design is not ergonomic, can exceed any potential savings. This separation may also often cause each of these four separate responsible sectors not to use ergonomics, because they cannot see the cost justification within their own cost limits. Only the production manager in charge of the user sees the ultimate cost, but can do little to alter the basic design.

Now here is a factor which could substantially help to convince managers and governmental decision makers of the direct value of greater involvement in ergonomics.

(5) An economic aid to ergonomics – total system/total life costing? Whilst each sector of responsibility is separate, as noted above, the cost-benefit evaluation of ergonomics can often be difficult to prove. Therefore, a recent new concept may be helpful. Organisations using new systems (i.e. the buyers) are beginning to realise that the running and repair costs (including selection, training, maintenance and labour turnover) may far exceed the capital costs. Some are beginning to ask the manufacturer/marketer not only to sell machines or systems at the capital purchase price, but also to guarantee the total running costs not to exceed some annual value over an agreed 'life' usage; this is called total system-life costing. This development should be strongly advocated by ergonomists, because it will show much better the cost-benefit value of ergonomics.

Finally, but not of least importance, is the methodology factor and related issues.

(6) The emphasis given to these various inherent structural and functional factors within industry at large should not belittle the importance of the methodology by which ergonomics is implemented (for example, see Singleton *et al.* 1971; Shackel 1974; Shackel and Klein 1976). More important still is the fairly recent development (i.e. from about 10 years ago) of a different orientation towards industrial problems. Instead of taking over the problem as presented, working upon it (often in the remote laboratory) and prescribing a solution to be implemented, there is a growing tendency to involve the users fully in the whole process. The extent of user participation in design can vary considerably, but the ethos and relevance of this type of approach is gaining wide acceptance. It is being adopted especially in the development of computer systems applications (Eason 1977; Damodaran 1977; Eason and Damodaran 1979; Mum-

ford 1978) and some of the papers presented at the IEA/NES Conference discussed this development in methodology and illustrated its value (Lenior *et al.* 1980; Sell 1980).

The above more specific and more general factors are based upon our experience and upon the opinions and experience of other ergonomists. However, we must emphasise that they do not have any great scientific validity and they have no empirical evidence or even controlled data gathering to support them. Therefore, a first empirical study was planned.

Empirical study

Magnitude estimation

It was decided that an appropriate information source for the study would be the subjective opinions of individuals who are directly involved in ergonomic implementations in their respective firms. Magnitude estimation was chosen as the method by which these individuals rated their perceptions of the importance of various factors in influencing the implementation of ergonomics in their firms. This relatively recent scaling technique, which was developed by the late S. S. Stevens at Harvard University as a psychophysical method of measuring subjective sensations of the magnitudes (intensities) of various types of stimuli, has found a number of useful applications for measuring subjective perception of more complex phenomena in behavioural science (see Stevens 1975 for a summary of some such applications; Kvålseth 1980).

A primary advantage of the magnitude estimation method, which also has an almost disarming simplicity, is that it is thought to lead to the highest level scale, i.e. the ratio scale. For such a scale, which possesses all the characteristics of an interval scale and in addition has a true zero point as its origin, it is meaningful to consider both the difference between any two values (scale points) and their ratio with the ratio being independent of the unit of measurement. Clearly, for the purpose of the present study, such a scale would have considerable advantage over the frequently used ordinal scale, since the latter would not provide any meaningful information about either the relative importance of the various factors (other than the rankings 'more important' or 'less important') or the relative differences between pairs of rankings. For these reasons, it was decided that the magnitude estimation method would be used in the present study, although this method is not yet firmly established as a universally accepted method of scaling non-metric stimuli, and has so far had very limited impact (too limited in the authors' opinions) as a measurement tool in ergonomics. In fact, part of the objective of the present study was to assess the feasibility of using this method for the relatively complex task of scaling subjective opinions about the importance of various work-related factors by individuals with a variety of different educational and training backgrounds and job responsibilities.

Procedure

The different factors to be considered were selected partly by the investigators and partly on the basis of interviews in a few firms. A total of 16 factors were chosen as defined in Table 16.1. Each of these factors was typed on a separate page of a small booklet. The factors or pages were arranged in a different random order for each booklet. Each subject was given one such booklet, and his task was to rate each factor at a time in terms of how important he felt each factor was in influencing whether and to what extent ergonomic implementations were made in his firm.

Rather than using the term 'ergonomics' (Norwegian: ergonomi), which is still a foreign word to (too) many, such terms as 'improve working environments and work place design' were used. No time constraint was imposed on the subject. On average, it took no more than about 15–20 min to complete the rating task. Furthermore, no constraint was imposed on the subject in terms of a common modulus by designating any one of the factors as a standard. Instead, each subject was free to choose his own modulus as has been strongly recommended by Stevens (1975). The written instruction on the cover page of each booklet, which was patterned after Stevens' general format, was as follows.

'This booklet contains some factors that may influence whether or not and to what extent your firm makes satisfactory efforts to improve working environments and work place design. These factors are presented in random order in this booklet with one factor per page.

'Your task is to judge the importance that you believe these factors have on the implementation of satisfactory undertakings to improve working environments and work place design in your firm. To the first factor (i.e. the one given on the first page in this booklet), assign any number that seems appropriate for your feeling about the importance that this factor has on the implementation of undertakings to improve working environments and work place design. For the subsequent factors given on the next pages, assign those numbers that your feel represent your subjective impression of the factors' importance.

'If you believe that the second factor is twice as important as the first factor, assign it a number that is twice as large as the first; if the second factor seems to be one-fifth as important as the first, assign it a number one-fifth as large, etc.

'Write each number at the bottom of each page as indicated. Write clearly! You may use whole numbers, decimals, or fractions, as well as a mixture of these. Please do not use the number zero or negative numbers.

'Take one page at a time. Try to avoid looking back on earlier pages and avoid changing previous judgements.'

Data sample

A total of 34 individuals of both sexes representing 21 different firms participated in the study. Their ages ranged from 26–56 years and the range of their employment with the present firms was 0.5–31 years. These individuals were, to varying degrees, involved in ergonomic activities in their respective firms. They represented such typical position categories as health personnel (physiotherapists and physicians), production manager, union steward (for ergonomic activities) and safety engineer.

The 21 firms, which were essentially located throughout Norway, were primarily industrial firms involved in either manufacturing or service activities. Their sizes ranged from less than 100 to a few thousand employees.

Results and discussion

The mean and variation of the importance ratings of the various factors by the individuals from the 21 firms are given in Table 16.1. The geometric rather than the arithmetic mean was used since the data obtained from magnitude estimation generally appear to be log normally distributed (Stevens 1975, pp. 269–270). The rating variations given in Table 16.1 were determined in terms of the semi-interquartile range. Since it was desirable that the ratings from the different firms should be weighted equally, the ratings by more than one individual in the same firm were first averaged (geometrically) before the mean and variation values in the table were calculated. In a few instances in which a zero rating was used, which was not permitted according to the written instruction to the subjects (since it would cause the geometric mean to be undefined), the arbitrary value 0.01 was substituted.

The results in the table emphasise clearly the importance of management's perception of the need for and potential benefits of ergonomic implementations as factors determining whether or not and to what extent such implementations will be made. These 'need perception' and 'potential benefit' factors appear to be somewhat more important from the point of view of management than from that of the workers (i.e. shop-floor personnel). The cooperation between individuals from these two job categories in ergonomic matters is ranked as the third most important factor. The real involvement by both management and the workers in ergonomic implementations is also ranked high on the import-ance scale. These results provide clear support for some of the arguments that we raised earlier in this chapter and for those raised by others (e.g. Sell 1980).

Public laws governing working conditions appear to be thrice as impor-tant as local laws and regulations. A firm's financial and technological abilities and ergonomic competence to undertake ergonomic implementa-tions seem to be of nearly identical importance. The firm's own financial ability and ergonomic competence for solving ergonomic problems are rated as nearly twice as important as the availability of external assistance, i.e. grants and favourable low-interest federal loans and ergonomic consulting services.

Perhaps somewhat surprising is the relatively low importance rating given to factor 12 in the table relating to accident rates and health problems, although a few of the firms did place this factor towards the top of the importance scale. Also, the likelihood of a firm being inspected and ordered to make ergonomic implementations by the Directorate of Labour Inspection (equivalent to the Factory Inspectorate in Britain and to OSHA in the USA) seems to have relatively little influence on the degree of ergonomic implementation in a firm.

Table 16.1 Mean (geometric) and variation (semi-interquartile range) of magnitude estimates for the perceived importance of the various factors (*N* = 34 individuals in 21 Norwegian firms)

Factor No.	Factor description	Importance ratings	
		Mean	Variation
(1)	Management's perception of the need for ergonomic implementations	10.02	3.11
(2)	Management's knowledge of the potential benefits of having satisfactory working conditions and environment	9.68	1.82
(3)	Degree of cooperation between management and the workers regarding environmental problems and work place design	9.49	2.45
(4)	Workers' perception of the need for ergonomic implementations	9.04	1.66
(5)	Management's real involvement in ergonomic implementations	8.91	2.21
(6)	Workers' real involvement in ergonomic implementations	8.09	1.99
(7)	Public laws that impose general demands on the work place (e.g. 'Act relating to Worker Protection and Working Environment')	7.93	2.18
(8)	Workers' knowledge of the potential benefits of having satsifactory working conditions and environment	7.72	2.38
(9)	The firm's financial ability to carry out ergonomic implementations	7.70	2.39
(10)	The firm's professional qualifications (competence and available information) for identifying and solving ergonomic problems	7.69	2.08
(11)	The firm's technological ability (i.e. available equipment and technology) for carrying out ergonomic implementations	7.64	1.92
(12)	The extent of work accidents and incidents of damage to health in the firm	4.55	2.11
(13)	The firm's opportunity of acquiring external assistance (consultants) for identifying and solving the firm's ergonomic problems	4.48	2.57
(14)	Availability of government economic support for improving working conditions and environment	3.92	1.55
(15)	Directorate of Labour Inspection's frequency of inspection and likelihood of ordering ergonomic implementations	3.85	1.51
(16)	Local laws and regulations that impose general demands on the work place	2.64	2.10

From the data in the right-hand column in the table, it is apparent that there is a considerable degree of variation in how important the various factors are perceived to be by individuals in different firms. This is clearly not an unexpected finding since the firms involved in this study represent a wide variety in terms of types of manufacturing/service activities, size, etc. It should be pointed out that since no standard or common modulus was used in this study, the data were transformed such that each subject's (or each firm's rating when more than one individual from the same firm participated) mean rating (i.e. geometric mean) across all factors coincided with the grand mean before the semi-interquartile range values in the table were calculated (see Stevens 1975, p. 289). That is, in logarithmic terms the difference between the grand mean of the importance ratings of all factors by all subjects and the mean of each subject's ratings for all factors was added to that subject's individual ratings. In general, the data in the table do not reveal any clear systematic relationship between the variation and the mean of the importance ratings across the subjects.

Although it was the first time any of the subjects had used this scaling method, they did not seem to have any particular difficulty with it with only a few exceptions. Even though it was made clear to them in the written instruction that their ratings were not restricted to any specific range (see instruction above), about two-thirds of the subjects limited their ratings to the range 0–10, which is also reflected in the data in the table.

Conclusion

We have raised some specific issues and postulated a number of causal factors of the ergonomic implementation process, that is in turning theory and expectation into practice and achievement. There may well be many other factors which are relevant and important to the implementation of ergonomics. We have attempted to acquire some empirical support for some of our propositions and to determine the relative importance of the various causal factors through an empirical study in a number of industrial firms. The results of our study must be interpreted as being specific to the situation in Norway, and may not extend across different social, cultural or political boundaries. Also, the specific findings from the study ought to be interpreted with some caution because of the rather limited sample of subjects and firms used. Nevertheless, the results reveal some interesting information about the relative importance of various causal factors in the ergonomic implementation process and would seem to be sufficiently encouraging to warrant an expanded investigation. Clearly, empirical results such as those of the present study may provide useful information so that our teaching of ergonomists, and of ergonomics knowledge and simple methods to designers and managers, can be significantly improved, which in turn may aid the propagation of ergonomics to the work place.

Perhaps the finding of most general interest from this study is the fact that magnitude estimation appeared to be an appropriate technique for the ratio scaling of subjective perceptions or opinions as considered in the study. In retrospect, and as a consideration for future studies, it should perhaps have been emphasised even more clearly than was done in the written instruction to the subjects that there was no limit to the range of numbers that may be used; this would further help to ensure that a subject does not feel compelled to use a scale from zero to ten, say, as appeared to be the case for several of the subjects in the present study.

References

CHAPANIS, A. (ed.). (1975). 'The ethnic variables in human factors engineering', (papers presented at *NATO Symposium on National and Cultural Variables in Human Factors Engineering*, 1972) John Hopkins Press, Baltimore, USA.

DAMODARAN, L. (1977). 'User involvement insystem design – Why and how?', (in *Computing and People*, Parkin, A. (ed.)) Edward Arnold, London.

EASON, K. D. (1977). 'Human relationships and user involvement in systems design', *Computer Management*, **19** 10–12.

EASON, K. D. & DAMODARAN, L. (1979). 'Design procedures for user involvement and user support', (in *Man–Computer Communication*, Infotech State of the Art Report, Shackel, B. (ed.)) Infotech International Ltd, Maidenhead.

KVÅLSETH, T. O. (1980). 'Quantitative measures of job variety: an experimental study based on a psychophysical scaling technique', *Int. J. Production Research*, **18**, 441–454.

LENOIR, T. M. J. *et al*. (1980). 'From field operators to central control room operators: an integrated educational, research and consultancy approach', *Ergonomics*, **23**, 741–749.

MUMFORD, E. (1978). 'A strategy for the redesign of work.' (in *Designing Organizations for Satisfaction and Efficiency*, Legge K. and Mumford, E. (eds.)) Gower Press, London.

SELL, R. G. (1980). 'Success and failure in implementing changes in job design', *Ergonomics*, **23**, 809–816.

SHACKEL, B. (1963). 'An introduction to ergonomics', (Paper B.64 to *UN Conference on Science and Technology for Less Developed Areas*, Geneva 4–20 February) UNCSAT Proceedings, Geneva.

SHACKEL, B. (1966). 'Ergonomics and design'. (in *The Design Method*, Gregory, S. H. (ed.)), chap. 7, 49–58. Butterworth, London.

SHACKEL, B. (ed.), (1974). *Applied Ergonomics Handbook*, IPC Science & Technology Press Ltd, Guildford.

SHACKEL, B. (1975). 'Proposed university course for Algeria in ergonomics', Report on mission for Ministry of Higher Education and Scientific Research, Algerian Republic. Department of Human Sciences Rep. No. DHS 180.

SHACKEL, B. & KLEIN, L. (1976). 'ESSO London airport refueling control centre redesign – An ergonomics case study', *Appl. Ergonomics*, **7**, 37–45.

SINGLETON, W. T. *et al*. (eds.), (1971). *Measurement of Man at Work*, Taylor & Francis Ltd, London.

STEVENS, S. S. (1975). *Psychophysics*, Wiley, New York.

Appendix 1

Sources of ergonomics information for industrial job design

T. O. Kvålseth

This guide to the published literature on ergonomics is intended for those concerned with the application of ergonomics to practical design problems and is not a complete bibliography of ergonomics publications. The list of ergonomics texts and handbooks is relatively complete, but the list of journal publications represents only a small sample of articles (an accession number of approximately 68 000 publications is reported by an ergonomics database for the period 1959–1975 (Kraiss and Moraal (1976), p. 497). The journal publications selected for inclusion in this bibliography represent some excellent review articles as well as useful data sources for industrial job design. The task of selecting the journal articles was greatly aided by a recent unpublished bibliography prepared by the Industrial Ergonomics Technical Group of the Human Factors Society.

The various references are identified with a set of topics or areas of ergonomics using a numerical code. Cross-coding between areas is also used to some extent. Attempts have been made to assign each reference to the most appropriate areas, which were again selected with particular relevance to industrial applications. Finally, a list of journals is given and some abstracting or bibliographic services are identified as additional useful ergonomics information sources.

Topics

General texts and handbooks

21, 33, 36, 41, 46, 48, 57, 61, 62, 63, 70, 71, 72, 74, 82, 83, 86, 89, 90

Man–machine systems

Displays and controls

2, 10, 12, 17, 21, 24, 25, 28, 29, 33, 36, 37, 41, 48, 49, 53, 57, 61, 62, 63, 64, 69, 70, 72, 73, 74, 82, 83, 86, 89, 90

Instrument layout

17, 21, 25, 33, 41, 48, 49, 53, 57, 61, 62, 63, 69, 70, 72, 73, 74, 82, 86, 89, 90

Operator functions (alternative control and monitoring tasks, man–machine task allocation, operator performance capabilities and limitations)

10, 24, 29, 30, 33, 36, 41, 48, 57, 62, 63, 64, 73, 82, 86, 90

Design of tools and equipment

2, 19, 21, 25, 37, 38, 41, 46, 57, 62, 69, 70, 80, 81, 83, 84, 86, 87, 89, 90

Design of workstations

8, 10, 12, 14, 15, 18, 19, 21, 25, 27, 28, 29, 33, 35, 36, 37, 41, 43, 46, 48, 50, 52, 56, 57, 60, 61, 62, 63, 66, 69, 70, 72, 74, 76, 81, 82, 83, 84, 86, 87, 89, 90

Job analysis and design

10, 13, 22, 23, 24, 29, 30, 34, 36, 42, 44, 58, 63, 66, 68, 73, 75, 77, 78, 79, 85, 88

Anthropometry (physical dimensions of body members, mobility, strength, sex and age differences)

15, 16, 21, 25, 26, 35, 36, 41, 46, 48, 54, 57, 62, 63, 65, 67, 69, 70, 74, 82, 83, 86, 89, 90

Work environmental factors
Noise

4, 11, 20, 31, 36, 41, 46, 48, 51, 57, 62, 63, 67, 68, 72, 74, 82, 84, 86, 89, 90

Illumination

5, 6, 9, 32, 33, 36, 40, 41, 46, 48, 57, 62, 63, 67, 68, 70, 72, 74, 82, 84, 86, 89, 90

Climate

3, 28, 36, 41, 45, 46, 47, 48, 57, 59, 62, 63, 67, 68, 72, 74, 82, 84, 89, 90

Vibration

7, 20, 36, 39, 41, 48, 57, 62, 63, 67, 68, 82, 84, 90

Toxicology

46, 55, 62, 67, 84

Comments

Some additional general remarks may be appropriate concerning a few of the general textbooks and reference sources listed. Among the classical books providing a fairly broad coverage of ergonomics were those of McCormick [57, first edition in 1957], Morgan *et al*. [62], Murrell [63], Van Cott and Kinkade [86, first edition in 1963] and Woodson and Conover [89, first edition in 1954]. As a textbook for introductory ergonomics courses, McCormick's book has probably been the most widely used one, at least in the USA. Of the more recent books, those of Grandjean [36], Huchingson [41], Konz [46], Salvendy [71], Shackel [74] and Woodson [90] provide excellent treatise covering most of the important aspects of ergonomics relevant to systems design. The book by Konz also covers topics from methods engineering and work measurement (time and motion study), but does not cover man–machine interface design. Its coverage of workstation design, tool design, anthropometry, work physiology and work environmental factors is comprehensive and clearly presented. While Shackel [74] provides a good and broad survey of ergonomics with quite extensive design data, it is somewhat out of date and is apparently in the process of being revised. Grandjean's book, which is a revision of its 1969 English edition, is one of the best sellers among the Taylor & Francis ergonomics books. While the earlier edition placed a particularly strong emphasis on work physiology, this latest edition provides a much more balanced presentation. It also contains material on night and shift work, mental activity and boredom. Finally, the ergonomics chapters in Salvendy [71] and the books by Huchingson [41] and Woodson [90] provide up-to-date data, design guidelines and reference sources useful for ergonomists, designers and engineers in practical design situations.

Journals and proceedings

The primary journals of ergonomics are the following:

Ergonomics. Publisher: Taylor & Francis, London.
Human Factors. Publisher: Human Factors Society, Santa Monica, CA.
Applied Ergonomics. Publisher: IPC Science and Technology Press, Surrey, England.
Ergonomics Abstracts. Publisher: Taylor & Francis, London.

Additional journals publishing papers relevant to various aspects of ergonomics include the following:

Journal of Occupational Psychology. Publisher: British Psychological Society, Leicester.
Journal of Applied Psychology. Publisher: American Psychological Association, Washington, DC.
Journal of Applied Physiology. Publisher: American Physiological Society, Bethesda, Maryland.
Behaviour & Information Technology. Publisher: Taylor & Francis, London.
Journal of Occupational Behaviour. Publisher: Wiley, New York.

Conferences sponsored by various ergonomics societies also publish proceedings of the papers presented. In particular, the Human Factors Society publishes proceedings from each of its annual meetings. These may be purchased from The Human Factors Society, PO Box 1369, Santa Monica, CA 90406, USA.

Abstracting services

Ergonomics Abstracts, UK.
Psychological Abstracts, USA.
Science Citation Index, USA.
Social Science Citation Index, USA.
MEDLARS (Medical Literature Analysis and Retrieval System), USA.

The *Ergonomics Abstracts* is published quarterly in journal format by Taylor & Francis, Inc. in cooperation with

Ergonomics Information Analysis Centre
Department of Engineering Production
University of Birmingham
PO Box 363
Birmingham B15 2TT, UK.

This Centre also maintains up-to-date bibliographies for a certain set of subject areas. Such bibliographies, as well as special bibliographies requested personally by a user, are subject to nominal charges.

With the exception of the Ergonomics Information Analysis Centre, these various databases are also available for computerised bibliographic searches. In this author's experience, such computerised searching is not entirely complete and it may be advisable to supplement it by manual searching.

References

1. AIHA Technical Committee on Ergonomics. (1971). 'Ergonomics guide to assessment of metabolic and cardiac costs of physical work', *Am. Industrial Hygiene Assoc. J.*, **32**, 560–564.
2. ALDEN, D. G. *et al.* (1972). 'Keyboard design and operation: a review of the major issues', *Human Factors*, **14**, 275–293.
3. American Industrial Hygiene Association. (1975). *Heating and Cooling for Man in Industry*, 2nd edition, Akron, Ohio.
4. American Industrial Hygiene Association. (1975). *Industrial Noise Manual*, 3rd edition, Akron, Ohio.
5. ANSI Standard All.1-1973. (1973). *American National Standard Practice for Industrial Lighting RP-7*, Illuminating Engineering Society, New York.
6. ANSI Standard Al32.1-1973. (1973). *American National Standard Practice for Office Lighting RP-1*, Illuminating Engineering Society, New York.
7. ANSI Standard S3.18-1979. (1979). *American National Standard: Guide for the Evaluation of Human Exposure to Whole-Body Vibration*, Acoustical Society of America, New York.
8. AYOUB, M. M. (1973). 'Workplace design and posture', *Human Factors*, **15**, 265–268.

9. Bennett, C. A. (1982). 'Lighting' (in *Handbook of Industrial Engineering*, Salvendy, G. (ed) chap 6.11). Wiley, New York.

10. BROWN, S. C. & MARTIN, J. N. T. (eds.). (1977). *Human Aspects of Man-Made Systems*, Open University Press, London.

11. BURNS, W. (1968). *Noise & Man*. Murray, London.

12. CAKIR, A. *et al.* (1980). *Visual Display Terminals*, Wiley, New York.

13. CAPLAN, R. D. *et al.* (1975). *Job Demands and Worker Health*. HEW Publication No. (NIOSH) 75–160, US Government Printing Office, Washington, D.C.

14. CHAFFIN, D. B. (1973). 'Localized muscle fatigue – definition and measurement', *J. Medicine*, **15**, 346–354.

15. CHAFFIN, D. B. (1975). 'Ergonomics guide for the assessment of human static strength', *Am. Industrial Hygiene Assoc. J.*, **36**, 505–511.

16. CHAFFIN, D. B. (1982). 'Engineering anthropometry and occupational biomechanics', (in *Handbook of Industrial Engineering*, Salvendy, G. (ed.), chap. 6.3.) Wiley, New York.

17. CHAPANIS, A. (1965). *Man–Machine Engineering*, Wadsworth Publishing Company, Belmont, California.

18. CORLETT, E. N. & BISHOP, R. P. (1976). 'A technique for assessing postural discomfort', *Ergonomics*, **19**, 175–182.

19. CORLETT, E. N. (1982). 'Design of handtools, machines, workplace, office and buildings', (in *Handbook of Industrial Engineering*, Salvendy, G. (ed.), chap. 6.9) Wiley, New York.

20. CROCKER, M. J. (1982). 'Noise and vibration', (in *Handbook of Industrial Engineering*, Salvendy, G. (ed.), chap. 6.10) Wiley, New York.

21. DAMON, A. *et al.* (1966). *The Human Body in Equipment Design*, Harvard University Press, Cambridge, Massachusetts.

22. DAVIS, L. E. & TAYLOR, J. C. (1979). *Design of Jobs*, 2nd edition, Goodyear Publishing Company Inc., Santa Monica, California.

23. DAVIS, L. E. & WACKER, G. J. (1982). 'Job design', (in *Handbook of Industrial Engineering*, Salvendy, G. (ed.), chap. 2.5) Wiley, New York.

24. DeGREENE, K. B. (ed). (1970). *Systems Psychology*, McGraw-Hill, New York.

25. Department of Defense. (1974). *Human Engineering Design Criteria for Military Systems, Equipment and Facilities*, MIL-STD 1472B.

26. DIFFRIENT, N. *et al.* (1978). *Human scale 1/2/3*, MIT Press, Cambridge, Massachusetts.

27. DRURY, C. G. & FOX, J. G. (eds.). (1975). *Human Reliability in Quality Control*, Taylor & Francis, London.

28. EDHOLM, O. G. (1968). *The Biology of Work*, Weidenfeld & Nicholson, London.

29. EDWARDS, E. & LEES, F. P. (1972). *Man and Computer in Process Control*, The Institution of Chemical Engineers, London.

30. EDWARDS, E. & LEES, F. P. (eds.). (1974). *The Human Operator in Process Control*, Taylor & Francis, London.

31. EMERSON, P. D. (1975). 'Practical noise control', *Industrial Engineering*, **7**, 24–28.

32. FAULKNER, T. W. & MURPHY, T. J. (1973). 'Lighting for difficult visual tasks', *Human Factors*, **15**, 149–162.

33. FOGEL, L. J. (1963). *Biotechnology*, Prentice-Hall, New York.

34. FOLKARD, S. & MONK, T. H. (1979). 'Shiftwork and performance', *Human Factors*, **21**, 483–492.

35. GARG, A. & AYOUB, M. M. (1980). 'What criteria exist for determining how much load can be lifted safely?', *Human Factors*, **22**, 475–486.

36. GRANDJEAN, E. (1980). *Fitting the Task to the Man: An Ergonomic Approach*, 2nd edition, Taylor & Francis, London.

37. GRANDJEAN, E. & VIGLIANI, E. (1980). *Ergonomic Aspects of Visual Display Terminals*, Taylor & Francis, London.

38. GREENBURG, L. & CHAFFIN, D. (1976). *Workers and Their Tools*, Pendell Publishing Co., Midland, Michigan.

39. GRETHER, W. F. (1971). 'Vibration and human performance', *Human Factors*, **13**, 203–216.

40. HOPKINSON, R. & COLLINS, J. (1970). *The Ergonomics of Lighting*, McDonald, London.

41. HUCHINGSON, R. D. (1981). *New Horizons for Human Factors in Design*, McGraw-Hill, New York.

42. HUNT, V. R. (1979). *Work and the Health of Women*, CRC Press, Inc., Boca Raton, Florida.
43. IRVINE, C. H. (1976). 'Evaluation of some factors affecting measurements of slip resistance of shoe sole materials on floor surfaces', *J. Testing and Evaluation*, **4**, 133–138.
44. KAMON, E. (1982). 'Physiological basis for the design of work and rest', (in *Handbook of Industrial Engineering*, Salvendy, G. (ed.), chap. 6.4) Wiley, New York.
45. KERSLAKE, K. McK. (1972). *The Stress of Hot Environments* (Monograph No. 29 of the Physiological Society), Cambridge University Press, London.
46. KONZ, S. (1979). *Work Design*, Grid Publishing, Columbus, Ohio.
47. KONZ, S. (1982). 'Climate', (in *Handbook of Industrial Engineering*, Salvendy, G. (ed.), chap. 6.12) Wiley, New York.
48. KRAISS, K. F. & MORAAL, J. (eds.). (1976). *Introduction to Human Engineering*, Verlag TUV Rheinland GmbH, Köln, West Germany.
49. KROEMER, K. H. E. (1971). 'Foot operation of controls', *Ergonomics*, **14**, 333–361.
50. KROEMER, K. H. E. (1971). 'Seating in plant and office', *Am. Industrial Hygiene Assoc. J.*, **32**, 633–652.
51. KRYTER, K. D. (1970). *The Effects of Noise on Man*, Academic Press, New York.
52. KUORINKA, I. (1982). 'Bodily discomfort', (in *Handbook of Industrial Engineering*, Salvendy, G. (ed.), chap. 6.5) Wiley, New York.
53. KVÅLSETH, T. O. (1982). 'Design of man–machine systems', (in *Handbook of Industrial Engineering*, Salvendy, G. (ed.), chap. 6.8) Wiley, New York.
54. LAUBACH, L. L. (1976). 'Comparative muscular strength of men and women: a review of the literature', *Aviation, Space, and Environmental Medicine*, **47**, 534–542.
55. LINDSTRÖM, K. (1982). 'Toxicology', (in *Handbook of Industrial Engineering*, Salvendy, G. (ed.), chap. 6.13) Wiley, New York.
56. Materials Handling Unit, University of Surrey, United Kingdom. (1980). *Force Limits in Manual Work*, IPC Science and Technology Press, Guildford, Surrey, UK.
57. McCORMICK, E. J. & SANDERS, M. S. (1982). *Human Factors in Engineering and Design*, 5th edition, McGraw-Hill, New York.
58. McCORMICK, E. J. (1979). *Job Analysis: Methods and Applications*, AMACOM, New York.
59. McINTYRE, D. A. (1980). *Indoor Climate*, Applied Science Publishers, London.
60. MEGAW, E. D. (1979). 'Factors affecting visual inspection accuracy', *Appl. Ergonomics*, **10**, 27–32.
61. MEISTER, D. (1971). *Human Factors: Theory and Practice*, Wiley, New York.
62. MORGAN, C. T. *et al.* (1963). *Human Engineering Guide to Equipment Design*, McGraw-Hill, New York.
63. MURRELL, K. F. H. (1965). *Ergonomics: Man in his Working Environment*, Chapman & Hall, London.
64. MURRELL, K. F. H. (1976). *Men and Machines*, Methuen, London.
65. National Aeronautics and Space Administration. (1978). *Anthropometric Source Book*, volumes I, II and III, NASA Reference Publication 1024, Scientific and Technical Information Office, Washington, DC.
66. NORTH, K. (1980). 'Ergonomics methodology – an obstacle or promoter for the implementation of ergonomics in industrial practice?', *Ergonomics*, **23**, 781–795.
67. PARKER, J. F. & WEST, V. R. (1973). *Bioastronautics Data Book*, 2nd edition, NASA SP-3006, US Government Printing Office, Washington, DC.
68. POULTON, E. C. (1970). *Environment and Human Efficiency*, Charles C. Thomas, Springfield, Illinois.
69. ROEBUCK, J. A. *et al.* (1975). *Engineering Anthropometry Methods*, Wiley, New York.
70. Royal Naval Personnel Research Committee and Medical Research Council, United Kingdom. (1975). *Human Factors for Designers of Naval Equipment*.
71. SALVENDY, G. (ed.). (1982). *Handbook of Industrial Engineering*, Wiley, New York.
72. SINGLETON, W. T. (1972). *Introduction to Ergonomics*, World Health Organization, Geneva.
73. SINGLETON, W. T. (1974). *Man–Machine Systems*, Penguin, London.
74. SHACKEL, B. (ed.). (1974). *Applied Ergonomics Handbook*, IPC Science and Technology Press, Guildford, Surrey, UK.
75. SLEIGHT, R. B. & COOK, K. G. (1974). *Problems in Occupational Safety and Health: A Critical Review of Select Worker Physical and Psychological Factors*, HEW Publication No. (NIOSH) 75-124, US Government Printing Office, Washington, DC.

76. SNOOK, S. H. (1978). 'The design of manual handling tasks', *Ergonomics*, **21**, 963–985.
77. SWAIN, A. D. (1980). *Design Techniques for Improving Human Performance in Production*, revised, Albuquerque, New Mexico.
78. SWAIN, A. D. (1980). *The Human Element in Systems Safety: A Guide for Modern Management*, revised, Albuquerque, New Mexico.
79. TASTO, D. L., *et al.* (1978). *Health Consequences of Shift Work*, DHEW (NIOSH) Publication No. 78-154, US Government Printing Office, Washington, DC.
80. TICHAUER, E. R. & GAGE, H. (1977). 'Ergonomic principles basic to hand tool design', *Am. Industrial Hygiene Assoc. J.*, **38**, 622–634.
81. TICHAUER, E. R. (1978). *Biomechanical Basis of Ergonomics*, Wiley, New York.
82. US Air Force Systems Command Design Handbook 1–3. (1977). *Human Factors Engineering*, 3rd edition.
83. US Department of Defense. (1975). *Human Factors Engineering Design for Army Material*, MIL-HDBK-759.
84. US Department of Health, Education and Welfare. (1973). *The Industrial Environment – Its Evaluation and Control*, National Institute of Occupational Safety and Health, US Government Printing Office, Washington, DC.
85. US Department of Health, Education and Welfare. (1973). *Work in America*, MIT Press, Cambridge, Massachusetts.
86. Van COTT, H. P. & KINKADE, R. G. (eds.). (1972). *Human Engineering Guide to Equipment Design*, revised edition, US Government Printing Office, Washington, DC.
87. WEINER, J. S. & MAULE, H. G. (eds.). (1977). *Human Factors in Work, Design & Production*. Taylor & Francis, London.
88. WELFORD, A. T. (1976). 'Thirty years of psychological research on age and work', *J. of Occupational Psychology*, **49**, 129–138.
89. WOODSON, W. E. & CONOVER, D. W. (1964). *Human Engineering Guide for Equipment Designers*, 2nd edition, University of California Press, Berkeley, California.
90. WOODSON, W. E. (1981). *Human Factors Design Handbook*, McGraw-Hill, New York.

Index